Industrial Electronics—second edition

Industrial Electronics

second edition

Noel Morris
Principal Lecturer in Electrical and Electronic Engineering
North Staffordshire Polytechnic

McGRAW-HILL Book Company (UK) Limited

London · New York · St Louis · San Francisco · Auckland · Bogotá · Guatemala
Hamburg · Johannesburg · Lisbon · Madrid · Mexico · Montreal · New Delhi
Panama · Paris · San Juan · São Paulo · Singapore · Sydney · Tokyo · Toronto

Published by
McGRAW-HILL Book Company (UK) Limited
MAIDENHEAD · BERKSHIRE · ENGLAND

Morris, Noel Malcolm
  Industrial electronics.—2nd ed.
  1. Electronic apparatus and appliances
  I. Title
  621.381   TK7870   77-30564
  ISBN 0-07-084225-6

456 SWB 8321

PRINTED AND BOUND IN GREAT BRITAIN

Contents

Preface

Developments in technology have resulted in the evolution of a wide range of courses in electronic engineering which cover a vast spectrum of applications. This edition of the book is intended to cover the electronics requirements of technicians in both certificate and diploma courses, including electrical technicians, electronics technicians and telecommunications technicians. It also provides useful information for the reader attending other electronics courses.

The arrangement of the chapters in this edition has been altered to emphasize the importance of semiconductor devices; the book has been thoroughly revised, new material has been added and dated material removed. It is felt that these changes will enhance the book both as an electronics text book for technician courses and for background reading in other fields. The text includes numerous worked examples which supplement the characteristics and design principles described. It also contains a large number of unworked problems (with answers).

The contents can broadly be divided into two sections: basic devices and their characteristics are described in the first eight chapters, whilst circuits and their applications are dealt with in the final twelve chapters. Throughout the book, emphasis is placed on semiconductor devices, but thermionic devices are not ignored as they fulfil useful engineering functions. The book provides a broad coverage of devices and circuits including diodes, rectifiers, bipolar and field-effect transistors, thyristors, integrated circuits, optoelectronics, a.c. and d.c. amplifiers (including operational amplifiers), noise in electronic circuits, feedback amplifiers, oscillators, pulse shaping circuits, multivibrators and other relaxation oscillators, digital electronics, stabilized power supplies, oscilloscopes and digital instruments.

I would like to thank the electronics industry for supplying information relating to the devices and circuits described in the book. I am also grateful for the comments I have received from colleagues and others both inside and outside the teaching profession. I would also like to thank the McGraw-Hill production and editorial staff for their efforts in producing this book.

On a personal note, I would like to thank my wife for her not inconsiderable efforts during the preparation of the manuscript, and for her patience and understanding during its writing.

NOEL M. MORRIS

1. Semiconductor theory and p-n junction diodes

1.1 The constitution of matter

Elements, compounds, and molecules: There are approximately 100 basic substances known to man and these are called *chemical elements*; elements are fundamental to nature, and cannot be reduced further by any chemical process. Chemical elements are made up of a number of smaller particles known as *atoms*. Two or more different elements can combine to form a *chemical compound,* and the smallest particle of a compound is called a *molecule.* Each molecule has the chemical properties of the compound, and comprises one or more of each of the atoms contained in the compound. The word molecule also describes combined atoms of the same element, e.g. ozone (O_3) which is *triatomic,* that is it contains three atoms of oxygen.

Certain elements are very *active* and readily combine with other substances; an example is sodium (Na), which is very corrosive. One of the reasons for the combination of elements is that they are either short of electrons, or have too many for an 'ideal' atomic design. Gases known as *noble gases* have this ideal design, and do not combine with other elements under normal conditions, or even with atoms of their own kind. These gases are helium (He), neon (Ne), argon (A), krypton (Kr), xenon (Xe), and radon (Rn). Molecules of *noble* gas are monatomic, and consist of only one atom. Some elements also become monatomic in their gaseous state, an example being mercury.

The atom: From an engineering point of view the atom consists of two types of *charged* particles—*protons* and *electrons*. To complete the basic chemical properties of the atom, a further particle known as the *neutron* is introduced. The proton carries a positive charge of electricity, and the electron a negative charge of electricity. The two charges are equal in magnitude and opposite in polarity, and are given the symbol e, where

$$e = \pm 1 \cdot 6 \times 10^{-19} \quad \text{coulomb}$$

1

The mass of the proton is 1.66×10^{-27} kg, which is about 1840 times greater than the mass of the electron. The neutron carries no charge and has a mass equal to that of the proton. The mass of the electron varies with its speed, but at the velocities normally associated with electronic devices it is approximately 9.1×10^{-31} kg. Atoms do not carry any electrical charge in their normal state, since they contain equal numbers of positive and negative charges. The addition or removal of an electron gives the atom a net negative or positive charge, respectively. An atom carrying an electrical charge is an *ion*, and is said to be *ionized*. Both positive and negative ions exist in nature.

The structure of all atoms is broadly the same. At the centre of the atom is the *nucleus,* which contains the protons and neutrons, and has a positive charge. The nucleus is surrounded by electrons in concentric layers or *shells.* The distance between the nucleus and the orbiting electron is determined by the kinetic energy of the electron. The greater the kinetic energy, the further out it will orbit, subject to the limitation that it must orbit in one of a given number of shells. When an electron moves to a higher orbit, as a result of receiving energy from an external source, the atom is said to be *excited*, and the process is known as *excitation.* For convenience the shells are lettered alphabetically, commencing at the letter K. The numbers of electrons that the shells can possess when filled are: K,2; L,8; M,18; N,32; etc. Some of the shells comprise a number of sub-shells. For instance, the M shell consists of three sub-shells containing 2, 6, and 10 electrons, respectively, when they have their full complement of electrons.

The atomic structures of different elements differ only in the arrangement and numbers of the three basic particles. For example helium has two protons and two neutrons in the nucleus, and two electrons in the K shell, thereby 'filling' that shell. The nucleus of pure oxygen contains eight protons and eight neutrons, while eight electrons are in orbit, two in the inner or K shell, and six in the L shell. Thus helium is chemically inert since its outer shell is full of electrons, while the L shell of oxygen is incomplete since it can hold eight electrons, and oxygen reacts with other substances to gain extra electrons to fill the shell.

Valency: Atoms with unfilled outer shells combine together to acquire full outer shells. They do so in one of three ways. They either *lose electrons* to other atoms to empty their incomplete outer shell, or *gain electrons* from other atoms, or they *share electrons* with other atoms. In the sharing process, an electron from one atom in the structure orbits around the parent atom and one other atom, binding the two atoms together. This is known as *covalency*, and the atoms are said to be joined by a *covalent bond.* This process is particularly important in semiconductor devices.

Some elements are known as *electro-positive elements* since they readily lose one or more electrons to become positive ions. An *electro-negative element* acquires one or more electrons, becoming a negative ion. Broadly speaking, metals are electro-positive elements, and non-metals are electro-negative elements. The number of electrons which an atom gains, loses, or shares, according to the method of chemical combination, is known as the *valency* of the element. The electrons in the outer shell are called the *valence electrons*. Elements are *mono-, di-, tri-, tetra-, penta-, hexa-,* or *heptavalent,* if the number of valence electrons involved is 1, 2, 3, 4, 5, 6, or 7.

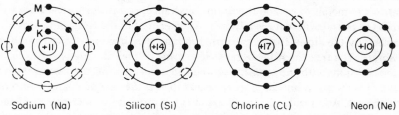

Sodium (Na)   Silicon (Si)   Chlorine (Cl)   Neon (Ne)

Fig. 1.1   The atomic structure of some well-known elements.

Figure 1.1 shows the basic atomic structure of some well known elements. Electrons in the shells are shown as black dots, and a shell is said to have a *hole* in it if an electron is missing. Holes are represented by the circles drawn in broken lines in the figure. The element sodium is an electro-positive substance, while chlorine is electro-negative. Silicon is one of those chemical substances which combines with other elements by means of covalent bonds, while neon is a noble gas. A hole may be regarded as the absence of an electron in a position where one would normally be found, and it can be regarded as a *positive charge carrier,* much as an electron is a negative charge carrier.

The broad outline of the structure of matter given here is adequate for the purpose of this book, but a closer investigation into the chemical properties of matter soon shows up the limitations of simple man-made theories.

1.2 Conduction in metals

From a chemical standpoint a metal is an electro-positive element, and readily gives up its valence electrons. A metal may therefore be thought of as a number of fixed positive ions (the atoms themselves), and a number of mobile negative ions (the valence electrons). In an isolated piece of metal the electrons move about in a random fashion, and the net charge on the metal is zero. Since the electrons move in a random fashion, the charge distribution throughout the metal varies with time. If the electrons tend to group at one point in the metal, that region acquires a net negative charge, and other regions a net positive charge. Thus, the region with the negative charge repels further electrons from entering it, and the regions with a positive charge attract electrons to it, resulting in further migration of electrons.

The application of an e.m.f. between the ends of a metal bar results in the free electrons drifting towards the positive pole of the supply source. To maintain the balance of electrons in the bar, electrons enter it from the negative pole of the source of supply. Although the flow of current from one end of the bar to

the other appears to be almost instantaneous, as measured by electrons entering
at one end and other electrons leaving at the other end, the net drift velocity of
an individual electron is very small, being 0·1 mm/s typically.

Electrical resistance of metals: At absolute zero of temperature ($-273°C$), free
electrons in metals move about without hindrance, and the electrical resistance
is zero (or the conductivity is infinite). When energy in the form of heat is
absorbed by the atoms from an external source, they become excited and begin
to vibrate. The free electrons begin to lose some of their kinetic energy as a result
of the collisions with the atoms, and when an e.m.f. is applied between the ends
of the metallic bar a smaller current results than is the case at absolute zero of
temperature. As a result, the metal exhibits the property of increasing resistance
to flow of current with increasing current. That is to say metals have a *positive
resistance-temperature coefficient*.

1.3   Semiconductors

There are many ways of classifying materials, a common method being by their
electrical conductivity. Broadly speaking, materials may be divided into conductors, semiconductors, and insulators. *Conductors* are defined as materials
having a low resistivity, in the range zero to 10^{-4} Ωm. *Insulators* have
conductivities greater than 10^3 Ωm, while *semiconductors* have conductivity
values at room temperature in the range 10^{-4} Ωm to 10^3 Ωm.

There are many semiconductor materials available, but very few of them
have a practical application in electronics. The two most useful materials are
silicon (Si) and germanium (Ge), both of which are tetravalent. The atoms in a
single crystal of either pure silicon or pure germanium are joined together by
covalent bonds, and the valence electrons are shared between the atoms. At
absolute zero temperature (0 K), all the electrons are at their lowest energy
levels, and the valence electrons are taken up in the covalent bonds of the
structure. As a result there are no free electrons at this temperature and, in
theory, both silicon and germanium are perfect insulators. This does not occur
in practice, since it is not possible to manufacture a perfect crystal, and
impurities exist within the crystal (a crystal is said to be pure if the impurity
content is less than one part in 10^{10}).

At room temperature, some valence electrons acquire sufficient energy to
break away from the parent atom to become free. Simultaneously, a *hole* is
said to be generated in the crystal structure (it has already been stated that a
hole is equivalent to a positive charge carrier). This process is known as *thermal
generation of an electron-hole pair*. Electron-hole pairs are generated at many
points within the crystal, with the result that an electron from one part of the
crystal lattice soon *recombines* with a hole from another part of the structure.
The average time that either charge carrier exists is known as the *lifetime* of the
carrier, which is typically 10^{-2} to 10^{-4} s. When a hole and an electron recombine,

they cease to exist as charge carriers. Thermally generated electron-hole pairs give rise to *intrinsic conduction* in the semiconductor when an electrical potential difference is applied between the ends of the sample.

Electron-hole pairs can also be generated by other sources of energy, such as light. Light can be considered to consist of a series of small packets of energy, known as *photons,* whose energy is proportional to frequency. Thus, blue light is more 'energetic' than red light. Atomic radiation can also generate electron-hole pairs in semiconductor materials.

An increase in ambient temperature (or in other incident radiation) causes the number of electron-hole pairs generated to increase. In turn this results in an increase in conductivity (that is a reduction in resistance) with increase in temperature. For this reason most semiconductor materials have a *negative resistance-temperature coefficient.*

1.4   Extrinsic conduction

The deliberate introduction of a small quantity of impurity (of the order of 1 part in 10^8) modifies the electrical properties of semiconductors. It results in a new type of conduction, known as *extrinsic conduction.*

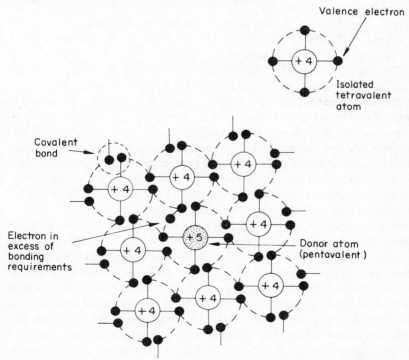

Fig. 1.2   The lattice structure of an *n-type* semiconductor material which has tetravalent 'host' atoms.

If the impurity atom has a valency of five, i.e., it is *pentavalent,* it has one more electron in its outer shell than have the host atoms (assuming them to be either silicon or germanium), as shown in Fig. 1.2. The atomic structure in the figure is simplified by representing it in planar form, or flat form, without loss of accuracy. Since there are only four electrons in the valence shell of the parent tetravalent atoms, the net charge on these atoms if the valence electrons were stripped off would be + 4 electronic units. The additional electron orbiting the pentavalent atom is surplus to the covalent bonding requirements, and can be removed more readily from the crystal lattice than can the valence electrons of the parent atoms. This type of impurity is known as *n-type* impurity (*n* for *n*egative

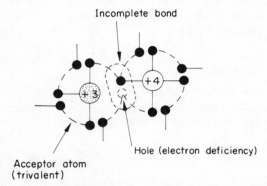

Fig. 1.3   The structure of a *p-type* semiconductor.

charge carrier), and the impurity atom is a *donor* atom since it donates an electron for the purposes of conduction.

In n-type semiconductors, free electrons are the major means of conducting charges through the lattice, and electrons are described as *majority charge carriers.* Holes generated by thermal or other means also act as charge carriers but, since these are relatively few in number when compared to the majority charge carriers, they are known as *minority charge carriers.* Typical donor elements include phosphorous (P), arsenic (As), and antimony (Sb).

If a germanium or silicon atom in the crystal is replaced by a trivalent atom (valency 3), as shown in Fig. 1.3, a *hole* is generated in the lattice due to incomplete bonding. This hole can be 'filled' by any free electron in the crystal lattice, causing a hole to appear at some other point. This type of impurity is known as *p-type* impurity (*p* for *p*ositive charge carrier), and the impurity atom is known as an *accep*tor atom, since it results in the acceptance of an electron into the lattice. Typical acceptor elements include boron (B), aluminium (Al), gallium (Ga), and indium (In). The mobile hole has all the characteristics of a positive charge carrier, and holes are the majority charge carriers in p-type semiconductors. Electrons generated by thermal and other effects are minority charge carriers.

Gallium arsenide (GaAs) is another material which is used in many electronic devices including light-emitting diodes (LED). Gallium has a valency of three, and arsenic has a valency of five. The same general rules for doping apply to gallium arsenide as to silicon and germanium. If the valency of the impurity atom is less than the lowest valency of the host atoms, then the crystal becomes a p-type semiconductor as, for example, if zinc is used, which has a valency of two. If the valency of the impurity atom is greater than the highest valency of the host material, then the crystal becomes an n-type semiconductor. Selenium, which has a valency of six, is a suitable donor impurity element. Tetravalent impurity atoms, e.g., germanium, can be used if the process is correctly controlled. If a germanium atom replaces a gallium atom, an n-type semiconductor is formed, whereas a p-type semiconductor results if it replaces an arsenic atom.

The simple theory outlined here is adequate to explain the operation of most of the devices we come across in electronics, but some devices require a more sophisticated theory. One such theory, the *energy-band theory* is given in simplified form below.

In an atom, electrons can only orbit in certain *levels* or *bands,* in much the same way that a car in a multi-storey car park can only park on one of the floors, and not between the floors. In semiconductors, the highest energy band containing electrons is the valence band, the next higher being an empty band known as the *conduction energy band.* Since electrons are forbidden to appear at energy levels in the range between the two levels, the gap between them is known as the *forbidden energy gap.* In pure semiconductor materials (those exhibiting only intrinsic conduction), the breaking of a covalent bond is equivalent to an electron gaining sufficient energy to leap the forbidden energy gap. This leaves an electron in the conduction band and a hole in the valence band.

The reverse *leakage current* of a semiconductor device is related to the size of the forbidden energy gap, since a large gap results in a smaller intrinsic leakage current at a given temperature. Since the forbidden energy gap in silicon is greater than in germanium, the leakage current in silicon devices is much less than in otherwise similar germanium devices.

At this point, we reach the first significant difference between the simple covalent bond theory and the energy-band theory. Since an electron in the conduction band is at a higher energy level in the atom than is the hole in the valence band, we find that the electron is more *mobile* than the hole. The difference in the *mobilities* of electrons and holes is of the order of 2:1 in the more usual semiconductors. This significant fact is not apparent from the simple theory.

In the energy-band theory, the effect of adding impurities is to introduce additional available energy levels in the forbidden energy gap. In the case of n-type materials, a 'full' level (i.e., full of electrons) is introduced close to the conduction band. This means that electrons can be transferred into the conduction band by only acquiring a small amount of energy, much less than is necessary to jump across the forbidden energy gap. In p-type semiconductors, an 'empty' level (i.e., one containing no electrons) is introduced into the gap close to the valence band. As a result, electrons can leave the valence band and enter the new energy level with much less energy than is required to cross the forbidden gap, leaving a hole in the valence band.

1.5   Diffusion and drift

Charge carriers move through semiconductor materials by two distinct and separate mechanisms: diffusion and drift. *Diffusion* occurs when there is a concentration of free charge carriers in one part of the crystal. The mutual repulsion between the charge carriers (assuming that they are of the same kind) results in a net movement of charges from an area of high concentration to one of low concentration.

Drift is an effect resulting from the application of an electric field (i.e., the application of a potential difference across the material) to the semiconductor. In p-type semiconductors, the drift current consists of holes which move towards the end of the semiconductor at a more negative potential. In n-type semiconductors, the drift current consists of electrons drifting toward the more positive end of the material. In both cases, the charge carriers are replenished by the supply source which sets up the electric field.

1.6   The p-n junction diode

A p-n junction diode is formed from a *single crystal* containing an n-region and a p-region, as shown in Fig. 1.4. When the p-region is connected to the negative pole of a battery and the n-region to the positive pole, as in Fig. 1.4(a), the mobile holes in the p-region are attracted away from the junction by the negative pole, as are the electrons in the n-region by the positive pole. As a result, the number of charge carriers in the region of the junction is depleted, and is known as the *depletion layer*. The greater the applied voltage, the greater the width of the depletion layer. Theoretically, the flow of current between the two regions should be zero since no mobile charge carriers are available at the junction. In fact, a small *leakage current* flows due to thermal generation of minority carriers in both halves. These are indicated by arrows in Fig. 1.4(a). The leakage current is of the order of a few nanoamperes in a silicon signal diode, and slightly greater in a germanium diode. In this operating state, the diode is said to be reverse biased, and is in its *reverse blocking mode.* The effect of an increase in temperature is to increase the number of minority carriers generated, so increasing the leakage current. The effect on the diode characteristic of an increase in temperature is shown in Fig. 1.5. The leakage current under reverse bias conditions, known as the *reverse saturation current,* is substantially constant at any given temperature. As the temperature increases, the number of

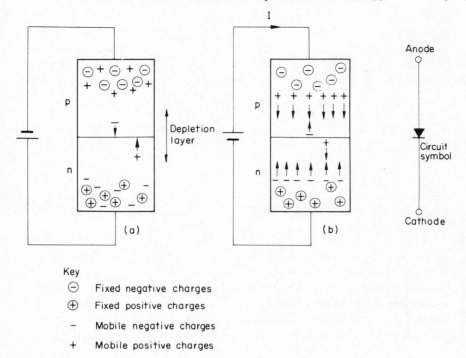

Key

⊖   Fixed negative charges

⊕   Fixed positive charges

−   Mobile negative charges

+   Mobile positive charges

Fig. 1.4   The operation of the p-n junction diode under (a) reverse bias and (b) forward bias.

thermally generated minority carriers increases, and with it the reverse leakage current.

The application of a reverse voltage in excess of the *peak inverse voltage* rating of the diode can lead to an electrical breakdown of the diode. It then operates in the *reverse breakdown* or *reverse conducting* mode. In this phase of its operation, the diode current increases rapidly for a very small increase in applied voltage. Unless the current is limited by some means, breakdown can result in the destruction of the p-n junction. Diodes known as *Zener diodes* are designed to operate in the reverse breakdown mode, and are described in section 1.9.

By reversing the polarity of the applied voltage, see Fig. 1.4(b), the majority carriers are attracted towards the junction under the influence of the electric field. In the region of the junction, the numbers of charge carriers diminish due to recombination of charge carriers. Thermally generated minority carriers also contribute to the current flow. The net result is that the potential drop across the diode in the forward conduction mode is small, being typically 0·8 V to 1 V at full load in a silicon diode, and one-half this value in a germanium diode. An increase in temperature gives rise to the generation of more minority carriers,

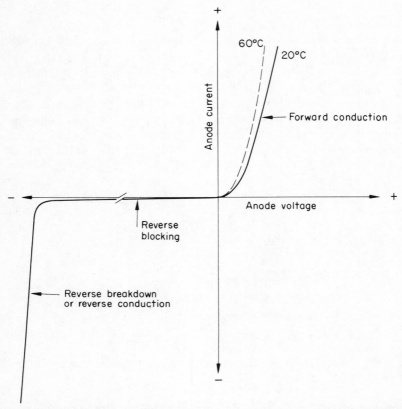

Fig. 1.5   The static anode characteristic of a p-n junction diode. An increase in temperature causes the forward characteristic to change in the manner shown.

giving an increased forward current for a given forward p.d. The junction is said to be *forward biased* in this mode of operation. Due to its characteristics, the p-n junction diode finds greatest application as a rectifying device.

1.7   Capacitance of the p-n junction diode

When a reverse voltage is applied to a p-n junction diode, a depletion layer is formed whose width is dependent on the applied voltage. An increase in the reverse voltage causes the majority charge carriers to move further away from the junction, and a reduction in reverse voltage causes them to move closer to the junction. Movement of charges within the diode during the time the applied voltage is changing manifests itself in the external circuit as a current.

Thus, a reverse biased p-n junction diode appears to the external circuit as a capacitor whose capacitance is a non-linear function of the applied voltage. The capacitance usually has a value in the range 5 pF to 20 pF, and is known as the *transition capacitance* of the diode. Diodes which are deliberately operated under reverse biased conditions to give a variable reactance effect are known as *varactor diodes.* Another version, the *step recovery diode,* is a variant of the varactor diode.

In addition, another effect known as *storage capacitance* occurs under forward biased conditions. It was stated earlier that holes and electrons diffuse throughout the crystal in order to unify the charge density. This effect is independent of the drift current. Hence, holes from the p-region diffuse into the n-region, and electrons diffuse in the reverse direction. This charge is effectively stored, and returns when a reverse bias is applied, as shown in Fig. 1.6. The storage current is principally hole flow, since the p-type anode region is doped more heavily with impurity atoms than is the n-type cathode. As a result, this phenomenon has become known as *hole storage.* The storage capacitance may have a value of several hundred picofarads. It is a transient effect and should not be confused with the transition capacitance, which is always present under reverse biased conditions.

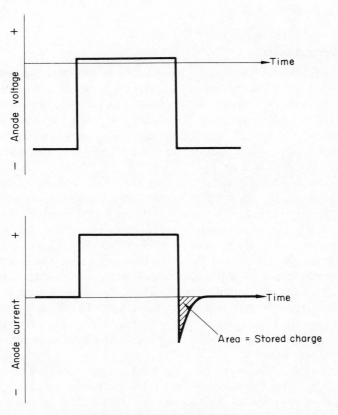

Fig. 1.6   Charge storage effect.

1.8   The Schottky barrier diode

A Schottky barrier diode or *hot carrier diode* is a rectifying metal-to-semi-conductor junction diode. Several metals may be used, including gold, molybdenum, titanium, chromium, nickel, nichrome, and aluminium in conjunction with either n-type or p-type silicon. Since the mobility of electrons is greater than that of holes, n-type silicon is nearly always used as the semiconductor since it ensures better high frequency performance.

Current flow in the Schottky barrier diode differs from current flow in conventional p-n junction diodes in that minority carriers (holes in n-type semi-conductors) do not take any part in the process. This has the effect of eliminating charge storage effects, enabling switching speeds less than 0·1 ns to be achieved. As a consequence of this, Schottky barrier diodes can be used at frequencies up to about 40 GHz

The electron flow results from the property of solids under the influence of a strong electric field to emit electrons. The electrons have energies which are normally associated with electrons which leave a 'hot' body, hence the name hot carrier diode.

1.9   Zener diodes

One of the first useful theories on the breakdown of dielectrics was put forward in 1934 by C. Zener. He suggested that, under the influence of very intense electric fields (several million volts per centimetre), electrons can tunnel through the forbidden energy gap. This theory is certainly true in semiconductor p-n junction diodes with a relatively thin depletion layer, when breakdown occurs with anode voltages in the region of $-2·6$ V to -5 V. This type of breakdown is known as *Zener breakdown*.

With wider depletion layers, obtained by modifying the impurity doping, breakdown occurs at a much higher voltage than is expected by Zener's theory. In such cases, the breakdown mechanism is thought to be due to *avalanche breakdown*. The breakdown mechanism is explained as follows. Leakage current in p-n junction diodes is largely due to minority carriers drifting across the junction under the influence of the reverse bias. If the electric field in the region of the junction is sufficiently great, the electrons are accelerated and acquire enough energy to ionize atoms by collision, i.e., they strip off valence electrons to generate electron-hole pairs in the depletion layer. The effect is multiplicative, causing a very rapid transition from a reverse blocking state to a reverse conducting state. Both avalanche and Zener breakdown diodes are traditionally known as Zener diodes.

Typical static anode characteristics of various types of Zener diodes are shown in Fig. 1.7(a), together with one form of circuit symbol (b).

An approximate equivalent electrical circuit of the Zener diode is shown in Fig. 1.7(c). Diode D1 allows conduction in the conventional manner when the anode is positive with respect to the cathode. Conduction takes place through D2 when the cathode potential exceeds the breakdown potential V_Z. Resistance r_Z represents the reverse breakdown slope resistance of the diode, which has a value between 0·5 Ω and about 150 Ω, depending on the operating point and the diode rating.

The anode current of the 4·7 V diode in Fig. 1.7(a) is largely composed of carriers which have tunnelled through the potential barrier, and the characteristic is typified by a smooth 'knee'. Avalanche breakdown diodes have a characteristic with a sharp 'knee', which is due to the sudden transition from reverse blocking to reverse breakdown, and the slope resistance is generally higher than that of a Zener breakdown diode. This is illustrated in the 15 V

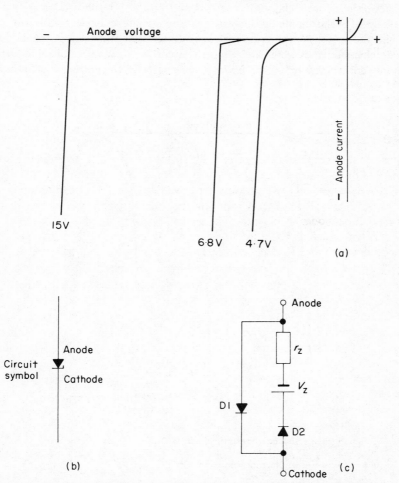

Fig. 1.7   (a) Reverse breakdown characteristics of Zener diodes. (b) Shows one form of circuit symbol, and (c) an equivalent electrical circuit.

characteristic. When breakdown occurs between 5 V and 7 V, there is a range of diodes whose breakdown mechanism is partly due to Zener effect and partly due to avalanche breakdown. The forward characteristics of both Zener and avalanche breakdown devices are generally similar to a conventional p-n junction diode.

It is found that Zener and avalanche breakdown mechanisms react in different ways to a change in temperature. In Zener breakdown, the tunnelling effect increases with temperature, resulting in a greater flow of current for a given anode voltage, as illustrated in Fig. 1.8. In avalanche breakdown devices, the increased temperature results in increased activity in the atomic structure, and the free charge carriers find it more difficult to acquire the critical energy to ionize other atoms. As a result, the breakdown voltage of avalanche diodes increases with temperature. Between the two, in the region of −5 V, the two variations balance each other out, giving diodes with characteristics which are relatively insensitive to temperature. The latter are used as *voltage reference diodes,* having voltage-temperature coefficients

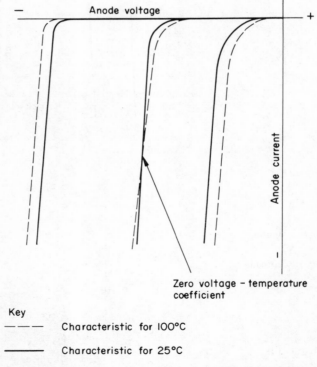

Key

——— Characteristic for 100°C

——— Characteristic for 25°C

Fig. 1.8   Illustrating the effect of temperature change on the reverse breakdown characteristics of Zener diodes.

of the order of zero (at one point on the characteristic only), combined with a very low slope resistance.

Ratings of Zener diodes range from breakdown voltages of 2·6 V to over 200 V, at power ratings up to 75 W and over. They are frequently used as voltage reference sources, and other applications include meter protection circuits, instrument scale expanders, and low speed computing circuits.

Problems

1.1 Explain the following terms: (a) donor atom, (b) acceptor atom, (c) valence electron, (d) n-type material, (e) p-type material, (f) covalent bond, (g) intrinsic conductivity, (h) extrinsic conductivity.

1.2 What are minority charge carriers and majority charge carriers in semiconductor materials, and what is their function?

1.3 Show how tetravalent semiconductors can be converted into p-type and n-type semiconductor materials. Illustrate your answer with a lattice diagram of the crystal structure. Give the names of commonly used impurity atoms.

1.4 Explain how it is possible for substances like gallium arsenide to be converted into extrinsic conductors.

1.5 Give a simple explanation of the energy-band theory of semiconductors.

1.6 What is meant by the term *mobility* in connection with charge carriers?

1.7 What is meant in semiconductor theory by (a) drift current, and (b) diffusion current. Using these concepts, describe the principle of operation of the p-n junction diode.

1.8 Explain, with the aid of a characteristic curve, the principle of operation of a Zener diode. What is meant by Zener breakdown and avalanche breakdown? What are the essential differences between them?

1.9 If you were selecting a Zener diode for a voltage reference source from the following range, which one would you select and why would you select it? 2·5 V, 4·7 V, 15 V. Explain the effects of temperature variation on the reverse breakdown voltage of the three types.

1.10 Two copper oxide rectifier elements have the following forward conduction characteristics:

Voltage	0·4	0·6	0·8	1·0	1·2
Current (rectifier 1)	0·4	1·8	5·5	12·5	23
Current (rectifier 2)	1·5	4·5	11	21	—

If the two rectifiers are connected in series to a 1·2 V d.c. supply, estimate the value of the voltage developed across each diode, and the circuit current.

1.11 Draw a diagram of a circuit which makes use of the properties of a Zener diode, and briefly explain its operation.

2. Rectifier circuits

2.1 Requirements of a power supply

The power supply is the most basic section of any electronic circuit. Practically all electronic systems require one or more power supplies, the simplest and most effective being a dry battery. While this has the advantages of being simple and having a low output impedance, it suffers from a limited useful life and poor long-term voltage stability.

The most common form of power supply comprises a *rectifier circuit*, which provides a unidirectional but unstabilized output, followed by a *filter circuit* to smooth out ripples in the output voltage and current.

In some cases, an a.c. power supply must be derived from a d.c. supply, in which case an *invertor circuit* is necessary.

2.2 Single-phase half-wave circuit

The simplest rectifier circuit is the *single-phase half-wave circuit* of Fig. 2.1(a). With a sinusoidal supply voltage $v_s = V_{SM} \sin \omega t$, the current in the conducting half-cycle is

$$i_l = \frac{V_{SM} \sin \omega t}{R_s + r_a + R_L} = I_M \sin \omega t \tag{2.1}$$

where R_s is the source resistance, r_a is the slope resistance of the diode, and R_L is the resistance of the load. In practice, both R_s and r_a are small compared with R_L, and eq. (2.1) becomes

$$i_l = \frac{V_{SM}}{R_L} \sin \omega t = I_M \sin \omega t \tag{2.2}$$

In the negative half-cycle, the diode is reverse biased, and only leakage current flows in the circuit. The diode has then to sustain its *peak inverse anode voltage* (p.i.v.), which is $- V_{SM}$ in Fig. 2.1(b).

16

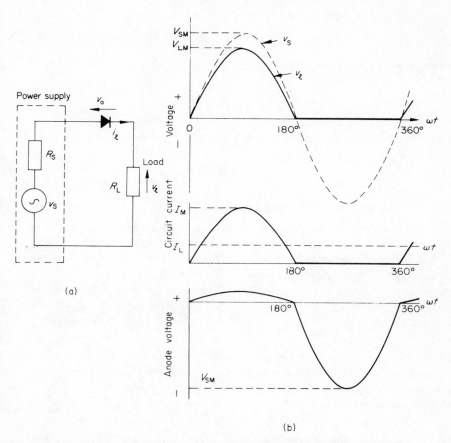

Fig. 2.1 (a) A single-phase half-wave rectifier circuit, and (b) typical wave-forms.

The *average value** or *d.c. value* of the load current is given by the equation

$$I_L = \frac{1}{2\pi} \int_0^{2\pi} i_l \, d(\omega t)$$

$$= \frac{1}{2\pi} \left[\int_0^{\pi} I_M \sin(\omega t) \, d(\omega t) + \int_{\pi}^{2\pi} 0 \, . \, d(\omega t) \right]$$

$$= (2I_M + 0)/2\pi = 0 \cdot 318 \, I_M \tag{2.3}$$

* A convenient fact to remember is that the *area* of *one half-cycle of a sinusoidal wave* is twice the peak value. Thus, if the peak value is 10 A, then the area of one half-cycle is 10 x 2 = 20 ampere-radians.

and the average value of the load voltage is

$$V_L = I_L R_L = 0 \cdot 318 I_M R_L = 0 \cdot 318 V_{LM} \tag{2.4}$$

For a sinewave supply of r.m.s. voltage V_s, then $V_{SM} = \sqrt{2} \, V_s$ and

$$V_L = 0 \cdot 45 V_s \, \frac{R_L}{R_s + r_a + R_L} \tag{2.5}$$

In the case where the sum of R_s and r_a is small compared with R_L, eq. (2.5) reduces to

$$V_L \simeq 0 \cdot 45 V_s \tag{2.6}$$

2.3 Single-phase full-wave circuits

The full-wave *centre-tap circuit* or *bi-phase circuit* is shown in Fig. 2.2(a). In this circuit a centre-tapped transformer is used to provide a bi-phase supply. The dots by the windings in Fig. 2.2(a) indicate the ends of the windings which are at the same instantaneous potential. Thus, when the upper end of the primary winding is at a positive potential, the corresponding ends of the two secondary windings are also positive. In this operating state, the upper diode is forward biased, and the lower diode is reverse biased. In the following half-

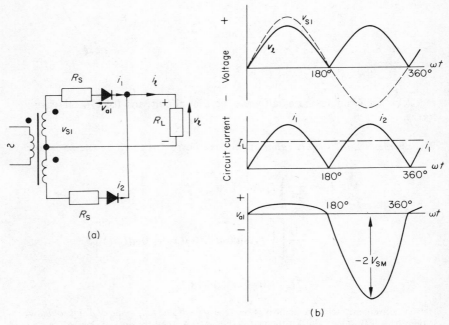

Fig. 2.2   (a) Full-wave centre-tap circuit, and (b) waveforms.

cycle the operating states are reversed, and the lower diode is forward biased
and passes load current.

Since current flows in both half-cycles, the average load current and voltage
are twice the values of the half-wave circuit. That is

$$I_L = 0.636 I_M \tag{2.7}$$

$$V_L = 0.9 V_s \tag{2.8}$$

In the second half-cycle, the upper diode is reverse biased while the lower
diode is forward biased. Under peak voltage conditions, the potential of the
anode of the upper diode is $-V_{SM}$ while its cathode is $+V_{SM}$. The peak inverse
voltage applied under this condition is, therefore, twice the peak supply voltage,
or

$$\text{p.i.v.} = 2V_{SM} = 2\sqrt{2}V_s = 2.828 V_s$$

This is the value of the repetitive inverse voltage applied to both diodes, and the
p.i.v. rating of any diodes used in this type of circuit should be greater than this
value. As a general rule of thumb, the p.i.v. rating should be at least four times
the r.m.s. value of the supply voltage.

A *bridge* configuration of four diodes is shown in Fig. 2.3. In this arrangement, diagonally opposite pairs of diodes conduct simultaneously, so that when
point A is positive with respect to point B, diodes D1 and D2 conduct, D3 and
D4 being reverse biased. When point B is positive with respect to point A,
diodes D3 and D4 conduct, while D1 and D2 are reverse biased.

This circuit possesses two advantages over the centre-tap circuit. Firstly, a
centre-tapped transformer is not required and secondly, the repetitive peak
inverse voltage is one-half that in the centre-tap circuit. A disadvantage
of this circuit is that it is not possible to simultaneously earth one side of

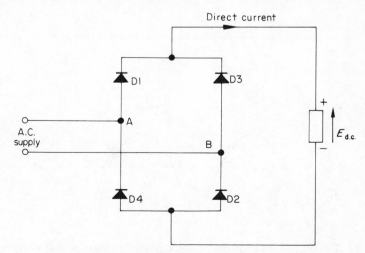

Fig. 2.3 Single-phase bridge rectifier circuit.

the power supply and one side of the output, otherwise part of the bridge circuit will be short-circuited.

The bridge circuit is commonly used in measuring instruments to convert alternating voltage signals into unidirectional signals, the load resistor being replaced by a microammeter or a milliammeter.

2.4 Harmonic generation

The output voltage from a simple rectifier circuit consists of a direct potential (or current), with a superimposed alternating ripple component. These are

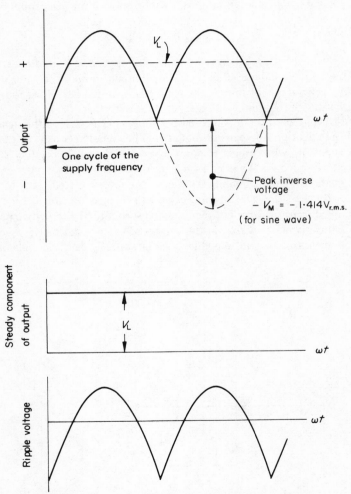

Fig. 2.4 The output waveform of a single phase full-wave circuit showing its constituent unidirectional and harmonic components.

shown in Fig. 2.4 for a single-phase full-wave rectifier. The unidirectional output V_L is the time-average of the waveform taken over one cycle, and has a constant value. The ripple voltage waveform is usually non-sinusoidal, and consists of a large number of *harmonics* of the supply frequency. A harmonic is a frequency which is an integral multiple of the supply frequency.

The number and magnitude of the harmonics are dependent on the supply frequency and the connection used. Both the number and the magnitude can either be calculated from a knowledge of the waveshape by *Fourier analysis,* or be measured in the laboratory by harmonic analyzers, which are basically highly selective tuned circuits. In the waveform in Fig. 2.4, the second harmonic (100 Hz with a 50 Hz supply) predominates. Other harmonics present include the fourth (200 Hz), the sixth (300 Hz), the eighth (400 Hz), etc. Fortunately, the magnitude of the harmonics diminishes rapidly as their order increases. It is the function of *filter circuits* to reduce or even eliminate the harmonic content of the output from a rectifier circuit.

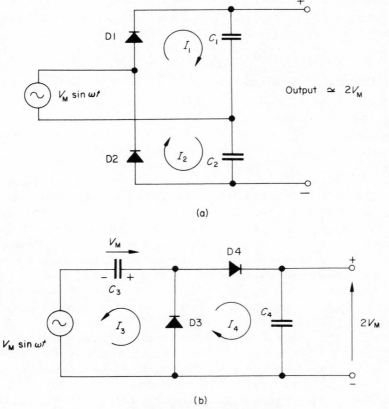

(a)

(b)

Fig. 2.5   Voltage doubling circuits.

2.5   Voltage multiplying circuits

There is a need in some instruments for a d.c. power supply which has a very
high voltage as, for example, in the oscilloscope where a voltage of the order of
several kilovolts is required. In these applications, voltage multiplying circuits
can be employed. The circuits in Fig. 2.5 develop an unloaded output voltage of
approximately twice the peak value of the a.c. input signal. Figure 2.5(a) shows
a bridge configuration in which diode D1 charges capacitor C_1 to V_M volts in
one-half of the input cycle. In the second half-cycle, diode D2 charges C_2 to V_M
volts. Since the two capacitors are series connected, the output voltage is
approximately $2V_M$ volts.

In the circuit in Fig. 2.5(b), C_3 is charged to V_M during the *negative* half-
cycle of the supply voltage. The potential between the terminals of C_3 now
acts as a battery in series with the supply. In the positive half-cycle of the
supply voltage, C_4 is charged to a voltage equal to the sum of the peak supply
voltage and the voltage across C_3.

When a current is drawn from either of these circuits, a large ripple voltage
is generated; this factor limits the use of these circuits to low current applications.
By cascading voltage multiplying circuits, d.c. voltages greater than four times
the peak alternating supply voltage can be generated.

2.6   Capacitor filter circuit

The simplest form of harmonic filter circuit is the shunt capacitor circuit shown
in Fig. 2.6(a). To provide adequate filtering with this circuit, the reactance
of the capacitor at the ripple frequency should be much lower than the resistance of the load. In this case, the load presented to the rectifier is no longer
completely resistive, and a large proportion of the diode current flows into the
capacitor. The voltage and current waveforms associated with the circuit are
shown in Fig. 2.6(b). Between t_1 and t_2 (Fig. 2.6(b)), the supply potential is
greater than the voltage across the capacitor, and current flows from the supply
into the capacitor and load. This circuit condition is illustrated in Fig. 2.6(c).
Between t_2 and t_3, the supply potential is lower than that on the capacitor,
causing both diodes to be reverse biased. During this period, the capacitor discharges and maintains the load potential. The capacitor voltage during the
discharge period is a function of the resistance of the connected load, and with
a small load resistance the capacitor voltage drops rapidly between charging
pulses.

To reduce the ripple voltage to a low level, a large value of capacitance
must be used, resulting in a larger charging current flowing for a shorter period
than is the case with a small value of capacitance. Figure 2.7 illustrates the
change in charging current waveform when the capacitance is increased by a
factor of 100. Values of capacitance used vary between a few microfarads and
several thousand microfarads, electrolytic capacitors being used to achieve the

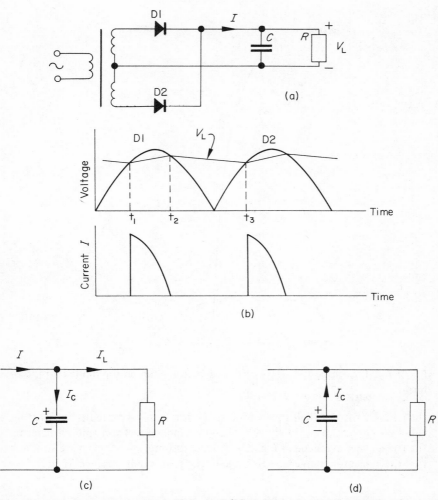

Fig. 2.6   (a) A simple capacitor filter, and (b) the waveforms diagram for the load circuit. The circuit conditions between t_1 and t_2 are shown in (c), and those between t_2 and t_3 are shown in (d).

high value required. It is permissible to connect high values of capacitance directly to the terminals of thermionic diode circuits, since the maximum current that may be drawn is limited by the temperature of the cathode. In the case of semiconductor diodes, excessive peak current can be drawn during the charging periods, resulting in overheating of the p-n junction and possibly leading to the diode being damaged. It is common practice to include a current limiting resistance R in series with the rectifier, shown in Fig. 2.8.

If the discharge time constant of the capacitor circuit is long compared with

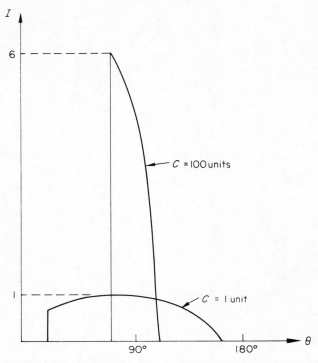

Fig. 2.7 Illustrating the effect of the capacitor value on the diode current waveform.

the periodic time of the ripple waveform ($1/f$ in half-wave circuits and $1/2f$ in full-wave circuits), i.e., if $CR_L \gg T$, then the ripple waveform approximates to the triangular waveshape in Fig. 2.9. A basic assumption of this waveform is that the capacitor charges in zero time to the peak supply voltage. If the

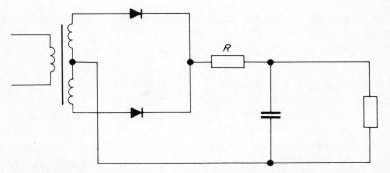

Fig. 2.8 Resistor R is frequently necessary in semiconductor circuits to avoid damage to the diodes.

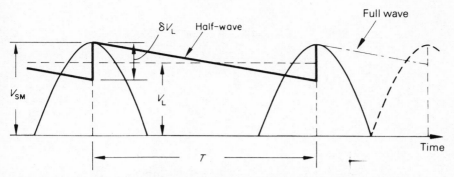

Fig. 2.9 A method of estimating the output voltage from a rectifier circuit.

assumption is valid, the capacitor voltage falls linearly at the rate of $V_{SM}/R_L C$ volts/second, which continues for T seconds. Thus, the total change in potential δV_L is given by

$$\delta V_L = V_{SM} T / R_L C$$

and the average output voltage of a half-wave circuit is

$$V_L \cong V_{SM} - \frac{\delta V_L}{2} = V_{SM} - \frac{V_{SM} T}{2 R_L C} = V_{SM} \left(1 - \frac{T}{2 R_L C} \right) \qquad (2.9)$$

For example, if a unidirectional output voltage of 200 V is required from a 50 Hz half-wave rectifier circuit with a simple capacitor filter, the load resistance being 1 kΩ and the shunt capacitance 100 μF, then the peak supply voltage must be

$$V_{SM} = 200/(1 - 0 \cdot 02/(2 \times 10^3 \times 100 \times 10^{-6})) = 222 \text{ V}$$

that is to say, the r.m.s. voltage provided by the transformer secondary must be $222/\sqrt{2} = 157$ V. In selecting a suitable transformer, the secondary no-load voltage should be greater than 157 V by about 10 to 15 per cent to allow for the voltage drop in the diode and the transformer windings, and also to allow for the errors introduced by the simplifying assumptions made in the theory.

In the full-wave rectifier circuit, the discharge period is $T/2$ s, and eq. (2.9) is modified as follows:

$$V_L \simeq V_{SM}(1 - T/4 R_L C)$$

If a full-wave rectifier is used in the above example, the r.m.s. value of the transformer secondary voltage needs to be 150 V (i.e., a 150-0-150 V bi-phase secondary).

2.7 Inductor filter

This filter depends for its operation on the property of an inductance to oppose any change of current in its winding. A simple inductor filter is shown in Fig 2.10. The inductor or *choke* fulfils the function of providing a high series

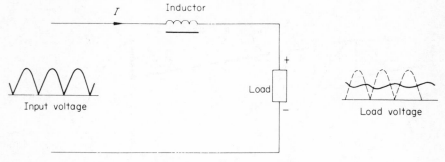

Fig. 2.10   A simple inductor filter.

impedance to the alternating ripple frequencies, while presenting only a low
resistance to the flow of unidirectional current. For example, a typical 10
henry choke has a resistance of about 225 Ω. If the supply frequency is 50 Hz,
then the reactance of the inductance to the lowest ripple frequency (100 Hz)
in the output of a full-wave rectifier is 6300 Ω. The rejection of the higher
harmonics of the supply frequency is further improved, since the reactance
of the inductor increases with frequency.

The design of an inductor filter is often a compromise, since the weight,
inductance, and resistance are interdependent. An increase in inductance
improves the performance of the filter, but it causes an increase in weight,
resistance, and cost of the choke. The resistance can be reduced by the use of
larger diameter wire, but this increases the weight and cost further.

Inductor filters are seldom used with half-wave rectifier circuits, since the
output voltage in such cases is very low when compared with the average value
of the rectified wave. This type of filter circuit, when used with a full-wave
circuit, provides a steady output voltage even with a large load current variation.
Also, the inductor has the effect of 'smoothing out' current impulses, and the
peak current drawn from the diodes is low when compared with the capacitor
filter circuit.

2.8   Choke input filter

The *choke input filter* or *inverted-L filter* is shown in Fig. 2.11(a). In this
circuit, the inductor provides a high impedance to harmonic currents, while
the capacitor shunts the remaining ripple current from the load. For low values
of load current, the circuit tends to operate as a simple capacitor filter; under
this condition, the rectifier current is discontinuous during the capacitor discharge periods. This operating condition is associated with a rapid reduction
in terminal voltage with load current, shown in Fig. 2.11(b). When the average
value of the load current reaches the value shown by I_K in the figure, the slope
of the characteristic is reduced and the output voltage does not fall as rapidly

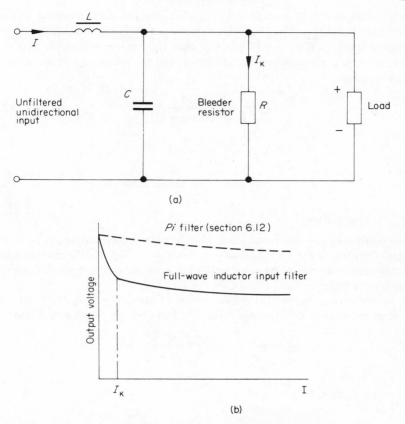

Fig. 2.11   (a) A choke input filter, and (b) its load characteristic.

with increase in load current as in the earlier part of the characteristic. This is the point at which the inductor causes the load current to become continuous, that is the rectifier current does not fall to zero. Beyond this point, the characteristic is generally similar to that of a simple inductor filter.

To overcome the problem of the rapid reduction in terminal voltage with load current at low values of load, the output is shunted by resistor R (see Fig. 2.11(a)), known as a *bleeder resistor,* which carries a current equal to or greater than I_K. Owing to the inductor-input nature of the circuit, the peak rectifier current is small when compared with capacitor-input circuits. Values of capacitance used lie between about 5 μF and 100 μF, and inductors between about 3 H and 30 H are used. The drop in terminal voltage with circuits incorporating a bleeder resistor is largely due to the effects of the resistance and leakage reactance of the transformer and choke.

A possible basis for the selection of the values of L and C is as follows. The reactance of C at the fundamental ripple frequency should be about one-tenth

of the minimum value of load resistance. Also, the resonant frequency of the
L-C circuit should not be greater than about one-fifth of the fundamental
ripple frequency. With a 50 Hz power supply the fundamental ripple frequency
generated by a full wave rectifier is 100 Hz, and the following relationships
may be used

$$C \geqslant \frac{0 \cdot 015}{\text{load resistance } (\Omega)} \text{ F} \qquad (2.10)$$

$$L \geqslant \frac{100 \times 10^{-6}}{C \text{(F)}} \text{ H} \qquad (2.11)$$

$$\geqslant 0 \cdot 007 \times \text{load resistance } (\Omega) \text{ H} \qquad (2.12)$$

2.9   The π filter

The performance of the choke input filter is improved by adding a capacitor in
parallel with its input terminals, as shown in Fig. 2.12. Since the configuration
of the reactive components is not unlike the mathematical π symbol, it gets its
name from this.

In this circuit, the rectifier delivers pulses of current to C_1 in much the same
manner as in the shunt capacitor filter. The filter section comprising L and C_2

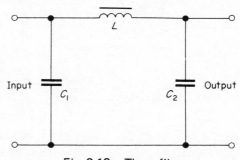

Fig. 2.12   The π filter.

smoothes out the ripple voltage appearing across the terminals of C_1. This
circuit provides a higher output voltage than the choke input filter described
above, but the rectifiers must provide a higher peak current to the π filter than
to the choke input filter because of the capacitor input nature of the circuit.

The component values for Fig. 2.12 supplied by a 50 Hz supply can be
estimated as follows $C_1 = C_2$ = twice the value computed from eq. (2.10)
L = the value calculated from eq. (2.11) or (2.12).

2.10   Ripple filters in a.c. circuits

The function of filters on the d.c. side of the circuit is to reduce the harmonic
currents in the load, and reduce inductive interference with nearby circuits. In

most rectifier circuits, harmonic currents also flow in the a.c. side, the order and magnitude of the harmonic currents depending on the rectifier connection.

The most satisfactory method of reducing harmonics on the a.c. side is to fit resonant filters to the circuit. These comprise tuned L-C circuits, one for each of the principal harmonics present. For higher frequency harmonics, broadband filters may be used to reduce groups of two or three harmonics.

2.11   Three-phase half-wave circuits

For outputs greater than about 2 kW the ripple content in the output from a single-phase rectifier is very high. If an output power greater than this is required, or a low ripple output is a desirable feature, then polyphase rectifier circuits must be employed. The simplest three-phase circuit is the half-wave circuit in Fig. 2.13(a). Here, a three-phase delta-star transformer is used to provide power to the circuit. When the potential of phase r is greater than that of either y or b, diode D1 conducts since it is forward biased and diodes D2 and D3 are reverse biased. This occurs between the two points marked 30 degrees and 150 degrees in Fig. 2.13(b). After the 150 degrees point, v_y has a greater potential than v_r, forcing the current to commutate to diode D2. The instant this occurs, the cathode of D1 is raised to a higher potential than that of its anode, and the current through it falls to zero. When v_b rises to a higher potential than v_y, the current commutates to diode D3. Later D1 takes the current up again, and the cycle is recommenced. The use of a three-phase supply increases the average output voltage to

$$V_L = 3 \times \frac{1}{2\pi} \left[\int_0^{30°} 0\, d(\omega t) + \int_{30°}^{150°} V_{SM} \sin \omega t\, d(\omega t) \right.$$

$$\left. + \int_{150°}^{360°} 0\, d(\omega t) \right]$$

$$= 0.827 V_{SM} = 1.17 V_s$$

The ripple magnitude at the output of a three-phase rectifier is much smaller than in either of the single-phase circuits, and the ripple frequency is higher (three times the supply frequency in Fig. 2.13). The inverse voltage waveform for diode D1 is plotted in Fig. 2.13(b), and it is found that there are two peaks, each having a magnitude of $\sqrt{3}\ V_{SM}$ or $2.449 V_s$.

2.12   Three-phase full-wave circuits

The *three-phase centre-tap circuit*, Fig. 2.14(a) is basically similar to the single-phase equivalent in that each secondary winding has a centre-tap and two diodes per phase are employed. The unidirectional output voltage is

$$V_L = 1.35 V_s$$

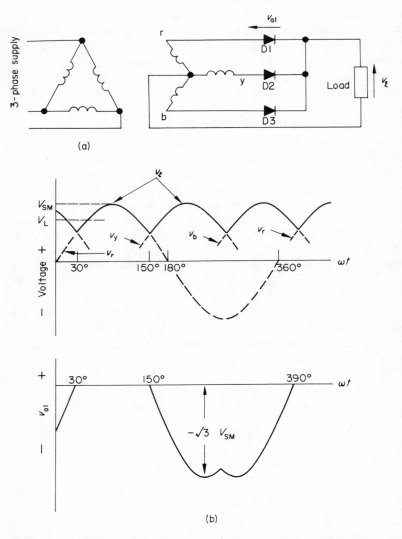

Fig. 2.13   (a) A three-phase half-wave rectifier circuit, and (b) typical waveforms.

and the diode p.i.v. is $2V_s$. This circuit is also described as a *six-phase half-wave circuit* since the centre-tap connection converts each single-phase supply into a bi-phase supply.

The three-phase bridge circuit of Fig. 2.14(b) is very frequently used since it is simple and does not require a centre-tap transformer. In the bridge circuit, when any one supply phase is more positive that the others, the upper

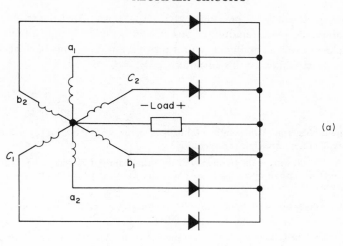

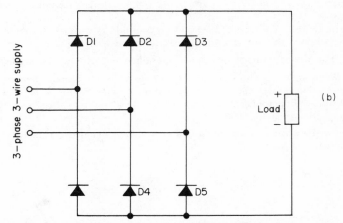

Fig. 2.14   (a) Three-phase full-wave centre-tap circuit, and (b) a three-phase bridge circuit.

connection of the load is connected to that supply line by the appropriate diode. Thus, when diode D1 is forward biased, and diodes D2 and D3 are reverse biased. The current is returned to the supply via diodes D4 and D5.

   This circuit gives the highest output voltage of those discussed so far, and is given by the expression

$$V_L = 2 \cdot 3 V_s$$

and each diode is subject to a peak inverse voltage of V_{SM}, which is not as great as in other polyphase rectifier systems.

The principal advantage of polyphase rectifier systems is that they are capable of supplying a large amount of power while generating only a low ripple signal. Six-, twelve-, and twenty-four phase rectifier circuits have been used in order to capitalize on this advantage.

Problems

2.1   Draw circuit diagrams of single-phase (a) half-wave, (b) centre-tap, and (c) bridge circuits, and explain their principles of operation.

2.2   Which of the following is the frequency of the principal ripple voltage at the output of a full-wave rectifier circuit operating from a 50 Hz power supply? (a) 25 Hz, (b) 50 Hz, (c) 100 Hz, (d) 150 Hz.

2.3   Explain the operation of one form of voltage multiplying circuit, and state one application.

2.4   State which of the following is a typical value for a capacitor for a filter circuit on a 50 Hz supply: (a) 10 pF, (b) 2000 pF, (c) 20 μF, (d) 10 F.

2.5   A rectifier circuit, operating at 50 Hz, supplies an output of 50 mA at 250 V. The output voltage is smoothed by a capacitor of 10 μF. Calculate the value of the load resistance.

Estimate the r.m.s. value of the transformer secondary voltage if the rectifier circuit is single-phase (a) half-wave, and (b) full-wave centre-tap.

2.6   Draw a circuit diagram of a choke input filter, and describe its operation.

2.7   When compared with a simple capacitor, does the choke input filter provide: (a) more filtering action and a smaller direct voltage drop, (b) more filtering action and a larger direct voltage drop, (c) less filtering action and a smaller direct voltage drop, (d) less filtering action and a larger direct voltage drop.

2.8   Explain why it is sometimes necessary to shunt an inductive load in an electronic circuit with a diode.

3. Bipolar junction transistors

3.1 The junction transistor

The junction transistor* was one of the first types of transistor to come into
commercial use, and many millions are now used in electronic circuits. The
junction transistor is a *bipolar transistor*, that is, it employs both p-type and
n-type semiconductor regions. Modern junction transistors are made from
silicon, and are mainly of the n-p-n type, shown in Fig. 3.1. That is, they
comprise a single crystal which contains two n-regions and a p-region. One of
the n-regions, known as the *emitter*, is of low resistivity material with a heavy
impurity doping. The emitter is the source of charge carriers in the transistor.
The central p-region is known as the *base region* of the transistor, and is a
relatively pure semiconductor of high resistivity. The base region is the control

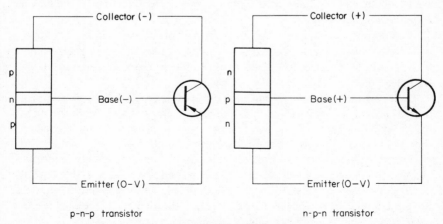

p-n-p transistor   n-p-n transistor

Fig. 3.1 Transistor symbols.

* The name transistor is derived from the expression *trans*fer re*sistor*.

33

electrode or control region of the transistor. The other n-region, known as the *collector region*, has a lower conductivity than the emitter region, and is the region in which the mobile charge carriers are finally collected.

The direction of the arrow on the emitter region in the circuit symbol indicates the *conventional direction of current flow* through the device. In a p-n-p transistor, the two extreme p-regions are the emitter and collector, respectively, while the central n-region is the base region. The rules for doping the regions of the n-p-n type apply to the p-n-p type.

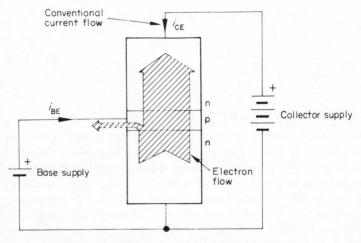

Fig. 3.2   The common-emitter connection.

In both transistor types, the junction between the emitter and the base is known as the *emitter junction*, and that between the collector and the base as the *collector junction*.

A simplified circuit diagram of an n-p-n transistor in the *common-emitter mode* or *common-emitter connection* is shown in Fig. 3.2. The circuit is known by this name since the emitter is common to the input (base) and output (collector) supplies.

Under normal operating conditions, the emitter junction is forward biased, and charge carriers are emitted by the low resistivity emitter region into the high resistivity base region. The collector supply voltage is normally much greater than the base circuit voltage, and the collector junction is reverse biased. The majority charge carriers (electrons) which leave the emitter become minority charge carriers when they arrive in the base region.

The base region is very thin (its thickness can be as little as 0·0005 mm) and the electrons (minority charge carriers) diffuse throughout it. Some of these electrons combine with holes (which are majority charge carriers in the p-type base) and disappear. The supply of holes is replenished in the form of base current (i_{BE}) from the external circuit.

When the electrons reach the collector junction they come under the influence of the positive potential connected to the collector region (see Fig. 3.2). The electrons are quickly swept into the collector region by this positive potential where they are 'collected'. In operation it is found that 98–99·8 per cent of the current leaving the emitter arrives at the collector.

It is therefore important in a bipolar transistor that the emitter region is heavily doped so that it readily emits charge carriers into the base region. Equally important, the base region must be very lightly doped so that very few charge carrier recombinations occur; also the base is very thin to allow the charge carriers leaving the emitter to reach the collector as quickly as possible.

3.2   Junction transistor configurations

When connected in an electronic circuit, one of the regions of the transistor is connected to the 'input' signal, another region is connected to the 'output' signal line, and the third region is connected to a line which is 'common' to the input and output signals. The circuit connection or configuration is named after the electrode which is connected to the common line. Thus we have *common-emitter circuits, common-base circuits* and *common-collector circuits.* Simplified versions of these circuits are shown in diagrams (a) to (c), respectively, of Fig. 3.3.

Important parameters of electronic circuits are their current gain, voltage gain and power gain. In this context the word 'gain' simply means the ratio of the *output signal* to the *input signal*, and does not necessarily have a direct relationship with the efficiency with which it utilizes its power supply. Other important parameters are the resistance (or impedance) between the input terminals (input resistance or impedance) and the resistance (or impedance) between the output terminals (output resistance or impedance). The latter is analogous to the 'internal' resistance of the circuit.

The common-emitter configuration is the most popular of the three circuits since it provides high values of current gain, voltage gain and power gain together with a reasonably high value of input resistance. The common-base circuit gives a high value of voltage gain together with a current gain of nearly unity; its input resistance is low and its output resistance is high. The common-collector configuration gives a voltage gain of slightly less than unity together with a high value of current gain; its input resistance is very high and its output resistance is low.

3.3   Bipolar transistor common-emitter characteristics

A typical test circuit to obtain the common-emitter static characteristics of an n-p-n transistor is shown in Fig. 3.4. Typical characteristics for a low power transistor are shown in Fig. 3.5. In the test circuit, the 500 Ω potentiometers are used to vary the base and collector supply voltages.

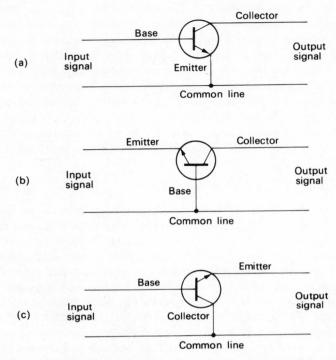

Fig. 3.3　n-p-n transistor configurations: (a) common-emitter, (b) common-base, (c) common-collector.

The *output characteristics*, Fig. 3.5(a), are particularly useful from a circuit design point of view, since they show how the collector current i_{CE} varies with the collector-to-emitter voltage v_{CE} over the normal working range of voltages. Initially, with the base circuit disconnected, the collector current is equal to the intrinsic leakage current in the common-emitter mode I_{CEO}. The subscript CE

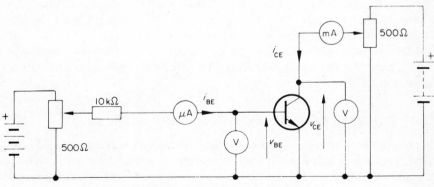

Fig. 3.4　Transistor test circuit.

indicates that current is flowing from collector to emitter, and the subscript O gives the value of the external base current. In a low power silicon planar transistor, I_{CEO} has a value of a few tens of nanoamperes. Under this condition, the base voltage is of the order of 100 mV, due to the flow of current through the transistor. Other values of leakage current of interest in the common-emitter mode are I_{CES} and I_{CEX}. I_{CES} is the collector leakage current with the base short-circuited to the emitter, and I_{CEX} is the collector leakage current with specified base circuit conditions.

When the collector voltage v_{CE} is held at a very low value (ideally zero), and voltage v_{BE} is applied to the base, the transistor is said to be operated in the *saturated region*. A very simple explanation of this is afforded by Fig. 3.5(c). To a first approximation, the transistor may be represented by the circuit in the figure, where diode D1 is the base-emitter junction diode, and D2 is the collector-base junction diode. When v_{BE} is greater than v_{CE}, both diodes are forward biased, and current flows from the base region to the emitter and collector regions. When this occurs, both diodes are 'saturated' with current carriers, hence the name saturated operation. This picture of the operation of the transistor is an imperfect one, and modifications are made to it as the chapter proceeds. When the transistor is used as a switching device, e.g., in electronic logic circuits, the transistor is frequently worked in the saturated region of the characteristic, and a parameter of some importance is the static value of the *saturation resistance* r_{CEsat}. This is the effective resistance between the emitter and collector at some specified point on the output characteristics. In Fig. 3.5, this may be specified at some point A, when the *saturated collector voltage* V_{CEsat} may be 0·6 V at a collector current of 10 mA. In this case,

$$r_{CEsat} = \frac{V_{CEsat}}{I_C} = \frac{0\cdot6}{0\cdot01} = 60 \ \Omega$$

To achieve this condition, the *base-emitter saturation voltage* V_{BEsat} is equal to, or greater than, the collector saturation voltage. In the above case, V_{BEsat} would be of the order of 0·8 V. When the transistor is working in its saturated region it is said to be turned ON, in much the same way that a switch is said to be turned ON when it carries a large current and has a small p.d. across it.

When the collector voltage is greater than the base voltage, the collector junction becomes reverse biased, and the transistor is said to be operating in its *unsaturated region*. In this region, collector current continues to flow as explained in section 3.1, and the greater the base current, the greater the collector current. When used in a *linear amplifier*, the transistor is biased to operate in the unsaturated region.

Under zero base-emitter current conditions, the transistor is said to be OFF, in as much as a switch is said to be OFF when it passes only leakage current and supports the whole of the supply voltage across itself. This region of the output characteristics is known as the *cut-off region*. If the polarity of v_{BE} is reversed,

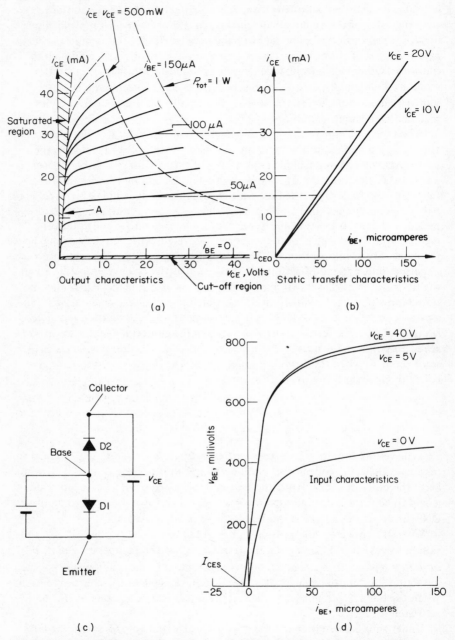

Fig. 3.5   (a) Common-emitter output characteristics, and (b) static transfer
characteristics. A simplified equivalent circuit in the saturated operating mode
is shown in (c), and the common-emitter input characteristics are shown in (d).

i.e., it it is made negative in Fig. 3.4, the emitter junction becomes reverse biased, and the collector current falls even further, to a value known as I_{CBO}. In this event, the emitter is effectively open-circuited, and the collector leakage current flows to the base circuit. The subscript CB designates collector-to-base current, and subscript O indicates the value of the external emitter current. In a low power silicon transistor, I_{CBO} is usually of the order of a few nanoamperes at normal values of collector current; for example, in the 2N929 it is less than 10nA. In transistors which handle several amperes, I_{CBO} may have a value of the order of 100 μA.

At values of v_{CE} well above the rated collector voltage, there is a sudden transition in the characteristics when the collector current rises very rapidly. This is due to *avalanche breakdown* of the reverse biased collector junction.

The *static transfer characteristic*, at a given value of v_{CE}, is predicted from the output characteristics by noting corresponding values of i_{CE} and i_{BE}. Thus, when v_{CE} = 20 V, i_{CE} = 30 mA when i_{BE} = 100 μA, and i_{CE} = 15 mA when i_{BE} = 50 μA, etc. These points are then plotted in Fig. 3.5(b) to give the static transfer characteristic for v_{CE} = 20 V. The static transfer characteristic for v_{CE} = 10 V is also given in the figure; it is curved due to its nearness to the curvature of the collector characteristics in that region.

The *static value of the forward current transfer ratio h_{FE}* (which is also known as the *large-signal common-emitter current gain*) of the transistor is given by the slope of the static transfer characteristic, and is quoted at a particular value of v_{CE}. In the case of Fig. 3.5(b), its value at v_{CE} = 20 V is h_{FE} = 30 mA/ 100 μA = 300. The numerical value of the current gain usually lies between about 20 and 600. The *parameter spread* of h_{FE} is about 4:1; that is, transistors of one type may have quoted minimum and maximum current gains of 150 and 600, respectively, while a typical value may be 350. Circuits must be designed to take account of the parameter spread. A moment's consideration of Figs. 3.5(a) and (b), indicates that h_{FE} falls in value as v_{CE} falls. The lowest value of current gain occurs when the transistor is working in its saturated mode, when the current gain is described by h_{FEsat}. In the case of the 2N929 transistor, one saturated condition is V_{CEsat} = 1 V when i_{BE} = 0·5 mA and i_{CE} = 10 mA. This corresponds to a current gain of 20, compared with a value of about 400 when working in the unsaturated region.

From the output characteristics, it appears that when a current flows in the base circuit, a much larger current flows in the collector circuit. The relationship between the two currents is given, neglecting leakage current, by the relationship

$$i_{CE} = k i_{BE}$$

where k is another parameter of the transistor. The simple equivalent circuit of Fig. 3.5(c) is modified to take account of this fact, by shunting the collector diode by a constant current generator, as shown in Fig. 3.6. For most low frequency applications, the equivalent circuit of Fig. 3.6 is adequate.

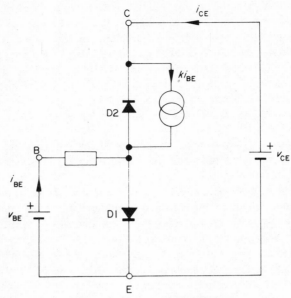

Fig. 3.6   One form of equivalent circuit.

Since the base-emitter circuit of a transistor corresponds roughly to a diode, the input characteristic, Fig. 3.5(d), has a diode-type shape. When $i_{BE} = 0$, i.e., the base circuit is disconnected, there exists a small potential at the base terminal due to the leakage current through the transistor. Only by short-circuiting the base and emitter regions together externally can v_{BE} be reduced to zero. In this event, leakage current I_{CES} flows out of the base region. In a low power silicon transistor, I_{CES} has the value of a few nanoamperes.

The input resistance of the transistor in the common-emitter mode is approximately equal to the sum of the forward conducting resistance of the diode and the ohmic resistance of the base region. The latter is represented by the resistance in series with the base lead in Fig. 3.6.

3.4   Transistor rating limitations

The regions on transistor characteristics which may be used are subject to certain limitations. In addition to the maximum collector voltage, which has already been discussed, there is a limit to the *maximum base-emitter reverse voltage*. Under certain conditions, e.g., in switching circuits, the emitter junction is reverse biased; due to the high impurity doping in the emitter region, the reverse breakdown voltage of the emitter junction is generally lower than the collector junction breakdown voltage.

The *maximum collector current* rating is rarely limited by the current carrying capacity of the device itself. It is often determined either by the power dissipation of the transistor, or by the reduction in current gain at high values of current.

The *maximum power* rating P_{tot} is related to the *maximum allowable junction temperature* T_{jmax}, which is about 85°C in germanium devices and 200°C in silicon devices. The *thermal resistance* of a transistor is an indication of the ability with which the transistor can dissipate heat, and is the junction temperature rise per unit power dissipated (C deg. per watt (or milliwatt)). For instance, a silicon transistor with a rating of 300 mW at 25°C and a maximum permissible junction temperature of 175°C, may have a thermal resistance of 0·5 C deg./mW. This results in a derating curve with a slope of 2 mW/C deg. The rating of this transistor at an ambient temperature of 50°C is $[300 - (50 - 25) \times 2]$ mW = 250 mW. Power derating curves for specific types of transistors are generally supplied by manufacturers.

It is found that the current gain has a constant value at low frequencies, but at higher frequencies its magnitude reduces. There are two principal reasons for this effect. Firstly, the minority charge carriers in the base region take a finite time, known as the *transit time*, to reach the collector. This time reduces with reducing base width, and planar transistors with a base width of about 0·5 μm exhibit a uniform gain up to frequencies of several hundred megahertz. The second effect is due to the capacitance of the collector junction. The *cut-off frequency* of a transistor in any given mode of operation is defined as the frequency at which the current transfer ratio is reduced to 0·707 of its initial value. The common-base cut-off frequency (the *alpha cut-off frequency* f_α or f_{hfb}) is much higher than the cut-off frequency of the same transistor operating in the common-emitter mode. For this reason common-base circuits are often used in applications which are beyond the frequency range of common-emitter amplifiers

3.5 Common-base characteristics

The common-base circuit [Fig. 3.7(a)] has the output characteristics and transfer characteristics shown in Figs. 3.7(b) and (c), respectively. In the common-base mode, the input circuit carries slightly more current than is carried in the collector circuit. Since the emitter current (the input current in this mode) is large, the input impedance of the common-emitter stage is low. Since the collector current is practically constant over the working range of v_{CB}, the output impedance of this configuration is very high, making it difficult to cascade common-emitter stages, since the output impedance of the driver stage is not matched to the input impedance of the driven stage.

The ratio i_{CB}/i_{EB} is known as the *static value of the forward current transfer ratio* h_{FB}. For convenience, in transistor circuit analysis, all currents are assumed to flow into the transistor and, as will be seen from the following, this leads to h_{FB} having a negative value. In Fig. 3.7(a) it is seen that both i_{CB} and i_{EB} appear to flow into the transistor, but a moment's consideration will show that, in fact,

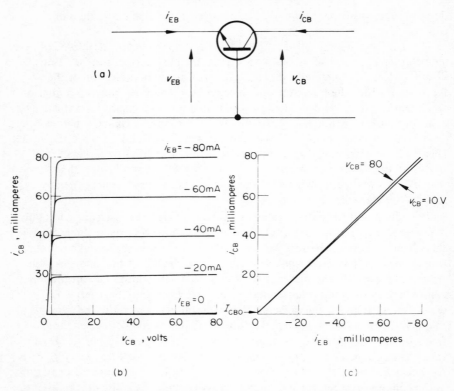

Fig. 3.7   (a) The common-base circuit, (b) output characteristics, and (c) the static transfer characteristics.

one of the two currents must flow out of the transistor. Thus, if a collector current of 98 mA flows *into* the transistor, and the base current is 2 mA, then an emitter current of 100 mA flows *out* of the transistor.

Hence,

$$h_{FB} = \frac{+98}{-100} = -0\cdot98$$

The value of h_{FB} usually lies between $-0\cdot98$ and about $-0\cdot998$. The *small-signal common-base current gain* α is the magnitude of the ratio i_c/i_e, without regard to sign, and

$$\alpha = -h_{fb}$$

The leakage current of the transistor in the common-base circuit is the collector-to-base current with the emitter (input circuit) open-circuited. This leakage current is designated I_{CBO} for the same transistor. To a first approximation, the relationship between the two values of leakage current is given by

$$I_{CBO} = I_{CEO}(1 + h_{FB})$$

3.6 The common-collector configuration

Transistors are frequently used in this configuration as buffer stages between circuits with widely differing impedances, but common-collector parameters are rarely quoted in manufacturers' literature. The common-collector amplifier will be dealt with at length in the chapter on feedback amplifiers.

3.7 Voltage and current sources

The principal requirement of an ideal voltage source is that its terminal voltage must be unvarying over a wide range of load conditions, i.e., from no-load to a value in excess of its rated power output. This is illustrated in Fig. 3.8(a). No-load operation is defined as the condition in which zero power is delivered into the load. In the case of a voltage source it occurs when the load current is zero, i.e., the load is disconnected.

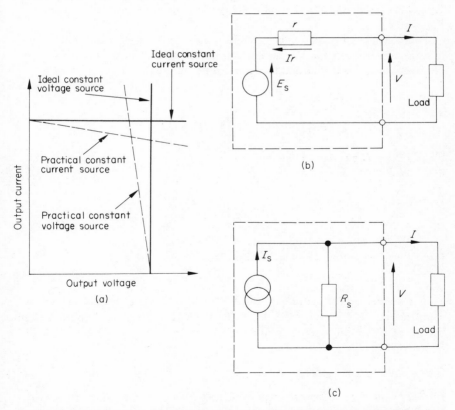

Fig. 3.8 (a) Characteristics of ideal and practical voltage and current sources. The equivalent circuit of a practical voltage source is shown in (b), and that of a practical current source is shown in (c).

An ideal current source must be capable of supplying an unvarying current to the load, from no-load to a value in excess of its rated power output. The no-load condition of a current source corresponds to the case where it delivers current into a load of zero resistance, i.e., when its terminals are short-circuited.

To satisfy the above conditions, the internal impedance or *output impedance* of the ideal voltage generator is zero, so that there is no reduction in terminal voltage with increase of load current. The output impedance of an ideal current generator is infinity, so that whatever load impedance is connected it does not alter the current delivered to the load. Ideal conditions are rarely achieved in practice, and a compromise must be made to obtain equivalent circuits which represent practical versions of the generators. The practical limitations are accounted for by including a resistor r in series with the ideal constant voltage source E_S, as shown in Fig. 3.8(b) (often known as a *Thévènin equivalent voltage source*), and by shunting the ideal current source I_S in Fig. 3.8(c) by resistor R_S (often known as a *Norton equivalent current source*). The characteristics of the two practical circuits are then as shown by the broken lines in Fig. 3.8(a).

In circuit design it is often convenient to use the voltage generator concept in some applications, and the current concept in others. The relationship between the two is deduced as follows. For the voltage source

$$V = E_S - Ir$$

or

$$I = \frac{E_S}{r} - \frac{V}{r}$$

therefore

$$\frac{E_S}{r} = I + \frac{V}{r} \tag{3.1}$$

For the current generator

$$I_S = I + \frac{V}{R_S} \tag{3.2}$$

For equivalence of eqs. (3.1) and (3.2)

$$I_S = E_S/r \quad \text{and} \quad R_S = r$$

Thus, a voltage source with $E_S = 50$ V and $r = 100$ Ω is equivalent to a current source having $I_S = 50/100 = 0.5$ A and $R_S = 100$ Ω. Both develop an open-circuit voltage of 50 V, and pass 0·5 A into a short-circuit.

3.8 Transistor *h*-parameters

Hybrid parameters or *h-parameters* are widely used in connection with bipolar transistors because they can be easily measured using simple circuits. Two types of hybrid parameters are quoted for transistors, namely *small-signal h*-parameters and *large-signal h*-parameters. Small-signal parameters are used in cases where the magnitude of the input signal is small (say a fraction of a volt). Large signal parameters are used where the change in the input signal is large, as occurs in the case of certain types of switching circuits or logic circuits and in power amplifiers. The parameters are so named because their dimensions are mixed. One of the h-parameters has the dimensions of resistance, one has the dimensions of conductance, while two are dimensionless. The small-signal h-parameters are defined by the equations

$$V_1 = h_i I_1 + h_r V_2 \qquad (3.3)$$

$$I_2 = h_f I_1 + h_o V_2 \qquad (3.4)$$

where V_1 is the r.m.s. value of the small-signal voltage applied to the input of the transistor, I_1 is the r.m.s. input current, V_2 is the r.m.s. value of the small-signal output voltage, and I_2 is the r.m.s. output current. The subscripts represent the relationships

   i = Input parameter, having the dimensions of resistance.

   r = Reverse parameter, which is dimensionless.

   f = Forward parameter, which is dimensionless.

   o = Output parameter, having the dimensions of conductance.

Depending on the circuit configuration, i.e., common-emitter, common-collector, or common-base, other subscripts are given to the parameters, viz.

   e = Common-emitter configuration.

   b = Common-base configuration.

   c = Common-collector configuration.

Thus, for the common-emitter configuration, eqs. (3.3) and (3.4) become

$$V_{be} = h_{ie} I_{be} + h_{re} V_{ce} \qquad (3.5)$$

$$I_{ce} = h_{fe} I_{be} + h_{oe} V_{ce} \qquad (3.6)$$

where h_{ie} is the input parameter in the common-emitter mode, etc., V_{be} is the r.m.s. input voltage, I_{be} is the r.m.s. input current, and V_{ce} and I_{ce} are the corresponding output quantities, respectively.

To be strictly accurate, h_{ie} and h_{fe} should both be measured with $V_{ce} = 0$, i.e., the output should be short-circuited to a.c. signals. This condition can be approximated to under small-signal conditions in a test circuit. Similarly, h_{re} and h_{oe} should be measured with $I_{be} = 0$, i.e., the input should be open-circuited to signal frequencies. In the following, a procedure is outlined for determining the parameters from the static characteristics, but in practice they are obtained by dynamic tests.

In determining the static characteristics of transistors, difficulty is experienced in taking reliable measurements close to the maximum power limit, and a practical solution is to use a transistor curve tracer in which the base current is applied impulsively so that the transistor does not operate for long periods of time at or near to its maximum power rating.

A qualitative explanation of the hybrid equations for the common-emitter mode of operation follows from an inspection of Fig. 3.6. When the transistor is conducting, the emitter diode D1 carries the collector current, resulting in a p.d. across the diode. The proportion of the collector signal voltage which appears between the base and emitter due to the collector current flowing in D1 is $h_{re}V_{ce}$. The net signal voltage acting in the input circuit is, therefore, $V_{be}-h_{re}V_{ce}$. Since the base and emitter regions are coupled together, there is an ohmic connection between them. If this resistance has a value $h_{ie}\Omega$, then the voltage drop in the base-emitter circuit when it carries current I_{be} is $h_{ie}I_{be}$. That is

$$V_{be} - h_{re}V_{ce} = h_{ie}I_{be}$$

or

$$V_{be} = h_{ie}I_{be} + h_{re}V_{ce}$$

which corresponds to eq. (3.5).

The total collector current I_{ce} is due in part to the collector voltage V_{ce}

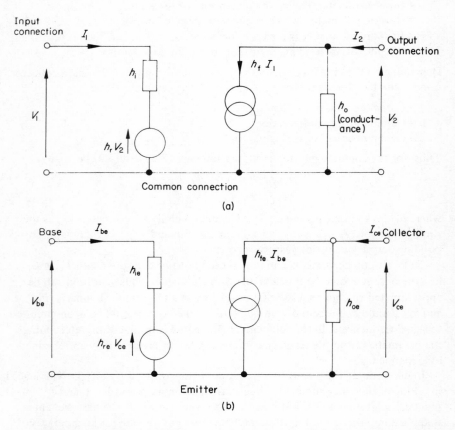

(a)

(b)

Fig. 3.9   (a) The general hybrid equivalent circuit, and (b) the common-emitter hybrid equivalent circuit.

appearing across the ohmic connections within the transistor. If h_{oe} is the effective conductance of the conducting path between the collector and the emitter, then the proportion of the collector current which flows in h_{oe} is $h_{oe} V_{ce}$. The remaining part of the collector current, which is usually the greater part, is due to the amplification of the base current. This is $h_{fe} I_{be}$. The total collector current is, therefore, the sum of the two components

$$I_{ce} = h_{fe} I_{be} + h_{oe} V_{ce}$$

which corresponds to eq. (3.6).

The equivalent circuit satisfying the general h-parameters, eqs. (3.3) and (3.4), is shown in Fig. 3.9(a), and that for the common-emitter equations, eqs. (3.5) and (3.6), is shown in Fig. 3.9(b). It is seen that both equivalent circuits contain two active elements, a voltage generator in the input circuit and a current generator in the output circuit. The parameters for any given configuration are obtained either from the static characteristics or by means of a dynamic test *in that particular configuration*. Typical h-parameter values for a silicon planar transistor in both the common-emitter and common-base modes are given in Table 3.1.

Table 3.1
Typical hybrid parameters of a silicon planar transistor

	Common-emitter	Common-base
h_i	$5 \text{ k}\Omega$	$30 \, \Omega$
h_r	$2 \cdot 5 \times 10^{-4}$	6×10^{-4}
h_f	200	$-0 \cdot 994$
h_o	$15 \, \mu\text{S}$	$1 \, \mu\text{S}$

A method of estimating the common-emitter parameters from the static characteristics is shown in Fig. 3.10. Using the input characteristics, Fig. 3.10(a),

$$h_{ie} = \delta v_{BE1} / \delta i_{BE} \qquad \text{at constant } v_{CE}$$

$$h_{re} = \delta v_{BE2} / \delta v_{CE} \qquad \text{at constant } i_{BE}$$

and from the output characteristics, Fig. 3.10(b),

$$h_{fe} = \delta i_{CE1} / \delta i_{BE} \qquad \text{at constant } v_{CE}$$

$$h_{oe} = \delta i_{CE2} / \delta v_{CE} \qquad \text{at constant } i_{BE}$$

h_{fe} is also given the symbol β. The common-base parameters are determined in much the same way from the common-base input and output characteristics, respectively.

The relationship between h_{fe} and h_{fb} may be deduced as follows. Since

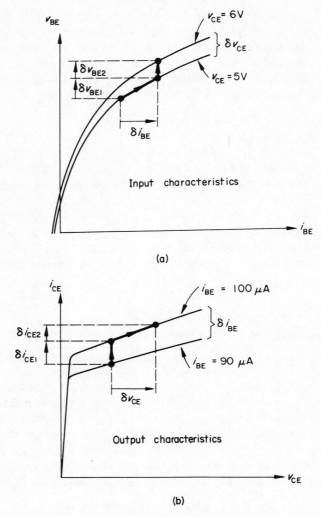

Fig. 3.10   (a) One method of evaluating h_{ie} and h_{re}, and (b) determination of h_{fe} and h_{oe}.

current is always assumed to flow into the transistor from the external circuits then

$$I_b + I_c + I_e = 0$$

or

$$I_e = -(I_b + I_c)$$

hence,

$$\frac{1}{h_{fb}} = \frac{I_e}{I_c} = \frac{-(I_b + I_c)}{I_c} = -\left(\frac{I_b}{I_c} + 1\right) = -\left(\frac{1}{h_{fe}} + 1\right)$$

therefore,

$$h_{fb} = \frac{-h_{fe}}{1 + h_{fe}} = -\alpha \tag{3.7}$$

$$h_{fe} = \frac{-h_{fb}}{1 + h_{fb}} = \frac{\alpha}{1 - \alpha} \tag{3.8}$$

For example, if h_{fe} = 99, then h_{fb} = $-99/100$ = -0.99, or α = 0.99, and if the transistor has a value of -0.98 for h_{fb}, then h_{fe} = $-(-0.98)/[1 + (-0.98)]$ = 49. This calculation illustrates the fact that a small change in h_{fb} gives a much greater change in h_{fe}; a change in h_{fb} from -0.99 to -0.98 gives a change in h_{fe} of 99 to 49.

When the transistor is used as a switch, we are primarily interested in the large-signal parameters, which are defined in the common-emitter mode by the equations

$$v_{BE} = h_{IE} i_{BE} + h_{RE} v_{CE} \tag{3.9}$$

$$i_{CE} = h_{FE} i_{BE} + h_{OE} v_{CE} \tag{3.10}$$

3.9 Simplified hybrid equivalent circuit

In some instances, it is possible to make simplifying assumptions to reduce the complexity of the equivalent circuit. Generally speaking, h_r is very small in both the common-emitter and common-base modes (see Table 3.1), so that the voltage generator $h_r V_2$ can be omitted from the input circuit without significant loss of accuracy. This gives the equivalent circuit in Fig. 3.11(a). In other cases, conductance h_o is small when compared with the conductance of any load connected to the output terminals. In this case, h_o may be neglected, giving the ultimate in simplicity in Fig. 3.11(b). It must be emphasized that the simplified equivalent circuits yield accurate results only when the assumptions are justified.

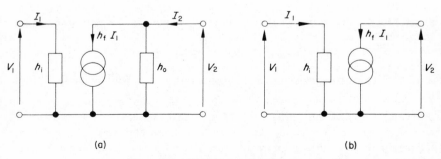

(a)   (b)

Fig. 3.11   Simplified hybrid equivalent circuits.

3.10 Transistor parameter variation and its working region

The numerical value of transistor parameters depends upon many factors, including the bias conditions, the collector current, the collector voltage, and the operating temperature. Bias conditions under which acceptance tests should be carried out are specified in data sheets, although it must be borne in mind that parameters vary considerably between transistors of the same type. Figure 3.12 shows the way in which the h-parameters for the common-emitter configuration vary with collector current and junction temperature.

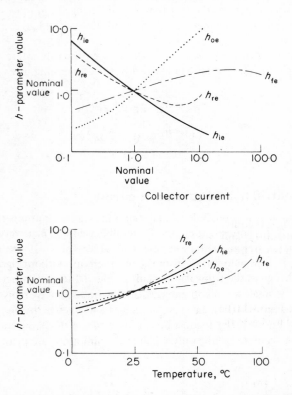

Fig. 3.12 Variation of the common-emitter parameters with collector current and temperature.

3.11 Choice of semiconductor materials

Transistors are often described as being suitable for entertainment, industrial or professional applications. Broadly speaking, transistors suitable for *entertainment* applications are produced by the most economical process available, and the parameter tolerances are normally very wide. The circuits in which they are used must be designed to accept the wide spread of parameters.

Devices intended for the *industrial* market, e.g., communications equipment and high quality instrumentation, are subject to more careful checks, including reliability tests. Transistors for the *professional* market are subject to the most exacting tests, and must meet stringent requirements. The price of an individual device reflects, to some extent, the degree of testing required in its selection.

So far as the bulk material of the semiconductor is concerned, manufacturing technology has reached a stage where both silicon and germanium devices are equally reliable. The choice then depends on other factors, such as leakage current, breakdown voltage, etc.

3.12 Semiconductor numbering and outline shapes

Semiconductor devices are registered under many numbering systems, some giving more useful information than others. American devices have numbers allocated to them in the order in which they were registered. These numbers are given by the Joint Electronic Device Engineering Council, the numbers being known as JEDEC numbers. In this system, the first numeral gives the number of p-n junctions, '1' for a diode, '2' for a triode-type transistor, '3' for a tetrode device or a thyristor, etc. This is followed by the letter N, and the registration number. Thus, a device numbered 2N2927 is a two-junction semiconductor device, which was the 2927th to be registered.

In the old European system, the first group of numerals gave the heater voltage (on the assumption that it is a thermionic device). When semiconductors came along, this numeral was '0'. The type of device was indicated by a letter, 'A' for a diode, 'C' for a triode, etc. Additional letters, e.g., 'P' for a photoeffect or radiation sensitive device, 'R' for a photoresistive semiconductor material, etc., are also used. Thus, the 0CP71 is a phototransistor.

In the *PRO ELECTRON* European system the type number has five alpha-numeric symbols, comprising either two letters and three numbers, or three letters and two numbers. The first letter indicates the semiconductor material used, 'A' for germanium, 'B' for silicon, 'C' for gallium arsenide, etc. The second letter indicates the most common application of the device. A list corresponding to this letter is given in Table 3.2. Where two numbers are included in the type symbol, e.g., BFX63, the device is intended for industrial and professional equipment, and when it contains three numerals, e.g., BF194, it is intended for entertainment or consumer equipment. The PRO ELECTRON system also provides for sub-classes by the addition of an alpha-numeric group separated from the basic number by a hyphen, e.g., BTY79-600R. This device is a silicon thyristor, registration number Y79, which has a rated maximum repetitive peak reverse voltage of 600 V. The 'R' denotes reverse connection, i.e., the stud is the anode.

When transistor construction was first commenced, manufacturers devised their own methods of encapsulations or *outlines.* In more recent years, there has been a great deal of standardization, based mainly on JEDEC outlines. The most

Table 3.2

PRO ELECTRON application type numbers

Letter Application

A	Signal diode
B	Variable capacitance diode
C	A.F. low power transistor
D	A.F. power transistor
E	Tunnel diode
F	H.F. low power transistor
G	Multiple device
H	Field probe
L	H.F. power transistor
M	Hall effect modulator
P	Radiation sensitive device
Q	Radiation generating device
R	Specialized breakdown device
S	Low power switching transistor
T	Power switching device (thyristors, etc.)
U	Power switching transistor
X	Multiple diode
Y	Power diode
Z	Zener diode

common metal-can forms for low power devices are cylindrical in shape (see Fig. 3.13(a)). Many types of transistors for the domestic market are encapsulated in plastic (see Fig. 3.13(b)). Where the collector power dissipation exceeds about 1 W, the canister has a diamond shaped metallic construction which is bolted to a heat sink. In power transistors, the collector is connected internally to the metal canister to minimize the thermal resistance to flow of heat.

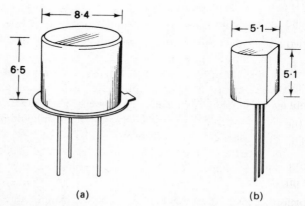

(a)   (b)

Fig. 3.13   Transistor packaging: (a) TO-5 canister (or can) and (b) one form of plastic encapsulation (all dimensions in mm).

Problems

3.1 Explain the following terms: valence electron, covalent bond.

3.2 Discuss the relative merits of the constant voltage (Thevenin) generator circuit and the constant current (Norton) generator circuit in electronic circuit analysis.

3.3 A certain generator provides an output voltage of 9 V when delivering 10 mA, and 8 V when delivering 20 mA. Derive both the Thevenin and Norton equivalent circuits of the generator.

3.4 Explain the principle of operation of a junction transistor.

3.5 Why are junction transistors sensitive to variations in temperature? Describe a circuit which minimizes the effects of temperature variation on the collector current.

3.6 Give an explanation why h-parameters are the most commonly quoted parameters of transistors.

3.7 With the aid of a circuit diagram briefly explain how you would obtain experimentally the output and transfer characteristics of an n-p-n transistor in the common-emitter mode.

Sketch on suitably scaled axes the curves you would expect to obtain for a low power general-purpose transistor. Give typical values of the h-parameters that would be obtained from this test.

Sketch also the characteristics which would be obtained from a p-n-p transistor in the common-emitter mode, clearly indicating the polarities of the voltages and the directions of the currents.

3.8 A certain transistor has a current gain of 0·99 in the common-base configuration; determine its current gain in the common-emitter configuration. Another transistor has $h_{FE} = 80$; determine h_{FB}.

3.9 The input characteristics of a low power transistor are as follows:

i_{BE} (μA)	v_{BE} (mV) at v_{CE} of	
	5 V	10 V
−5	68	75
0	103	108
5	125	128
10	140	142
15	152	155
20	162	165
25	171	174
30	180	183

The output characteristics are linear between the following points:

v_{CE} (V)	2	10	
i_C (mA)	1·9	2·9	when $i_B = 20$ μA
i_C (mA)	2·7	3·75	when $i_B = 30$ μA

Estimate the values of the hybrid parameters of this transistor if the quiescent base current and voltage are 25 μA and 170 mV, respectively, and the quiescent collector current is 2·7 mA.

3.10 Sketch the output characteristics relating the collector current and collector voltage of a bipolar junction transistor when connected in (a) the common-base configuration, and (b) the common-emitter configuration. State the type of transistor. e.g., n-p-n or p-n-p, for which the characteristics are drawn, clearly indicating the polarities of the quantities concerned on the characteristics.

Write down the hybrid parameter equations for the common-emitter configuration, and state typical values for a low power transistor. Sketch the circuit diagram of a suitable test circuit to evaluate the common-emitter parameters.

4. Field-effect transistors

4.1 Types of field-effect transistor

The flow of current through a field-effect transistor (FET) is controlled by means of an electric field in the semiconductor, the field being produced by a voltage applied between the *gate electrode* and the *conducting channel* of the device. There are two families of FETs, namely:

(a) junction-gate FETs (JUGFET or JFET)
(b) insulated-gate FETs (IGFET, MOSFET or MOST)

4.2 Junction-gate FETs

The principle of operation of the JUGFET can be explained by reference to the n-channel device in Fig. 4.1. The device (see Fig. 4.1(a)) comprises a bar or *channel* of n-type material with a *gate region* of p-type semiconductor diffused into it; practical devices have two p-type gate regions diffused into opposite sides of the bar, and are usually electrically connected together. The device shown is described as an *n-channel* JUGFET since the conducting channel between the source and drain electrodes is n-type material; p-channel devices are also manufactured having a bar or channel of p-type material together with an n-type gate diffusion.

Since the conducting channel of the FET illustrated is an n-type semi-conductor, current flow in the channel is due to flow of electrons which enter at the *source electrode* and leave at the *drain electrode*. Thus, in the FET shown, the source electrode is connected to the negative pole of the supply and the drain electrode to the positive pole. When the gate bias voltage (V_G) is zero, that is the gate and source are connected together, and when the drain voltage is low, the conducting channel of the FET has the characteristic of a resistor whose value lies between about 100 Ω and 1 kΩ. This fact is indicated

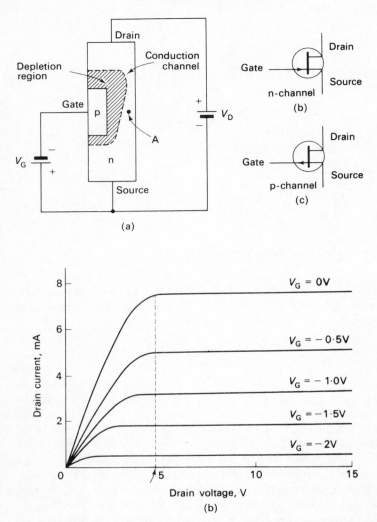

Fig. 4.1   (a) A cross-section through a simplified n-channel JUGFET. Symbols for (b) n-channel and (c) p-channel JUGFETs. (d) Typical family of output characteristics for an n-channel device.

in the circuit symbol (Fig. 4.1(b)) by means of the solid line (representing a conducting path) between the source and drain electrodes. The nature of the gate-to-source p-n junction is indicated by the arrow on the circuit symbol; it points in the direction of the arrow associated with a conventional diode, so that in an n-channel device it points towards the n-channel. In a p-channel device it points away from the channel (see Fig. 4.1(c)).

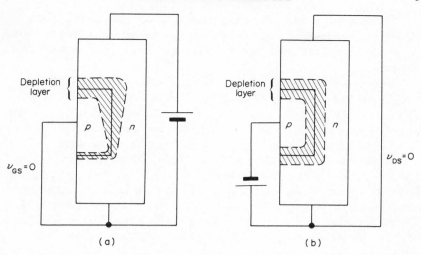

Fig. 4.2 Methods of producing a depletion layer in the conducting channel.

JUGFETs may be connected in one of three configurations, namely *common-source, common-gate* or *common-drain*. The common-source configuration in Fig. 4.1 is the most popular method.

The common-source operation of the JUGFET is described as follows. When the gate-to-channel junction is reverse biased, a depletion region is formed as shown in Fig. 4.1(a). The effect of the depletion layer is to reduce the width of the channel which is available for conduction. The depletion layer can be developed in one of two ways. One way is shown in Fig. 4.2(a), and occurs when the gate bias voltage has a constant value (which is zero in the case shown). The flow of drain current gives rise to a potential drop along the face of the gate region, and the potential at the end of the gate nearest to the source electrode is lower than that at the drain electrode end of the gate. Consequently the depletion region due to this effect has a greater depth at the drain electrode end of the gate. Increasing the drain voltage causes the depth of the depletion layer to progressively increase. A point is finally reached when the depletion region causes the conducting channel to be pinched into a very thin sheet. The drain voltage at which *pinchoff* occurs with zero gate voltage is known as the *pinchoff voltage*, V_P. At drain voltages greater than the pinchoff voltage the drain current becomes constant, and the drain current for zero gate voltage is known as the *drain-source saturation current*, I_{DSS}.

The second way of producing a depletion region is by applying a reverse bias to the gate-to-channel p-n junction (see Fig. 4.2(b)). In order to eliminate the effects of the depletion layer due to the drain voltage, described above, the conditions at zero drain voltage are described. Increasing the reverse bias applied to the gate increases the depth of the depletion layer, and vice versa. In operation, production of the depletion layer is due to both causes described above.

At drain voltages below V_P, the effective drain-source resistance of the JUGFET can be controlled by means of the gate voltage; in this way the device can be used as a voltage-controlled resistor, known as a *pinch-effect resistor.*

When the drain voltage is greater than V_P, the characteristics are flat and a large change in drain voltage produces only a small change in drain current. This type of characteristic is typical of a resistor having a very high value; the equivalent resistance of the FET on this part of the characteristics is known as the *slope resistance* or *drain resistance*, r_d, and it has a high value.

The effect of increasing the reverse gate bias on the *output characteristics* or *drain characteristics* is illustrated in Fig. 4.1(d). Increasing the reverse gate bias voltage results in the onset of pinchoff at a lower value of drain voltage, causing the drain current to be reduced or depleted. Field-effect devices having a finite drain current at zero gate voltage, and whose drain current is reduced when the reverse gate bias is increased are known as *depletion-mode* devices.

4.3   JUGFET common-source parameters

Under normal operating conditions the gate-to-channel p-n junction is reverse biased so that the gate current is practically zero. That is, the input resistance of the JUGFET is practically infinity, and can be represented on the equivalent circuit by an open-circuit.

The parameters relating to the output circuit are deduced from the output characteristics in Fig. 4.3. The change in drain current, δi_{D1}, between points X

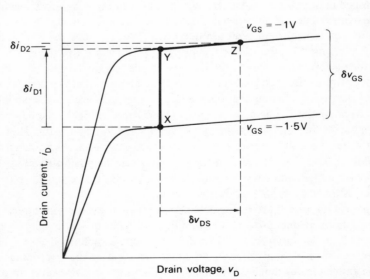

Fig. 4.3   Evaluating the output parameters of the JUGFET.

and Y (at constant drain voltage) is related to the change in gate-source voltage, δv_{GS}, by the *mutual conductance*, g_m, as follows

$$\delta i_{D1} = g_m \delta v_{GS}$$

or

$$g_m = \frac{\delta i_{D1}}{\delta v_{GS}} \qquad (4.1)$$

The mutual conductance is also known as the *transconductance*, and the symbols g_{fs} and y_{fs} are sometimes used. The value of g_m usually lies in the range 0·1–10 mS (mA/V).

The relationship between the change in drain current, δi_{D2}, and the change in drain-to-source voltage, δv_{DS}, at constant gate voltage is given by the *slope resistance* or *drain resistance*, r_d, as follows.

r_d = inverse of the slope of the output characteristic between Y and Z

$$= \frac{\delta v_{DS}}{\delta i_{D2}} \qquad (4.2)$$

and typically has a value in the range 0·1–1 MΩ. This parameter is sometimes quoted in terms of the slope of the output characteristic, when it is described as the *output conductance*, g_{os} or y_{os}, whose value is in the range 1–10 μS.

Example 4.1: The following measurements were taken on an n-channel JUGFET. Assuming that the output characteristics are linear, determine the value of the mutual conductance and the drain resistance for v_{DS} = 13 V and at a gate bias voltage of (a) − 0·5 V, (b) −1·5 V.

v_{DS} (V)	i_D (mA) at v_{GS} of				
	0 V	−0·5 V	−1·0 V	−1·5 V	−2·0 V
6	7·2	4·9	3·1	1·65	0·45
13	7·25	5·0	3·2	1·8	0·5
20	7·3	5·1	3·35	1·9	0·65

Solution: (a) Assuming that the gate voltage changes by ± 0·5 V about the bias voltage of −0·5 V, the instantaneous gate voltage changes between 0 V and −1 V. Hence δv_{GS} = 1 V (see also Fig. 4.3). The corresponding values of drain current at v_{DS} = 13 V are 7·25 mA (corresponding to point Y on Fig. 4.3) and 3·2 mA (corresponding to point X), hence

$$g_m = \delta i_{D1}/\delta v_{GS} = (7\cdot25 - 3\cdot2) \text{ mA}/1 \text{ V} = 4\cdot05 \text{ mS or mA/V}$$

The slope resistance is determined from the output characteristic for a bias voltage of v_{GS} = − 0·5 as follows. Assuming that the drain voltage changes by

±7 V about the quiescent drain voltage of 13 V, then the maximum and minimum values of drain voltage are 20 V and 6 V, respectively, hence δv_{DS} = 20-6 = 14 V. The corresponding change in drain current δi_{D2} is 5·1-4·9 = 0·2 mA, hence

$$r_d = \delta v_{DS}/\delta i_{D2} = 14 \text{ V}/0·2 \text{ mA} = 70 \text{ k}\Omega$$

(b) The corresponding values for v_{DS} = 13 V and a gate bias voltage of −1·5 V are

$$g_m = (3·2 - 0·5) \text{ mA}/(-1 - [-2]) \text{ V} = 2·7 \text{ mS or mA/V}$$

and

$$r_d = (20 - 6) \text{ V}/(1·9 - 1·65) \text{ mA} = 56 \text{ k}\Omega$$

Readers should note that a change in the operating point from −0·5 V to −1·5 V produces changes both in g_m and in r_d.

4.4   JUGFET common-source equivalent circuit

As explained in section 4.3, the gate current of the JUGFET is zero under normal operating conditions. This is represented by an open-circuit in the equivalent circuit in Fig. 4.4(a) between the gate and source electrodes.

Referring to the output characteristics in Fig. 4.3, readers will note that the total change in the drain current is the sum of δi_{D1} and δi_{D2}. The change δi_{D1} is due to a current generator $g_m \delta v_G$, and the change δi_{D2} is due to the current which flows in the drain resistance, r_d, which is connected between the drain and the source electrodes. The equivalent circuit of the output is therefore represented by a current generator which is connected in parallel with r_d. The equivalent circuit in Fig. 4.4(a) is drawn for small-signal a.c. conditions where

$$V_g = \text{r.m.s. value of the gate signal}$$
$$V_d = \text{r.m.s. value of the drain voltage}$$
$$I_d = \text{r.m.s. value of the drain current.}$$

Since Fig. 4.4 is drawn for small values of a.c. signals, it is known as the *small-signal a.c. equivalent circuit* of the FET.

Applying Kirchhoff's first law to the output circuit gives

$$I_d = g_m V_g + \frac{V_d}{r_d} \tag{4.3}$$

In many cases the value of r_d is very large, so that $g_m V_g \gg V_d/r_d$, and eq. (4.3) can be simplified to

$$I_d = g_m V_g \tag{4.4}$$

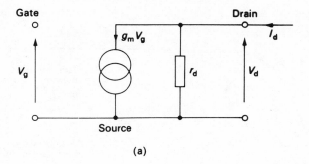

(a)

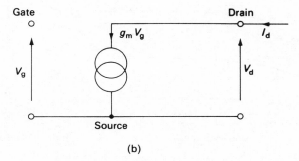

(b)

Fig. 4.4   (a) Equivalent circuit of the JUGFET at low frequencies; (b) simplified equivalent circuit.

The equivalent circuit corresponding to eq. (4.4) is shown in Fig. 4.4(b).

At high frequencies the self-capacitance effects of the reverse-biased gate-to-channel junction must be taken into account. These capacitors effectively shunt the input terminals, and since capacitive reactance reduces with increasing frequency, they result in a reduction in the voltage gain of FET amplifiers with increasing frequency. These effects must be accounted for in the equivalent circuits of FET amplifiers to be used at high frequencies.

4.5   Common-source static transfer characteristics of the JUGFET

The curve relating the drain current to the gate voltage for a given value of drain voltage is known as the *static transfer characteristic*. Other names given are the *mutual characteristic* and the *transconductance curve*. A family of curves exist for each device, each curve relating to one value of drain voltage.

The transfer characteristics are obtained from the output characteristics in the manner shown in Fig. 4.5. The transfer characteristic for $v_{DS} = 12$ V is obtained by projecting values obtained from the output characteristics in diagram (a) on to diagram (b). Point A on the $v_{GS} = 0$ V output characteristic in diagram (a) appears as point A′ on diagram (b); points B and C on the

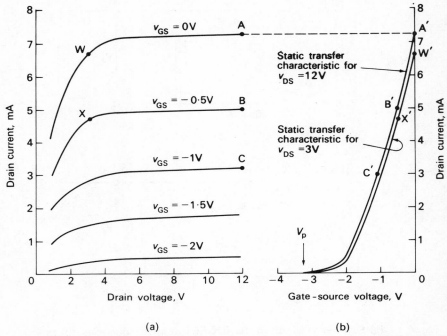

Fig. 4.5   Output and static transfer characteristics of an n-channel JUGFET.

output curves for v_{GS} of -0.5 V and -1.0 V, respectively, are plotted as points B′ and C′ on the transfer characteristic for a drain voltage of 12 V. The line joining A′, B′, C′, etc., is the transfer characteristic for $v_{DS} = 12$ V.

The transfer characteristics for other values of drain voltage are plotted in much the same way; for example, the transfer characteristic for $v_{DS} = 3$ V is plotted by projecting points W, X, etc., on diagram (a) as points W′, X′, etc., on diagram (b).

4.6   Insulated-gate FETs or MOSFETs

A cross-section through a p-channel IGFET is illustrated in Fig. 4.6(a), in which the reader will see that the gate electrode is insulated from the conducting channel by a very thin layer of silicon oxide (glass). The name MOSFET is derived from the gate-to-channel structure of the device, that is Metal-Oxide-Semiconductor FET.

Depending on the construction used, MOSFETs may either be described as enhancement-mode devices or as depletion-mode devices. The essential differ-ence between the two modes of operation is that in an *enhancement-mode device* the drain current is zero when the gate voltage is zero; the drain current is increased or enhanced in value by applying a gate voltage of the correct polarity. In a *depletion-mode device* the drain current is finite when the gate voltage is zero (see also section 4.2).

4.6.1   Enhancement-mode devices

In a p-channel device (see Fig. 4.6(a)), the drain and source electrodes are diffusions of p-type material in an n-type substrate. Since this device ultimately has a p-channel linking the drain and source, the source electrode is connected to the positive pole of the supply and the drain to the negative pole. When the gate voltage is zero, the p-n junction between the drain and the substrate is reverse biased and the drain current is zero.

The MOSFET is manufactured so that the substrate is nearly an intrinsic semiconductor. At normal operating temperatures, electron-hole pairs are generated so that a number of minority charge carriers (holes) are always available in the substrate. Should conditions be established in the substrate which

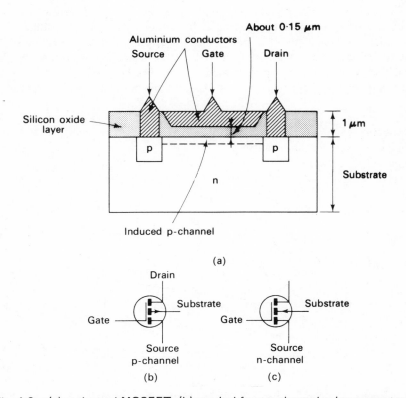

Fig. 4.6   (a) p-channel MOSFET, (b) symbol for a p-channel enhancement-mode MOSFET, (c) symbol for an n-channel enhancement-mode MOSFET.

allow the holes to accumulate, it would result in a local region of the substrate being converted n-type into p-type material. This is known as inversion, and is the principle on which the operation of MOSFETs is based.

The application of a negative potential to the gate of the MOSFET in Fig. 4.6(a) attracts the holes (minority charge carriers) in the substrate to the underside of the oxide layer just below the gate region. At a value of voltage known as the *threshold voltage* V_T, a sufficient number of holes has accumulated to form a conducting p-type channel between the source and the drain, and current begins to flow through the device. This channel is described as an *inversion channel* or *induced channel*. The value of V_T for a p-channel device lies between about −2 V and −5 V. Making the gate potential more negative than V_T increases the conductivity of the channel, and with it the drain current increases, i.e., the drain current is *enhanced* by increasing the gate voltage. A typical set of common-source output characteristics is shown in Fig. 4.7.

Information relating to the type of MOSFET is given by the circuit symbol (see diagrams (b) and (c) in Fig. 4.6). The break in the link between the source and the drain implies that the drain current is zero when the gate voltage is zero, i.e., it operates in enhancement-mode. The direction of the arrow associated with the conducting channel indicates the nature of the channel material, since it 'points' in the direction of the arrow associated with a conventional diode; an arrow pointing away from the channel indicates that the channel is p-type and that the substrate is n-type. The fact that the gate is insulated from the channel is symbolized by the gap between the gate and the channel.

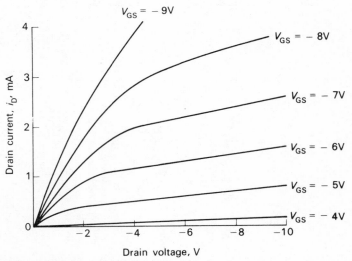

Fig. 4.7   Common-source output characteristics for a p-channel enhancement-mode MOSFET.

4.6.2 Depletion-mode devices

At the time of manufacture, depletion-mode MOSFETs have an *initial channel* diffused into the substrate between the source and the drain (this would be of p-type material in the case of the FET in Fig. 4.6). As a result, drain current can flow when the gate voltage is zero. A family of output characteristics for an n-channel depletion-mode MOSFET is shown in Fig. 4.8(a). Increasing the gate potential, i.e., making it more positive, attracts more minority charge carriers (electons in this case) to the channel and increase its conductivity.

If the gate potential is negative, some electrons in the initial channel are repelled so that the conductivity of the channel reduces; the result in this case is a reduction in drain current below the $v_{GS} = 0$ value of current. A large enough value of negative gate voltage will reduce the drain current to zero.

4.7 MOSFET common-source equivalent circuit and parameters

The low-frequency, small-signal equivalent circuit of the MOSFET is similar to that of the JUGFET (see Fig. 4.4) for the following reasons. Since the gate is isolated from the conducting channel the gate current is zero, and the input circuit can be represented as an open-circuit. Also the output characteristics of the MOSFET (see Figs. 4.7 and 4.8) are generally similar to those of the JUGFET (see Fig. 4.5(a)); hence the output circuit can be represented by a

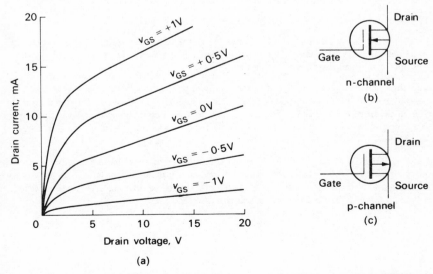

(a)

Fig. 4.8   (a) Output characteristics of an n-channel depletion-mode MOSFET, (b) and (c) symbols for depletion-mode MOSFETs.

current generator of value $g_m V_g$ connected in parallel with a resistor r_d, where

$$g_m = 0\cdot1 - 25 \text{ mS or mA/V}$$
$$r_d = 1 - 50 \text{ k}\Omega$$

4.8   Protection of the gate oxide of MOSFETs

The oxide between the gate and the channel in MOSFETs is very thin and can be permanently damaged by the application of a comparatively low voltage (a typical value of breakdown voltage lies in the range 30–100 V). Since it is possible for any human to generate a static voltage of several thousand volts merely by moving around, MOSFETs must be protected from damage by discharge of static electricity from anyone handling them.

As a general rule, MOS devices are shipped with their leads passing through a conductive plastic material, and should not be removed from this material until they are inserted in the circuit. Moreover, the technicians handling them should not wear nylon clothing and should be effectively 'earthed'.

Problems

4.1   Describe, with the aid of diagrams, the essential differences between enhancement mode FETs and depletion mode FETs.

4.2   Describe the construction of a junction-gate FET, and explain its principle of operation. Explain the meaning of the terms *pinchoff voltage* and *drain saturation current*.

4.3   Discuss the effects of change in temperature on the JUGFET.

4.4   Describe a test circuit suitable for the determination of the output characteristics of an n-channel JUGFET. State which types of instrument you would use in test, and give reasons for their selection.

4.5   In a test on a p-channel JUGFET the following results were obtained. At a constant gate voltage of −1 V, a change in drain voltage from 8 V to 10 V caused the drain current to increase from 2·8 to 3 mA. The drain voltage was then held constant at 10 V and the gate voltage changed from −1 V to −0·5 V, whereupon the drain current changed from 3 to 4·8 mA. Estimate the values of the parameters g_m and r_d.

4.6   With the aid of diagrams, describe the construction of an n-channel enhancement-mode MOSFET. Sketch the output characteristics and indicate the polarities of the voltages involved, and also the directions of the currents. Explain the difference between *threshold voltage* in MOSFETs and *pinchoff voltage* in JUGFETs.

5. Thyristors and other semiconductor devices

5.1 The reverse blocking thyristor

The *reverse blocking thyristor*, formerly known by the trade name of the *silicon controlled rectifier* (SCR), is a p-n-p-n semiconductor switching device with a bistable action. The thyristor has three terminals, an anode, a cathode, and a gate or control terminal, shown in Fig. 5.1. Connection G2 is available on some devices as an additional control region. A simple explanation of the operation of the thyristor, known as the *two-transistor analogy*, follows.

If the two centre regions of the thyristor are regarded as being split diagonally as shown, the structure reduces to two interconnected transistors T1 and T2. T1 is a p-n-p transistor, and T2 is an n-p-n transistor. When the anode is raised to a positive potential (with no signal applied to the gate), the collector junctions of both transistors are reverse biased, and the only current flowing is the leakage current through the two transistors.

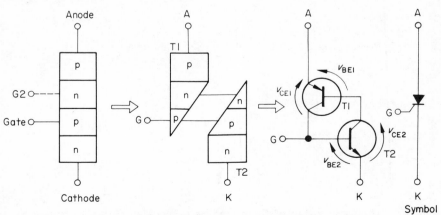

Fig. 5.1   The two-transistor analogy of the thyristor.

67

Breakdown can be made to occur in one of two ways. Firstly, if the anode voltage exceeds the breakdown voltage of either collector junction, collector current flows in that transistor. Since this current must also flow through the base region of the other transistor, it also turns that transistor on. This action is regenerative, one transistor holding the other in the ON state, since each provides the base current of the other. Once this has happened, the thyristor continues to conduct so long as the anode remains positive with respect to the cathode. The characteristic of the thyristor is shown by the full line in Fig. 5.2.

The second method of turning the thyristor ON is to inject a pulse of current into the gate terminal. This turns transistor T2 ON, providing a conduction path for the base current of T1. Once this has occurred each transistor holds the other in the ON state, as described above, and the signal applied to the gate terminal can be removed. This is by far the most common method of triggering a thyristor

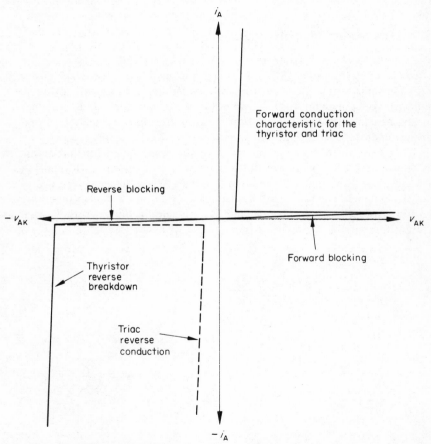

Fig. 5.2   The static characteristic of the reverse blocking thyristor is shown by the full line; the reverse characteristic of the triac is shown in broken line.

into its forward conduction mode, since an impulsive current of a fraction of an ampere of a few microseconds duration applied to the gate is adequate for the purpose. Generally speaking, a large gate current causes the thyristor to turn ON more rapidly than a smaller gate current, subject to the limitation that the peak gate current is not exceeded. Typical values of peak gate current are 1 A at $v_{GK} = 5$ V, and 0·5 A at $v_{GK} = 10$ V.

When the anode becomes negative, the emitter junctions of T1 and T2 are reverse biased. In this event, the thyristor assumes a blocking state, and it passes only leakage current. For this reason, the basic type of thyristor just described above is known as a *reverse blocking thyristor*. At some value of reverse voltage, reverse breakdown occurs, which may result in catastrophic failure of the device.

A feature of the conduction characteristic is that the p.d. across the thyristor is substantially constant at all values of current, up to its rated output. This may be explained by the two-transistor analogy as follows. When a transistor is working in its saturated mode, i.e., when it is turned ON, V_{BEsat} is of the order of 0·7 V, and V_{CEsat} is approximately 0·3 V to 0·5 V. From Fig. 5.1, it is seen that the anode-to-cathode voltage in the ON state is the sum of these two values, i.e., approximately 1 V. This voltage is found to increase slightly as the load current increases, but it may be regarded as substantially constant over the normal working range.

Once triggered into conduction, the thyristor continues to conduct so long as the anode current remains above a value known as the *holding current I_H*. The value of this current depends on the rating of the device and is typically 2·5 mA in a 1 A rated device, but can be a few hundred milliamperes in high-current devices. In a.c. circuits the thyristor automatically turns off when the current in the circuit falls below the holding current. To turn a thyristor off in a d.c. circuit, it is necessary to provide additional circuitry which forces the anode current to be reduced below I_H; this is known as *forced commutation*.

A value of current known as the *latching current I_L*, is also specified for thyristors. This is the minimum value of anode current which enables the thyristor to latch in its conducting mode. The value of I_L is typically twice the value of I_H.

5.2 The triac or bidirectional thyristor

The triac is a multilayer semiconductor device, and a simplified cross-section is shown in Fig. 5.3. This device is 'bidirectional' insomuch that it can be triggered into conduction when T2 is either positive or negative with respect to T1 (T1 and T2 being the main conducting terminals).

The 'forward' characteristic (when T2 is positive with respect to T1) is similar to that of the forward characteristic of the reverse blocking thyristor (see Fig. 5.2). The triac characteristic in the third quadrant (when T2 is negative with respect to T1) is shown dotted in Fig. 5.2. An important feature

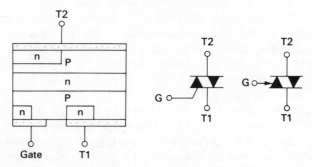

Fig. 5.3   The triac or bidirectional thyristor.

of the triac is that it can be triggered into conduction by a gate signal which has either positive or negative polarity with respect to T1. The triac generally needs a higher value of gate current to trigger it than does the reverse blocking thyristor. The operating modes of the triac are listed in Table 5.1; triacs are usually most sensitive to gate current in the I^+ and III^- modes, and least sensitive in the III^+ mode. The gate current I_{GT}, required to trigger a triac is typically 40 mA in the I^+ and III^- modes, and 60–100 mA in the I^- and III^+ modes (these values are for a 10 A device; higher rated devices will require somewhat higher values).

Table 5.1

Mode	Potential of T2 with respect to T1	Potential of gate with respect to T1
I^+	Positive	Positive
I^-	Positive	Negative
III^+	Negative	Positive
III^-	Negative	Negative

5.3   The diac or bidirectional breakdown diode

This is a two-terminal device and is similar in appearance to a signal diode. A symbol and typical static characteristic are shown in Fig. 5.4. For applied positive voltages less than V_{BR1} and negative voltages less than V_{BR2}, the device blocks the flow of current and is effectively an open-circuit. Voltages V_{BR1} and V_{BR2} are known as breakdown voltages, and usually have a value in the range 30–50 V; the two values of breakdown voltage in a particular device may differ by a few volts.

When the applied voltage exceeds the breakdown voltage, the diac begins to conduct and the voltage across it falls by a few volts. An important applica-

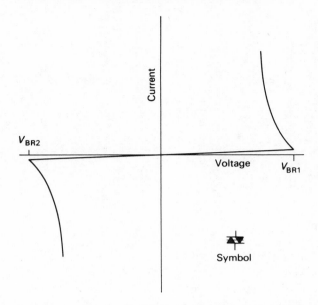

Fig. 5.4   The bidirectional breakdown diode or diac.

tion is as a capacitor discharge device in pulse generators used for triggering thyristors and triacs (see chapter 17).

5.4   Unijunction transistors

The unijunction transistor (UJT) or *double-based diode* has two ohmic connections to a bar of n-type material, shown in Fig. 5.5(a). These connections are known as *base-one* (B1) and *base-two* (B2), respectively. A p-n junction is formed between a p-type *emitter* and the bar. In the absence of a signal at the emitter, the interbase resistance is of the order of 5 kΩ to 10 kΩ, so that the leakage current is small. The bar acts as a potential divider, and a potential of about $0.4V_{BB}$ to $0.8V_{BB}$ appears between the emitter and base-one, where V_{BB} is the interbase voltage. The coefficient of V_{BB} above is known as the *intrinsic stand-off ratio η*.

If V_E, the emitter voltage, is less than ηV_{BB}, the emitter-to-bar junction is reverse biased, and the emitter current is very small. When the emitter voltage is increased to the point where the junction is forward biased, the UJT turns on, and the resistance between the emitter and base-one falls to a low value. This occurs at the *peak-point voltage V_{EP}*, which is given by

$$V_{EP} = V_j + \eta V_{BB}$$

where V_j is the forward voltage drop across the p-n junction, and is of the

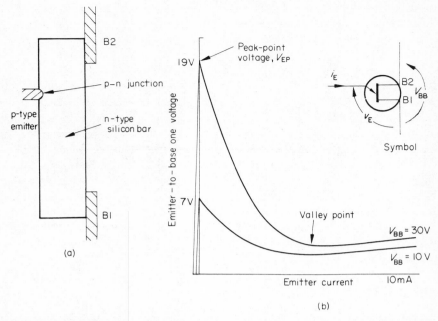

Fig. 5.5   (a) A section through a unijunction transistor, and (b) static characteristic curves.

order of 0·7 V. It is frequently possible to neglect V_j when compared with
ηV_{BB}.

   The UJT characteristics shown in Fig. 5.5(b) are typical only. For a
general-purpose UJT, the peak-point current is of the order of $1\mu A$ at
V_{BB} = 20 V, with a valley-point voltage of about 1·5 V at 6 mA. Complementary
UJT's with p-type bars are also manufactured. UJT's are commonly used
in relaxation oscillator circuits, in which they are used to periodically discharge
a capacitor. In these circuits, the peak emitter current may be several amperes,
which falls to a very low value after a few microseconds when the capacitor is
discharged (see chapter 17).

5.5   Thermistors

Thermistors are **THERM**ally sensitive res**ISTORS** whose resistance alters by a
significant amount with changes in temperature. There are two types, namely
those with a *negative resistance-temperature coefficient* (n.t.c. types) whose
resistance reduces with increasing temperature, and those with a *positive
resistance-temperature coefficient* (p.t.c. types) whose resistance increases
with increasing temperature (over a limited temperature range only). An n.t.c.
thermistor is a temperature sensitive resistor made of semiconductor material,

usually in the form of metallic oxides of cobalt, manganese, or nickel. The material is an intrinsic semiconductor with a negative resistance-temperature coefficient in the region of 3 per cent per C deg. to 4·5 per cent per C deg. at room temperature.

Thermistors are manufactured in rod, bead, and disc form, with diameters as small as 0·015 cm, and their working temperatures range from about −100°C to 400°C. Typical ohmic values at room temperature lie between 500 Ω and 100 kΩ. They are commonly used in one arm of a Wheatstone bridge circuit, the potential between opposite corners of the bridge being a measure of the thermistor temperature. Thermistors are also used in transistor bias circuits to provide compensation for the effects of temperature on the leakage current of transistors. In such circuits, the current flowing through the thermistor must be small, otherwise it will cause the temperature of the bulk of the thermistor to rise, resulting in a further change in resistance.

P.t.c. thermistors show a sudden increase in resistance over a relatively small temperature range, and are used in colour T.V. tube demagnetization circuits and in electric motor overload protection circuits.

Problems

5.1 Using the two-transistor analogy, describe the operation of the reverse blocking thyristor. With the aid of a static anode characteristic, explain the difference between the reverse blocking thyristor and the bidirectional thyristor (the triac).

5.2 In a test on a thyristor operating in its forward blocking mode, the voltage across the thyristor measured by an instrument having an internal resistance of 5 MΩ was 250 V. The current taken from the supply by the thyristor and voltmeter was found to be 55 μA. Determine the blocking resistance of the thyristor.

5.3 Explain the principle of operation of the thyristor. Sketch the static characteristic of a thyristor noting the salient features on the graph.

Draw a circuit diagram to show how two thyristors can be connected in inverse parallel to supply controlled armature current to a d.c. motor, which has constant excitation.

5.4 Explain the principle of the thyristor. Describe how thyristor convertors may be used to control the speed of an induction motor over a wide range.

A thyristor convertor is to be used to control the speed of a d.c. motor and the maximum average current is to be 10 A. The supply is from a single-phase alternating supply of 220 V r.m.s. and the armature current is to be limited by connecting a resistor in series with the armature. Calculate the minimum value of this resistance if the armature resistance is 1 Ω.

5.5 Describe any one type of solid state controllable rectifier. Show how this could be embodied in a system for the control of the voltage or current delivered to a variable load, and briefly describe the system operation. State what safety features should be incorporated in the system.

5.6 Draw a diagram of a unijunction transistor, and explain how the device operates.

6. Integrated circuits

Developments in miniaturization of circuits have resulted in improvements in the reliability of equipment together with a reduction in cost. A *micro-circuit* is simply a miniature assembly of electronic components, the two most popular types being known as *film circuits* and *monolithic integrated circuits*, respectively.

6.1 Film circuits

A film circuit is manufactured by depositing films of conducting material on an insulating surface or insulating *substrate*. Film circuits are classed as being either *thick-film* or *thin-film*, according to the manufacturing technique

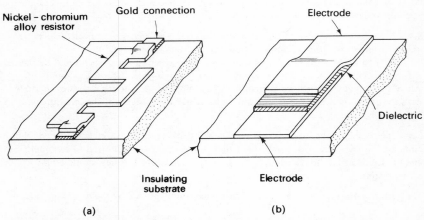

Fig. 6.1   Film circuit components: (a) a resistor and (b) a capacitor.

involved. In either case, the film is 'thin' by any normal standards. The construction of a film circuit resistor is shown in Fig. 6.1(a). This may be one of many resistors deposited on a substrate of size 1 cm square or less. A feature of a resistor of this kind is that its value can be mechanically trimmed by the manufacturing to provide an accurate value of resistance. Low values of capacitance can be manufactured in the form shown in Fig. 6.1(b). Inductors with low values of inductance are constructed by depositing a flat spiral of conducting material on the surface of the substrate. In general, when normal values of capacitance or inductance are required, they are best obtained by using standard components which are connected externally to the film circuit.

Transistors, in the form of field-effect transistors, can be manufactured in film form.

6.2 Monolithic integrated circuits

Since silicon possesses characteristics which are best suited to IC manufacturing processes, all monolithic ICs are manufactured from this substance. The term 'monolithic' simply implies that the IC is manufactured from a single crystal. The basic production processes are described below.

First, silica (common sand) is reduced to pure silicon, from which a cylindrical silicon crystal is grown having typical dimensions of 30 cm (12·25 in.) long and up to 5 cm (2 in.) diameter. The silicon crystal is then cut by a diamond saw to give a large number of cylindrical *wafers* which, after polishing, are about 200 μm (0·008 in.) thick. This is illustrated in diagrams (a) and (b) of Fig. 6.2. After the silicon wafer has been subjected to a number of processes which are described below, it contains a large number of individual circuits. The physical size of these circuits can be very small, in some cases being

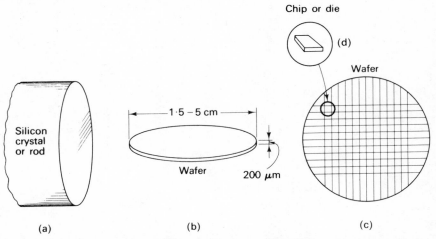

Fig. 6.2 Processes involved in the manufacture of monolithic integrated circuits.

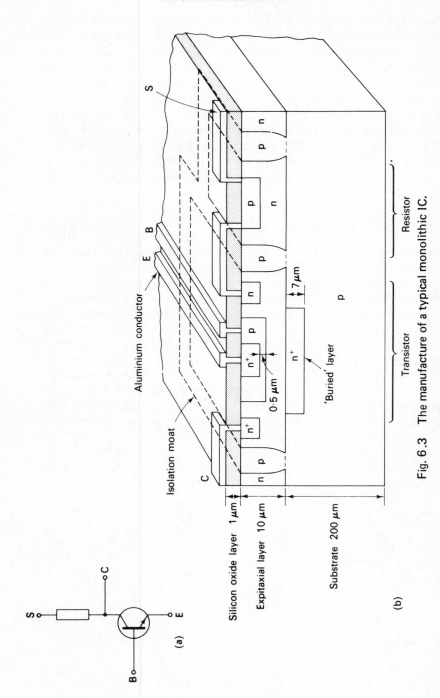

Aluminium conductor

Isolation moat

Silicon oxide layer 1 μm

Expitaxial layer 10 μm

Substrate 200 μm

S

E B

C

n p

n$^+$

p

n$^+$

p

n$^+$

0.5 μm

n p

n

p

p

n

p

p

n

7 μm

'Buried' layer

p

Transistor

Resistor

(a)

S

C

E

B

(b)

Fig. 6.3   The manufacture of a typical monolithic IC.

squares of sides a fraction of a millimetre. To separate the individual circuits, the wafer is divided into small *chips* or *dies* by a process similar to glass cutting. This is illustrated in diagrams (c) and (d) of Fig. 6.2.

The chip is then bonded to its mounting and, after connections are made between the IC and the external leads, it is encapsulated to prevent it from becoming contaminated by the surrounding atmosphere.

The type of IC produced by the above method is known as a *planar epitaxial* IC (epitaxial is derived from the Greek language, and means 'arranged upon'; planar epitaxial implies that the IC is arranged upon a plane surface).

6.3 Manufacture of a bipolar integrated circuit

We will now consider how the circuit in Fig. 6.3(a) can be constructed in IC form; the network shown could be a part of either a linear amplifier or a switching circuit. When completed, the IC appears as shown in Fig. 6.3(b), with the overall size of the transistor being typically 100 μm (0·004 in.) square. The steps involved are summarized below.

The n^+ buried layer: The silicon chip or dice manufactured in the initial process is used as a substrate, upon which the whole circuit is constructed. The resistivity of the substrate material is fairly high and would result in any transistor constructed in it being unsuitable as a switching device. In order to overcome this defect, a 'buried layer' of n^+ semiconductor material having a high conductivity is diffused into the substrate at a point on the chip which is to be directly below where the final transistor is to be placed. An n^+ material is one which has a higher value of conductivity than a conventional n-type material. The process of diffusion is described below under the two headings of *oxide growth and photomasking* and *diffusion*, and is generally similar to the diffusion process used in the construction of the remainder of the circuit. The reason that the buried layer is so named is because ultimately it is buried below the surface of the circuit.

Oxide growth and photomasking: After cleaning and inspection, the upper surface of the substrate is oxidized by passing steam over it; the oxide layer produced by this process is only about 1 μm thick. The upper surface of the oxide is then coated with a light-sensitive material known as *photoresist*, as shown in Fig. 6.4(a). The photoresist is exposed to ultraviolet radiation through a photographic mask (see Fig. 5.4(b)), and the exposed areas of the photoresist harden. The unexposed areas covered by the opaque areas of the mask are 'soft' and are dissolved by a solvent, leaving an aperture in the photoresist. The slice is then etched in acid to remove the exposed area of the oxide film, leaving a 'window' through to the upper surface of the substrate. The remaining photoresist is next removed by other solvents, after which the slice is rinsed and dried.

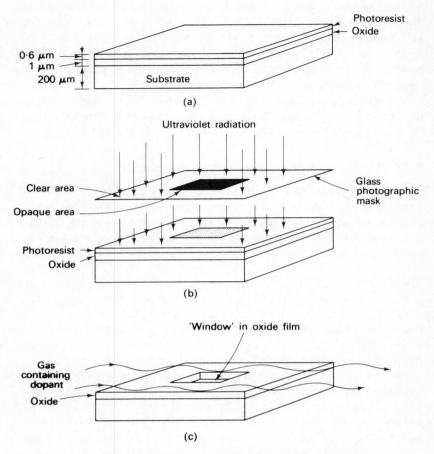

Fig. 6.4   Production of the n⁺ buried layer.

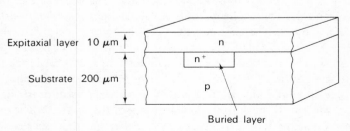

Fig. 6.5   A section through the wafer after the epitaxial layer has been formed.

Diffusion: In the next stage of manufacture the slice is passed through a diffusion furnace, where it is heated to a temperature of about $1200°C$ and gases containing appropriate dopants are passed over it (see Fig. 6.4(c)). The dopant in the gas causes the exposed area of the p-type substrate to be converted into n^+ material. The buried layer, diffused through the window in the oxide layer in this manner, finally penetrates to a depth of about 7 μm. After this, the oxide layer is etched away leaving the p-type substrate together with the 'buried' n^+ layer at its surface.

Epitaxial layer: Next, the slice is heated once more in a furnace and is subjected to a gas which causes an n-type *epitaxial layer* to 'grow' uniformly over the whole surface (see Fig. 6.5). It is in this 10 μm thick epitaxial layer that the whole integrated circuit is formed.

Circuit components: In order to isolate the components within the circuit from one another, it is next necessary to form isolation 'moats' around the areas in which the components are to be formed. By a process of masking, etching and diffusion similar to that described above, p-type isolation moats are diffused into the epitaxial layer (see Fig. 6.3(b)). The moat provides a link between the surface of the IC and the substrate, and electrically isolates the area it surrounds.

Next, windows are introduced in the oxide layer to allow the p-type base and resistor diffusions to be introduced. After this, the next diffusion process enables not only the emitter of the transistor but also the two n^+-regions in the collector to be introduced. The latter regions are required (a) to allow a connection to be made to the collector region itself and (b) to enable the collector and the resistor to be interconnected.

Completing the IC: A layer of aluminium about 1·5 μm thick is evaporated over the whole surface of the circuit, and the regions not required for electrical connections are removed by an etching process. Connections are then made between the remaining aluminium and the external 'pins' of the IC.

The above is a simplified description of the processes involved and, as the readers will appreciate, the sectional sketch in Fig. 6.3(b) is also a simplified picture. In all, about 80–100 individual processes are involved in the manufacture of a bipolar IC, some requiring a few hours to complete and others several weeks.

6.4 Manufacture of MOS integrated circuits

A sectional view through a p-channel MOSFET manufactured in IC form is shown in Fig. 6.6; it shows the essential features of the device. When compared with the bipolar IC circuit in Fig. 6.3, it is evident that the MOS device is simpler to construct. Also, it requires less surface area on the semiconductor

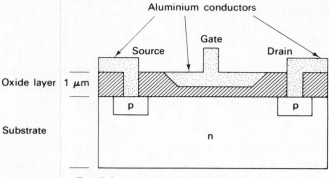

Fig. 6.6   A p-channel MOSFET.

chip than does a bipolar transistor. Consequently, it is possible with MOS elements either to produce a more complex circuit on a given chip area or to produce the same circuit at lower cost than with bipolar elements. Thus, the logic functions in most electronic calculating machines are invariably carried out by MOS devices in IC form.

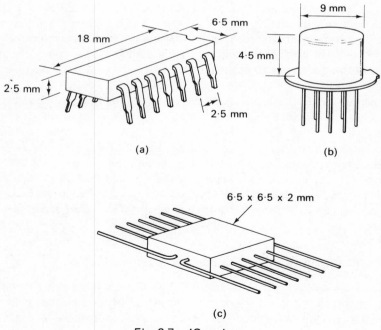

Fig. 6.7   IC packages.

6.5　Integrated circuit packaging

The three most popular forms of IC packages (or *packs*) are shown in Fig. 6.7. The most popular form is the plastic encapsulated 14-pin *dual-in-line* (DIL) pack in Fig. 6.7(a). The 14-pin DIL pack has seven connecting pins per side, pairs of pins being in line with one another and the pins being 2·5 mm (0·1 in.) apart to allow the IC to be fitted directly into standard printed circuit boards. The *canister* (or *can*) form, Fig. 6.7(b), contains the IC in a hermetically sealed metal can. The *flatback* (Fig. 6.7(c)), frequently of ceramic construction, is hermetically sealed also.

6.6　MSI and LSI circuits

The terms *medium-scale integrated* (MSI) circuit and *large-scale integrated* (LSI) circuit are commonly used when describing certain types of complex logic circuits. They refer to the number of complete logic gates in an IC pack and, though not precisely defined, may be interpreted as follows:

(a) MSI circuits contain between about 10 and 100 gates.
(b) LSI circuits contain more than about 100 gates.

ICs used in electronic calculators use LSI circuit chips.

Problems

6.1　With the aid of sketches, describe what is meant by (a) a film integrated circuit, and (b) a monolithic integrated circuit.

6.2　Show how (a) a capacitor, (b) a diode, and (c) a resistor can be constructed in a monolithic integrated circuit.

6.3　Explain how electrical isolation of components is achieved in monolithic integrated circuits.

6.4　With the aid of sketches, explain the following as they apply to solid-state device manufacture: (a) monolithic integrated circuit, (b) diffusion, (c) planar transistor, (d) epitaxial layer, (e) metallization, (f) encapsulation.

7. Thermionic valves

7.1   Electron emission

At room temperature very few free electrons in metallic bodies attain sufficient
energy to escape from the surface. It is necessary to increase the energy of the
electrons before escape is possible. The four principal methods of achieving
electron emission are

(a) Thermionic emission.
(b) Photoemission.
(c) Secondary emission.
(d) Field emission.

Thermionic emission: When a metal surface is raised to a sufficiently high temperature, a number of free electrons gain sufficient energy to escape from it. This
is known as thermionic emission. It is an unfortunate fact that many metals
melt, or even boil, at the temperature at which adequate thermionic emission
takes place. Emitting materials in common use today are tungsten, thoriated-
tungsten, and oxide coated materials.

Tungsten is used extensively in high voltage (i.e., over 10 kV) electronic
devices and in large transmitting valves. It has a melting point of 3380°C and
is worked as an emitter between 2300°C and 2500°C. A *thoriated-tungsten
filament* is a tungsten filament which has an atomic layer of the oxide thoria
on its surface. These filaments provide a greater thermionic emission than an
equivalent rated tungsten filament and work at a much lower temperature,
typically 1500°C. They are commonly used in electronic devices which operate
at voltages less than about 10 kV. *Oxide coated emitters* take the form of a
coating of oxides of barium and strontium on the surface of a metal sleeve,
usually made of nickel. The temperature of the metal sleeve is raised either
by passing a current directly through the metal sleeve, or by heating the sleeve

indirectly by a heating filament known as a *heater,* the latter method being the most common. The electron emission of oxide coated emitters is much greater than either tungsten filaments or thoriated-tungsten filaments, and the operating temperature is about 700°C. These emitters are restricted to use in electronic devices operating with anode voltage less than about 1 kV. If the temperature of an oxide coated emitter falls below its rated value, the cathode becomes susceptible to *cathode poisoning.* This term describes the reduction in emission that occurs as a result of surface contamination when small quantities of gas are present.

An illustration of a typical filament emitter is shown in Fig. 7.1(a), and of an indirectly heated oxide coated cathode in Fig. 7.1(c). The circuit symbols of the

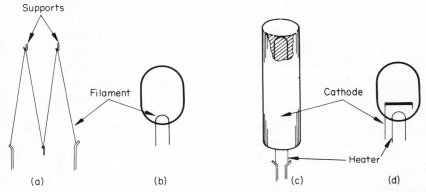

Fig. 7.1   The filament-type emitter shown in (a) is represented by the symbol in (b), and the indirectly heated cathode (c) is represented by symbol (d).

two forms of emitter are shown in Figs. 7.1(b) and (d), respectively. Owing to the high efficiency and reliability of oxide coated cathodes, the majority of industrial valves employ indirectly heated oxide coated cathodes.

Photoemission: Light is one form of energy, and if the frequency of the light waves impinging on a metal surface exceeds a threshold value, electrons are emitted from the metal.

Secondary emission: When a charged particle (an electron or a positive ion) strikes a conducting surface it transfers some, or all, of its kinetic energy to the atomic structure of the metal. If the energy transferred is sufficiently large an electron is dislodged from its surface.

Field emission: Electrons can be literally torn out of their orbits by the application of a very intense electric field of the order of 1 MV/cm at the surface of the material. This is known as field emission, and is thought to be the principal mechanism of electron emission in mercury-pool devices.

7.2   The diode

The thermionic diode is a valve containing only two electrodes, a *cathode* and an *anode* inside an evacuated container. When the cathode is heated to its working temperature, it releases electrons by thermionic emission and is surrounded by free negative charges. Under steady operating conditions, the negative *space charge* resulting from the presence of the electrons limits further electron emission from the cathode.

In the diode the anode, which is usually made from nickel in the form of a cylinder, surrounds the cathode as shown in Fig. 7.2(b). When the anode is at the same potential as the cathode it is found that some electrons have sufficient energy to cause them to travel to the anode, resulting in a small anode current. This is shown as I_{AO} on the *anode characteristic* or *output characteristic* in Fig. 7.2(c); I_{AO} has a value of the order of a few microamperes, and may be neglected for most practical purposes. I_{AO} is sometimes described as *splash current* and is due to *fast electrons* or electrons which have an energy level which is sufficient to carry them to the anode. To reduce this anode current to zero it is necessary to apply a small negative potential to the anode; this repels the electrons which approach the anode. If the anode potential is made progressively more negative, a small reverse leakage current (of the order of a few microamperes) flows from the anode to the cathode. The safe *peak inverse working voltage* that may be applied to the anode is restricted below the value at which a discharge would commence. When the diode operates with a negative anode voltage it is said to be operating in a *reverse blocking* mode, since it blocks the flow of current.

When the anode is positive with respect to the cathode, electrons are attracted to it, resulting in an increase in anode current. At first the anode current increases in an approximately linear fashion with voltage, between I_{AO} and point L on the anode characteristic; this section is described as the *linear* part of the characteristic. Owing to the effect of the cathode space charge, the anode potential can only influence the outer edge of the cloud of electrons, and in the linear region of the characteristic the anode current is said to be *space-charge limited*. As the anode voltage is increased, more electrons are drawn from the outer edge of the electron cloud, depleting the space charge and allowing more electrons to leave the cathode. The electrons in motion between the cathode and anode constitute a current, and are collectively known as the *space current*.

Strictly speaking, the relationship between the anode current and voltage between the points given above is not truly linear, but is given by the relationship

$$i_A = kv_A{}^{3/2}$$

which is known as the *three-halves power law* or the *Langmuir-Child law*, since the equation is due jointly to the work of Langmuir and Child.

When the anode voltage is increased beyond point L in Fig. 7.2(c), the curve begins to flatten out because all the electrons emitted by the cathode are collec-

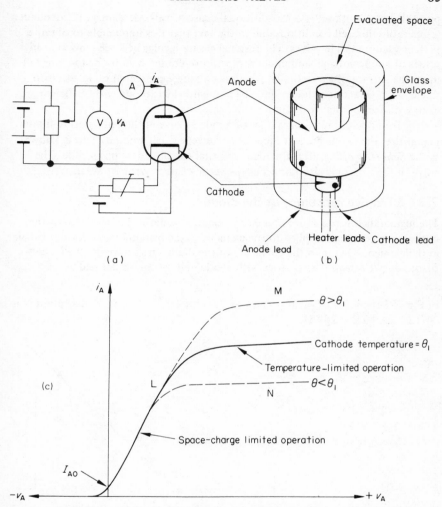

Fig. 7.2   (a) A typical test circuit for use with a thermionic diode. In (b) the anode
structure is cut away to show the electrode structure. The anode characteristics
for various values of cathode temperature are shown in (c).

ted by the anode. Further increase in anode voltage has negligible effect on the
anode current. In this region of the characteristic, the anode current is said to be
temperature-limited. Only by increasing the cathode temperature is it possible to
increase the anode current, corresponding to characteristic M in Fig. 7.2(c). The
maximum temperature at which the cathode may be operated is limited, of
course, by the temperature at which the oxide coating begins to evaporate. A
reduced cathode temperature reduces the value of the saturation current, shown
in characteristic N, in addition to which the cathode becomes susceptible to

poisoning (see section 7.1). An additional cause of cathode damage occurs under temperature-limited conditions due to the fact that it is impossible to obtain a perfect vacuum inside valves. The residual gas molecules become ionized at high values of anode voltage, and under temperature-limited conditions the ions fall upon the surface of the cathode, which is no longer protected by its electron shield. At high anode voltages the ions bombard the cathode with sufficient energy to destroy the oxide film.

It is found with increasing values of anode voltage in the temperature-limited region that the anode current increases by a very small amount. This is known as the *Schottky effect* after the man who first calculated its magnitude. The curve in Fig. 7.2(c) is also known as the *static characteristic of the diode.*

7.3   Effective resistance of the diode

The instantaneous resistance of a circuit element is defined as the ratio of the instantaneous voltage applied to the element to the instantaneous current flowing in the element. Owing to the curvature of the diode characteristic, the *instantaneous anode resistance r_A* varies with anode voltage, and is defined as

$$r_A = v_A/i_A$$

In Fig. 7.3 the value of r_A at point M is $22/75 \times 10^{-3} = 293\ \Omega$, and at point N is $34/132{\cdot}5 \times 10^{-3} = 257\ \Omega$.

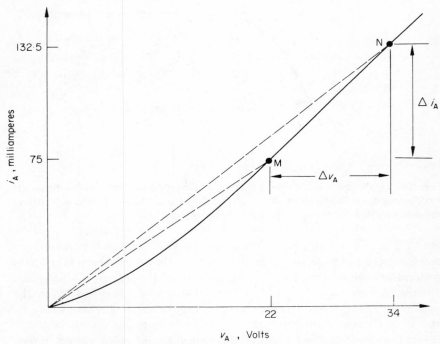

Fig. 7.3   Method of evaluating r_A and r_a.

When the anode voltage changes continuously between two points on the characteristic, the average operating point is known as the *quiescent point* or *operating point*. The effective resistance of the diode at the quiescent point is given by the slope of the static characteristic at that point and is known as the *slope resistance* r_a, and is defined by the relationship

$$r_a = \frac{\Delta v_A}{\Delta i_A} \ \Omega$$

where Δv_A and Δi_A are small changes in anode voltage and anode current respectively. The slope resistance of the diode in Fig. 7.3 between points M and N is

$$r_a = \frac{34 - 22}{(132 \cdot 5 - 75) \times 10^{-3}} = 209 \ \Omega$$

When the anode of the diode is positive with respect to the cathode, the diode is said to be *forward biased* and operates in its *forward conducting* mode. The effective resistance of the diode in this mode is generally taken to be equal to r_a. When the anode of the diode is negative with respect to the cathode, the space current of the diode is practically zero and the diode is said to be *reverse biased*. The slope resistance of a reverse biased diode is many megohms and is referred to as the *reverse blocking resistance*.

7.4 Equivalent circuit of the diode

The equivalent circuit of an electronic device is a circuit which has the same static characteristics as the device over a specified range of operating conditions. In the case of the diode the characteristic is non-linear, and a true equivalent circuit is very complex. The problem is simplified if only the linear parts of the characteristic are considered.

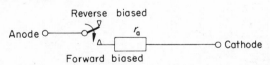

Fig. 7.4   The linear equivalent circuit of the diode.

A simplified *linear equivalent circuit* of the diode is shown in Fig. 7.4. The diode is regarded as a single-pole switch which is open (OFF) when the diode is reverse biased, and is closed (ON) when the diode is forward biased. The effective resistance in the forward biased condition is taken to be the slope resistance r_a.

7.5 The triode

Since space current in high vacuum thermionic diodes is in the form of electron flow, it can be modified by introducing a third electrode between the anode and the cathode, which is arranged to alter the electrostatic field distribution in the valve. The third electrode is known as the *control grid* or G1, which is in the form of a spiral wire mesh close to, and around the cathode, and is supported on metal rods. The geometry of a typical triode is shown in Fig. 7.5(a) together with its circuit symbol. The anode is cut away to display the electrode structure.

If the control grid is negative with respect to the cathode, some of the electrons in transit to the anode are repelled by the grid and return to the cathode. This has the effect of reducing the space current. Since the grid is physically close to the cathode, a small grid potential exerts a considerable influence on the space current of the triode. Increasing the negative potential on the grid reduces the space current further, and high values of negative grid voltage result in the anode current being reduced to zero. In this event, the anode current is said to be *cut-off* or simply OFF.

A typical triode test circuit is shown in Fig. 7.5(b), and the *static anode characteristics* or *output characteristics* corresponding to various values of v_{GK} are shown in Fig. 7.5(c). With negative grid potentials, electrons are not attracted to the grid, and the grid current for all practical purposes is zero. The *input impedance* measured between the grid and cathode (expressed by v_{GK}/grid current) is, therefore, very high indeed.

If the grid becomes positive with respect to the cathode it acts as a second anode, and the net space current increases. Since the grid is in the form of an open wire mesh, most of the increased space current passes through it and is

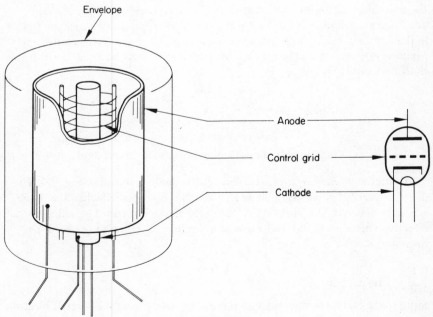

Envelope

Anode

Control grid

Cathode

Fig. 7.5(a)

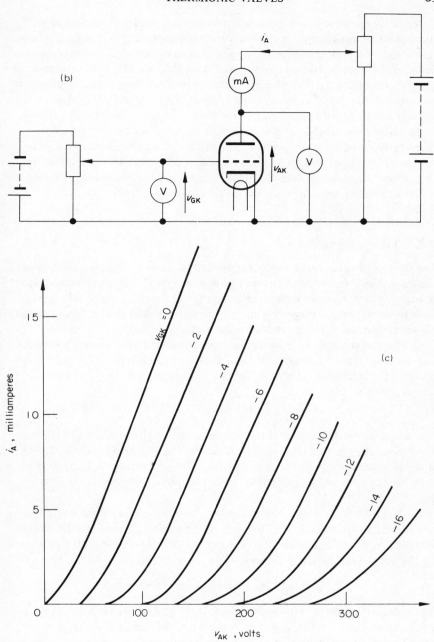

Fig. 7.5 The construction of the triode valve and its circuit symbol are shown in (a), the anode being cut away for clarity. The *static anode characteristics* in (c) are obtained using the test circuit in (b).

collected by the anode, so increasing the anode current. However, not all the additional electrons escape, and those that reach the grid return to the cathode via the external grid circuit. Since the grid now draws current, the input impedance of the valve is reduced to a value of the order of 1 kΩ. If the grid potential is to be maintained positive, the grid structure must be designed to dissipate heat, otherwise it may be damaged. In most applications the grid is maintained at a negative potential with respect to the cathode.

The triode output characteristics may be regarded as a family of diode characteristics, each characteristic corresponding to a particular control grid voltage. If the anode voltage is raised to a sufficiently high level, temperature-limited operation occurs as in the diode. In all normal applications the triode is operated in the space-charge limited region of its characteristics.

7.6   Triode parameters

The valve constants or *parameters* are defined in terms of the characteristics of the valve, Fig. 7.6. The total change δi_A in anode current is dependent upon the change δv_A in the anode voltage, and upon the change δv_G in the grid voltage. Each of these changes may occur independently or simultaneously, and the parameters enable the effects of these changes to be predicted.

In Fig. 7.6(a) the grid voltage is maintained constant at v_{G1} while the anode voltage is increased by an amount δv_A, resulting in an increase δi_A in the anode current. The relationship between the two changes is given by the *slope resistance* r_a, where

$$r_a = (\delta v_A / \delta i_A)_{\delta v_G = 0} \ \Omega$$

The suffix $\delta v_G = 0$ implies that there is no change in grid voltage, and this statement is usually omitted from the equation. From an inspection of Fig. 7.6(a), it appears that the equivalent circuit of the valve for a change in i_A at constant v_G is that of a resistor connected between the anode and cathode, as shown in Fig. 7.6(b).

If the grid voltage is made more positive, by being increased from v_{G1} to v_{G2} at constant anode voltage, as in Fig. 7.6(c), the current flowing into the anode increases by δi_A. The relationship between the changes (at constant v_A) is given by the *mutual conductance* or *transconductance* g_m, where

$$g_m = (\delta i_A / \delta v_G)_{\delta v_A = 0} \ \text{mA/V or mS}$$

The change in anode current is, therefore, $\delta i_A = g_m \delta v_G$. The equivalent circuit of the valve, based on Fig. 7.6(c), is as shown in Fig. 7.6(d), the change in anode current being generated by a current generator.

Changes in v_G and v_A can occur simultaneously to give zero net change in anode current if v_G is increased by δv_G, causing a change along the line XY in Fig. 7.6(e), and v_A is decreased by δv_A causing a change along the line YZ. The

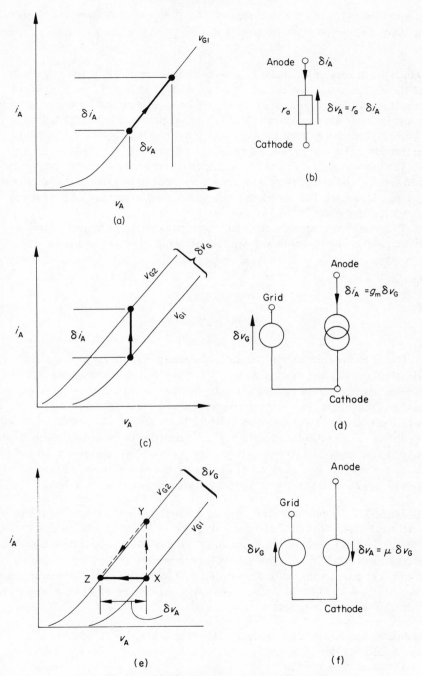

Fig. 7.6 Determination of triode valve parameters.

relationship between the two changes necessary to maintain a constant value of
i_A is given by the *amplification factor* μ, where

$$\mu = (\delta v_A / \delta v_G)_{\delta i_A = 0}$$

which is a dimensionless quantity (having dimensions of V/V). The magnitude
of the change in v_A, at constant i_A, is $\delta v_A = \mu \delta v_G$. It is seen from Fig. 7.6(e)
that it is necessary to reduce v_A by δv_A when v_G is increased by δv_G in order to
maintain a constant anode current. The equivalent circuit representing Fig.
7.6(e) is therefore as shown in Fig. 7.6(f), in which the equivalent generators
in the grid and anode circuits are of opposite polarity to one another.

The changes δi_A, δv_A, and δv_G considered here are small changes in current
and voltage, and the equivalent circuits so derived are known as the *small-signal
equivalent circuits*. The complete small-signal equivalent circuit of the valve is
developed in section 7.7.

The relationship between the small-signal parameters is obtained as follows.
For a given change in anode voltage, the following equations hold good

$$\delta v_A = r_a \delta i_A \qquad \text{and} \qquad \delta v_A = \mu \delta v_G$$

hence

$$\mu v_G = r_a \delta i_A$$

or

$$\mu = r_a (\delta i_A / \delta v_G)$$
$$= r_a g_m \tag{7.1}$$

Owing to the curvature of the static characteristics, the value of the small-
signal parameters depends upon the point at which they are measured. It is
normal practice for the parameters to be specified at particular values of anode
and grid potentials. Valves are often operated at a point on the characteristics
which is well away from the point at which the parameters are measured in order
to obtain some particular advantage, e.g., a greater value of μ or g_m. Also, owing
to physical imperfections in manufacturing processes, parameters are subject to
variation in value, even in valves of the same type. This is known as *parameter
spread*, which is more marked in semiconductor devices than in valves.

Example 7.1. To determine the small-signal parameters of a triode the following
tests were made. With an initial grid voltage of -6 V and an anode voltage of
175 V, the anode current was found to be 4·6 mA. The anode voltage was then
increased to 200 V, at constant grid voltage, when the anode current rose to
7 mA. The anode voltage was then maintained at 200 V and the grid voltage was
altered to -4 V, when the anode current was found to be 11·4 mA. Compute the
values of the valve parameters.

Solution: The first change corresponds to that in Fig. 7.6(a), where
$\delta v_A = 200 - 175 = 25$ V and $\delta i_A = 7 - 4·6 = 2·4$ mA.
    Hence
$$r_a = 25/2·4 \times 10^{-3} = 10,420 \ \Omega \text{ or } 10·42 \text{ k}\Omega$$

The second change corresponds to that in Fig. 7.6(c), where
$\delta i_A = 11\cdot4 - 7 = 4\cdot4$ mA and $\delta v_G = -4 - (-6) = +2$ V.
    Hence

$$g_m = 4\cdot4 \text{ mA}/2 \text{ V} = 2\cdot2 \text{ mA/V or mS}$$

From eq. (7.1),

$$\mu = r_a g_m = 10\cdot42 \text{ k}\Omega \times 2\cdot2 \text{ mA/V} = 22\cdot9$$

7.7 The small-signal equivalent circuit of the triode

A change in the characteristics from condition X to condition Y, in Fig. 7.7(a)
and (c), can occur in two basic ways, giving two types of equivalent circuit. In

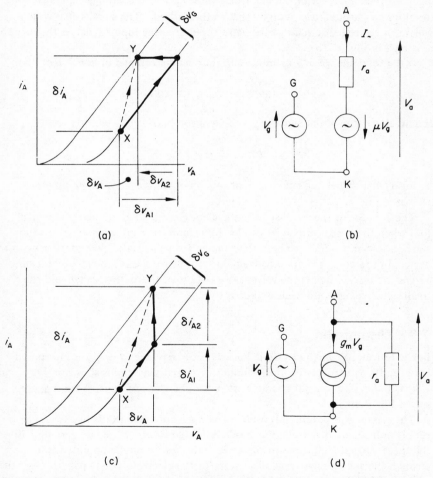

(a)   (b)

(c)   (d)

Fig. 7.7 The a.c. small-signal equivalent circuit of the triode in (b) is derived
from characteristic (a); equivalent circuit (d) is deduced from characteristic (c).

Fig. 7.7(a), the net change in anode voltage is

$$\delta v_A = \delta v_{A1} - \delta v_{A2}$$

Change δv_{A1} occurs at constant grid voltage, while change δv_{A2} occurs at constant anode current. The equation can thus be modified to

$$\delta v_A = r_a \delta i_A - \mu \delta v_g$$

From this equation, the equivalent circuit of the valve is that of a resistor r_a carrying a current δi_A, in series with a voltage generator with an output voltage $-\mu \delta v_G$, i.e., a generator which makes the anode less positive when the grid becomes more positive. If the grid signal is an alternating voltage of r.m.s. value V_g, then the anode current has an r.m.s. value I_a, and the voltage generator develops an output $-\mu V_g$ with respect to the cathode. The small-signal voltage generator equivalent circuit of the valve for alternating input signals is therefore as shown in Fig. 7.7(b).

If the total change δi_A in anode current occurs as shown in Fig. 7.7(c), then

$$\delta i_A = \delta i_{A1} + \delta i_{A2} = \frac{\delta v_A}{r_a} + g_m \delta v_G$$

For an alternating input signal V_g, this equation becomes

$$I_a = \frac{V_a}{r_a} + g_m V_g$$

giving a small-signal current generator version of the *a.c. equivalent circuit* shown in Fig. 7.7(d).

The concept of the small-signal equivalent circuit is a particularly powerful tool when the design principles of electronic amplifiers are considered. In the above, the parameters have been determined from the static characteristics of the device. In practice, it is more convenient to evaluate the parameters by means of a *dynamic test*, in which the valve is excited by an alternating signal, and the small signal changes are measured directly.

7.8   The tetrode

In the tetrode, a fourth electrode known as the *screen grid* or G2 is interposed between the control grid and the anode. The circuit symbol is shown in Fig. 7.8(a), and typical output characteristics for one value of control grid voltage and in Fig. 7.8(b).

The screen grid potential is usually fixed at about two-thirds of the anode supply voltage, so that when the anode potential is zero, i_A is also zero and all the space current (i_K) flows to the screen grid. As the anode potential is increased, the anode begins to collect some of the electrons which pass through the coarse mesh of the screen, and i_A begins to increase rapidly at first, as shown in Fig. 7.8(b).

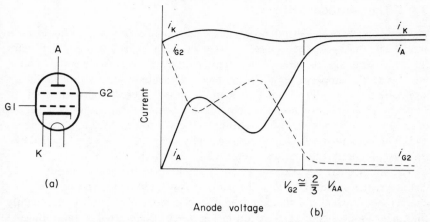

$$V_{G2} \cong \frac{2}{3} V_{AA}$$

Anode voltage   (b)

Fig. 7.8   (a) The circuit symbol of the tetrode, and (b) a typical set of character-istics for a constant value of control grid voltage.

The screen grid provides an effective electrostatic screen between the anode and the cathode, and for any given control grid potential the total space current is set by the potential of the screen grid. The anode potential has little influence on the total space current so effective is the 'screening' of G2. As a result, an increase in i_A causes a reduction in i_{G2}, and the screen grid current character-istic is almost a mirror image of the anode current characteristic (for a given value of v_{G2}).

Following the region in which i_A rises rapidly, there is a region in which it reduces with increasing anode voltage. This is equivalent to the tetrode having a negative slope resistance. This occurs because of secondary emission from the anode due to the impact of primary electrons. Since the screen grid potential is still higher than that of the anode, the secondary electrons which leave the anode are attracted to the screen grid, reducing i_A and increasing i_{G2}.

When the anode potential is increased further, some of the secondary elec-trons are attracted back to the anode, causing the characteristic to begin to flat-ten again. When $v_A > v_{G2}$, practically all of the space current flows to the anode. In this region of the characteristics the anode current, at a set value of control grid voltage, remains substantially constant over a wide range of anode voltages, the value of the current being limited by the screen grid voltage.

The tetrode is normally operated with an anode voltage greater than the screen voltage to avoid the kinks in the characteristic. Under these conditions, the anode current is almost independent of the actual anode voltage used, resulting in a slope resistance of the order of 10^5 to 10^6 Ω. Typical values for g_m and μ are 0·5 mA/V to 5 mA/V and 100 to 1500, respectively.

Owing to the inherent screening introduced between the control grid and the anode, the grid-anode capacitance of the tetrode is much less than that of the triode, being typically 0·001 pF to 0·01 pF.

7.9   The pentode

The pentode, or five electrode valve, has three grids between the cathode and the anode. The third grid, the *suppressor grid* or G3 is a coarse mesh grid between the screen grid and the anode. The circuit symbol of the pentode is shown in Fig. 7.9(a), the suppressor grid usually being connected to the cathode either internally or externally, although in some circuits it is used as an additional control grid. In its normal operating mode, the principal function of the suppressor grid is to form a region of zero potential between the anode and the screen grid. When secondary electrons are emitted by the anode, they are repelled by the zero potential region and are returned to the anode.

The anode characteristics are generally similar in shape to the output characteristics of the JUGFET. The pentode is worked on the flat parts of the characteristics which are characterized by a high slope resistance. Consequently, the current-source equivalent circuit in Fig. 7.9(b) is preferred to the voltage-source equivalent circuit; with normal types of construction, g_m has a maximum value of about 8 mA/V.

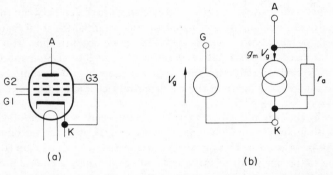

Fig. 7.9   (a) Pentode symbol, and (b) the small-signal a.c. equivalent circuit.

Since the grid/cathode geometry of a pentode is very similar to that of a triode, the mutual conductances of the two valves are much the same. However, the slope resistance of the pentode is much greater, with the result that the amplification factor of the pentode may have a value of the order of several thousand, compared with a value of about 20 in the triode.

7.10   Valve construction

The majority of industrial valve electrodes are made of nickel or iron, which are easily workable and are chemically stable materials. Electrodes are insulated from one another by spacers, usually made from mica, which are treated to remove surface impurities before being sealed. The electrode assembly is then connected to the valve base and inserted into the glass envelope, together with a small magnesium pellet, known as the *getter*.

The whole assembly is then heated to a temperature just below the softening temperature of the envelope, which is about $400°C$ for glass and $600°C$ for Pyrex, and the interior of the valve is evacuated by a vacuum pump. At the same time, the electrodes are heated by induction. The two processes have the effect of removing practically all traces of gas and water vapour from the inner surfaces of the valve.

Finally the getter, which is a chemically active material, is fired by induction heating. The getter combines with any further small quantities of gas that may be liberated during the lifetime of the valve. The getter deposits itself on the glass envelope of the valve, forming silvery film on the inside of the valve.

A valve which has a high vacuum inside it is known as a *hard valve*, while one containing gas is described as a *soft valve*. Since many gases are electro-negative, i.e., they acquire electrons, the presence of such gases (oxygen is an example) seriously affects the performance of the valve at high frequencies. Gas particles also increase the noise level introduced by the valve.

Problems

7.1   Describe a test made to obtain the static characteristic of a vacuum diode. Draw the circuit arrangement used; list the equipment necessary and indicate the ranges of instruments used. Sketch the characteristics, and show how the forward conduction resistance and reverse blocking resistance can be calculated.

7.2   When the anode current and the anode voltage of a certain vacuum diode are 5 mA and 70 V, respectively, the relationship between the anode current and anode voltage is given by $i_A = k v_A^{1.5}$. Determine the value of k, and calculate (a) the anode voltage for an anode current of 4 mA, and (b) the anode current for an anode voltage of 75 V.

7.3   A diode has the following static characteristic:

v_A	(V)	5	10	15	20	25	30	35
i_A	(mA)	8	22·5	42	65	88	113	137·5

Plot the characteristic, and determine (a) the instantaneous slope resistance r_A, and (b) the slope resistance r_a at anode voltages of (i) 10 V, and (ii) 30 V.

7.4   (a) Describe a test made to obtain the static characteristic of a vacuum triode. Sketch the circuit arrangement used.

(b) List all the equipment required giving typical ranges.

(c) Sketch the form of curves obtained by plotting typical test results and explain how (i) the anode slope resistance, (ii) the mutual conductance, and (iii) the amplification factor may be derived from these curves.

7.5   In a triode valve, $\mu = 20$ and $r_a = 5$ kΩ. Draw the equivalent constant current (Norton) generator circuit.

7.6   In a certain triode, the anode voltage and current were found to be 140 V and 12 mA, respectively, when the grid bias voltage was -2 V. When the anode voltage was increased by 10 V, at constant grid voltage, the anode current was found to be increased by 3 mA. The anode conditions were then returned to their initial values, and the grid bias voltage was increased to -3 V at a constant anode current of 12 mA. To maintain the anode current constant in the latter test, the anode voltage had to be increased by 10 V. Evaluate the parameters of the valve.

7.7   The following characteristics refer to a triode:

$v_A(V)$	i_A (mA) at grid voltages of				
	−2	−3	−4	−6	−8
130	10·5	8	5·6	2·7	0·9
150	13·5	10·6	8	4·3	2
170	16·8	13·5	10·6	6·2	3·3

Plot the characteristics and estimate the parameters of the valve at a grid bias of −3 V and an anode voltage of 150 V.

7.8   The following characteristics refer to a pentode valve.

$v_A(V)$	i_A (mA) at grid voltages of			
	−0·5	−1·0	−1·5	−2·0
150	13·0	10·5	8·25	6·25
200	13·2	10·7	8·3	6·3
250	13·3	10·8	8·4	6·4

Plot the characteristics and estimate the slope resistance on each curve for v_A = 200 V. Estimate the value of μ when v_A = 200 V, v_G = −1·5 V.

7.9   In a pentode valve, g_m = 6 mA/V and r_a = 200 kΩ. Draw the voltage generator (Thevenin) equivalent circuit.

7.10   The characteristic of a certain valve is given by $i_A = a + bv_G + cv_G^2$, where i_A is the anode current and v_G is the grid voltage. Draw a graph showing how mutual conductance varies with grid bias.

Given that a = 18, b = 6, c = 0·5, calculate the mutual conductance at a bias of 3V.

8. Optoelectronics

Optoelectronics is a name which covers a wide range of *photosensitive devices* (devices which are sensitive to light and other radiation) and *photo-emissive* devices (devices which radiate light and other near-visible radiations).

8.1 The visible electromagnetic spectrum

Light, radio, television, X-rays and cosmic rays have a common feature—they are all electromagnetic radiations. The wavelength of *visibie light* ranges from about 0·35 μm (violet) to about 0·75 μm (red), as shown in Fig. 8.1. Wavelengths shorter than 0·35 μm are known as *ultraviolet* radiations and those greater than 0·75 μm are *infrared* radiations.

The velocity at which electromagnetic waves travel in a vacuum is 3×10^8 m/s (or 186 000 miles/s) which, very approximately, is $\frac{1}{3}$ m/μs (1 ft/μs), and the frequency of the radiations in hertz is given by the equation

$$\text{Frequency} = f = \frac{3 \times 10^8}{\text{wavelength in m}} \text{ Hz}$$

For example, the frequency corresponding to a wavelength of 0·75 μm is

$$f = \frac{3 \times 10^8}{0 \cdot 75 \times 10^{-6}} = 4 \times 10^{14} \text{ Hz or 400 million MHz}$$

The eye, as with other radiation detectors, is not equally sensitive to all frequencies, and is most sensitive to colour with a wavelength of about 0·55 μm. A curve showing the approximate sensitivity of the eye to radiations within the visible spectrum is also given in Fig. 8.1. The colour we actually 'see' can, in some instances, be deceiving. Consider the case of an incandescent tungsten-filament lamp; the output from this type of lamp includes all the visible wavelengths, but the majority of its power output is in the red and infrared region,

99

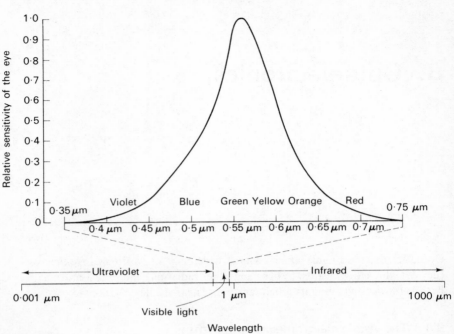

Fig. 8.1   A section of the radiation spectrum, together with the relative sensitivity of the human eye.

the latter being invisible. The eye acts to produce a 'mean' result, so that the lamp appears to humans to have a colour in the yellow–red region of the spectrum.

Certain types of radiation detector have their greatest response in the infrared region and are used where this feature is of advantage, e.g., in boiler flame failure detection systems, in burglar alarm systems and in aircraft and missile tracking systems.

At this point, a few words about the units of illumination would not be out of place. The *luminous flux* is the total visible light energy emitted by a source in unit time, the *lumen* being the unit of luminous flux. Some characteristic curves show *illumination* on one axis; the unit of illumination is the *lux* or lumen per square metre.

8.2   Photoconductive cells

When light falls upon a semiconductor, the energy taken up by the atoms causes the spontaneous generation of electron-hole pairs. The net effect is an increase in bulk conductivity, or a decrease in electrical resistance. Materials used as the semiconductor material include lead sulphide, lead selenide, indium anti-

monide, and cadmium sulphide (CdS). The last is the most commonly used
material since its spectral response curve closely matches the human eye.
Cadmium sulphide cells can, therefore, be used in applications where humans
could normally estimate illumination levels, e.g., camera exposure settings,
street lighting control circuits, smoke detectors, etc.

Other types of photoconductive cells generally have spectral response curves
with peak values at wavelengths of 2 μm to 3 μm. These cells are used to detect
radiation with a high infrared content.

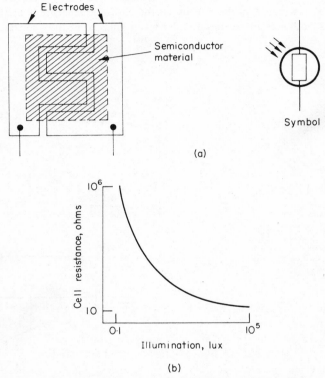

Fig. 8.2   (a) A photoconductive cell, and (b) its characteristic curve.

One form of construction is shown in Fig. 8.2(a), in which a film of semi-
conducting material is laid down on an insulating substrate, and electrodes
are evaporated on to its surface through a mask. The electrodes have the shape
shown in order to increase the contact area and decrease the resistance of the
cell. The 'dark' resistance of the cell generally has a value between 10^4 and
10^6 Ω, the characteristic of a typical cell being illustrated in Fig. 8.2(b). Photoconductive cells are also known as *light-dependent resistors* (L.D.R.).

Photoconductor arrays can be manufactured in the form of a film integrated
circuit. It is possible to connect active devices (e.g. transistors) to the array in

order to use it in encoding networks, such as in punched-card and punched-tape readers and in positioning systems.

8.3   Light-activated p-n junction devices

Radiant energy incident upon a semiconductor creates electron-hole pairs, giving rise to a drift current in the presence of an electric field.

The simplest *photojunction device* is the *photodiode*, Fig. 8.3. Photodiodes are generally similar to conventional p-n junction diodes, the difference being that there is a 'window' in the housing of the photodiode to allow light to fall upon it. Photodiodes are operated under reverse bias conditions so that only

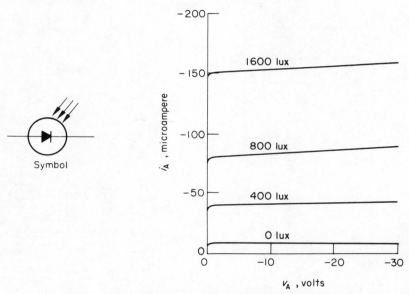

Fig. 8.3   A photodiode and its characteristics.

leakage current flows through them. The 'dark' current is typically 10 μA in germanium diodes, and 1 μA in silicon diodes. As the illumination intensity increases the leakage current increases, as shown in the characteristics; the sensitivity of photodiodes lies between 10 mA/lm and 50 mA/lm, and the spectral response covers the visible and near infrared frequencies. Incident light can be modulated at very high frequencies with this type of device, and some photodiodes designed for use with laser systems can operate at frequencies of several hundred megahertz.

As with all semiconductor devices, the leakage current increases with an increase in ambient temperature, and the characteristics of Fig. 8.3 are correct at only one temperature.

Bipolar *phototransistors* operate by exposing the base region to light, the radiant energy being equivalent to additional base current. The base connection is brought out for biasing purposes; a circuit symbol and a typical characteristic is shown in Fig. 8.4. The sensitivity of a general-purpose phototransistor is typically 500 mA/lm, and the collector current is usually a few milliamperes, which is adequate to energize the coil of a relay.

The gate insulation of a *photo-FET* is made transparent to light, and the light energy passing into the substrate causes charge carriers to be liberated in the substrate. This increases the conductivity of the source-to-drain conducting channel, resulting in the drain current being a function of the illumination intensity.

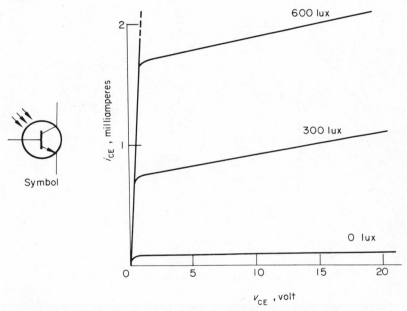

Fig. 8.4 A typical set of phototransistor characteristics.

Four-layer p-n-p-n *light-activated thyristors* are triggered by incident light, the light providing the energy to the gate region which is normally supplied by the gate circuit. Light-activated thyristors are very sensitive, and to prevent inadvertent triggering of the thyristor by induced voltage pulses, the gate and cathode region are usually coupled by a resistor. High power circuits can be controlled directly by photothyristors.

8.4 Photovoltaic cells or solar cells

A *photovoltaic cell* is a device which generates an e.m.f. between its terminals when light falls upon it, and is made in the form of a silicon p-n crystal. One of

the regions is a very thin diffused layer (about 1 μm deep) through which
light can pass without much loss of energy. When the light reaches the p-n
junction its energy is released into the crystal lattice, causing electrons and
holes to be generated in the junction. The normal process of charge carrier
diffusion then takes place. Since one of the regions is very thin, it rapidly
saturates with charge carriers, and a differential potential appears between the
two regions. The characteristics of a typical photovoltaic cell are shown in
Fig. 8.5.

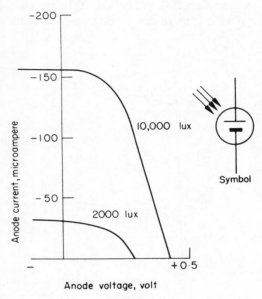

The characteristics of a photovoltaic cell.

Earlier types of photovoltaic cell operated on the barrier-layer principle, the
semiconductors being selenium or cuprous oxide.

Applications of photovoltaic cells include exposure meters, punched-tape
and card readers, and aerospace projects.

8.5 Light-emitting diodes (L.E.D.)

One form of light-emitting diode is shown in Fig. 8.6(a). The diode is shown in
sectional view, and consists of an epitaxial n-type layer of gallium arsenide
phosphide which is grown upon a gallium arsenide substrate. A very thin
p-region is diffused into the epitaxial layer, and an anode in the shape of a
comb or similar configuration is laid down on the p-region. The shape of the
anode is selected so as to minimize its masking effect on the emitted light.

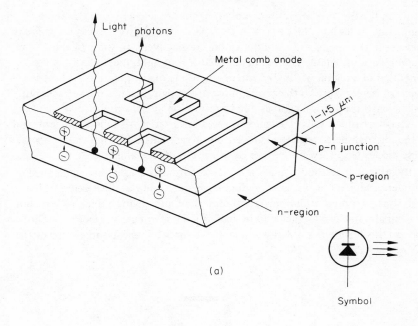

(a)

Symbol

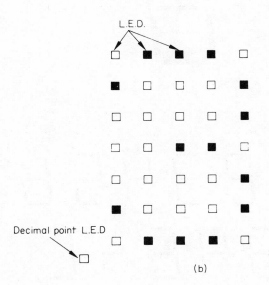

(b)

Fig. 8.6 (a) Sectional view of a light-emitting diode, and (b) a 7 x 5 array of light-emitting diodes which can be used to generate any alpha-numeric symbol. In the figure, decimal number 3 is illuminated.

When the diode is forward biased, electrons are injected into the anode region and holes into the cathode region. The charge carriers recombine when they reach the anode and cathode regions, respectively. In some of the recombinations, energy is given off in the form of light, most of which is generated in a region within 0·5 μm of the p-side of the junction. Since the junction is very close to the anode, most of the light reaches the surface, but only a small proportion escapes due to refraction at the surface.

The electroluminous efficiency of the diodes varies with diode current, and in the microampere range the light output is very small. It is normal to operate these diodes with forward current of some tens of milliamperes.

By arranging 35 diodes in a 7 x 5 matrix form, see Fig. 8.6(b), a decimal number or alphabetical character can be generated. In the illustration, the dark squares represent illuminated diodes, the figure giving a decimal 3 readout. A decimal point can be included by having a diode which is offset from the matrix; this is shown at the lower left of the figure. Typical dimensions of the

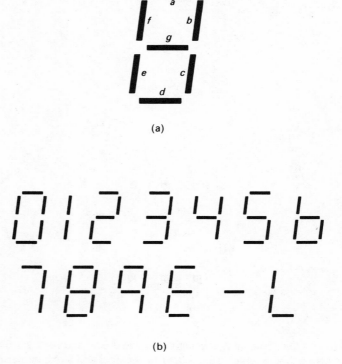

(a)

(b)

Fig. 8.7   A seven-segment display.

array in Fig. 8.6(b) are 1 cm x 0·75 cm, each lamp being energized by a current
of 50 mA to 100 mA at about 1·7 V. Popular colours are red, green, orange and
yellow. Each diode in the matrix can be driven either by a suitable code convertor circuit* or a single integrated circuit code convertor.

Applications of L.E.D.'s include digital read-out devices, tuning indicators,
overload indicators, line-of-sight communication systems, and communication
systems using fibre optics.

A popular form of display used in calculators is the *seven-segment display*
shown in Fig. 8.7(a). By energizing combinations of segments, the decimal
numbers 0 to 9 can be displayed together with a limited range of alphabetical
characters (see Fig. 8.7(b)). Two forms of seven-segment L.E.D. display are
shown in Fig. 8.8. A 'first generation' type is illustrated in Fig. 8.8(a) in

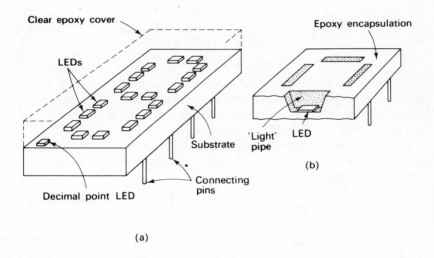

Fig. 8.8   Two forms of construction of a seven-segment L.E.D. display.

which several L.E.D.s are formed in a seven-segment pattern on a common
substrate, the whole having a transparent epoxy coating. Fig. 8.8(b) shows
a form of construction using a 'light' pipe to conduct light from the L.E.D.
The light pipe is a cone-shaped cavity containing glass-filled epoxy.

* See *Logic Circuits* by N. M. Morris (McGraw-Hill, 1976).

8.6 Optically coupled isolators

Circuit designers are often faced with the problem of providing electrical isolation between circuits, whilst still maintaining signal transmission at high frequency. Opto-isolators solve many problems of this kind.

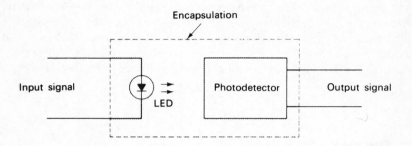

Fig. 8.9   An optically coupled isolator.

The basis of an opto-isolator is shown in Fig. 8.9, in which a L.E.D. and a photodetecting device are contained in a light-tight encapsulation. The photodetector may be a photodiode, a phototransistor, or a photothyristor; in some cases an amplifier is included in the encapsulation.

The opto-isolator provides complete isolation between the input and output signals, and this feature allows it to be used as an interface between high voltage and low voltage systems.

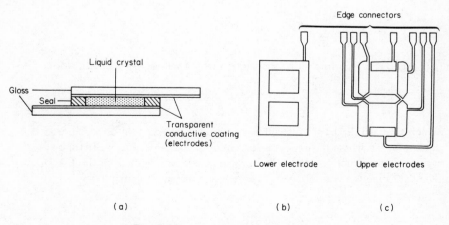

(a)   (b)   (c)

Fig. 8.10   Liquid crystal display.

8.7 Liquid crystal displays (L.C.D.)

Liquid crystals are organic fluids whose molecules can be re-aligned by the application of an electric field to the liquid crystal. The general form of seven-segment L.C.D. is shown in Fig. 8.10. The liquid crystal is sealed between two glass surfaces (see Fig. 8.10(a)) which have transparent conductive coatings on them; the space between the surfaces is typically 10 μm. The conductive coat on the lower electrode (b) is common to all electrodes, whilst the upper segments (c) are energized independently; the two sets of electrodes are aligned with one another in the display.

The display is designed so that when one of the segments is energized it causes the incident light either to be transmitted or to be reflected. In the latter case the energized electrode appears silver in colour. In the former case the display may either be silver or black, depending on the design of the L.C.D. L.C.D.s do not generate light and depend on incident illumination, to be observed under conditions of low ambient illumination, it is necessary to provde artificial illumination, e.g., from a tungsten filament lamp.

L.C.D.s suffer from electrolytic dissociation if energized by d.c., which leads to deterioration of the display. In practice they are energized by a.c., which gives a considerably extended lifetime.

Problems

8.1   Write an essay on the nature of light.

8.2   A substance is found to change its electrical resistance when it is illuminated by light; which of the following names is given to it? (a) Photoelectric, (b) photomultiplier, (c) photoconductive, (d) photovoltaic, (e) photoemissive.

8.3   Sketch the characteristics of a photodiode and a phototransistor, and explain how they operate.

8.4   Sketch the characteristics of a photovoltaic cell, and deduce one form of equivalent circuit for it.

8.5   Describe the principle of operation of the light-emitting diode. Illustrate your answer with suitable diagrams.

8.6   With the aid of a connection diagram, explain the operation of a circuit using a photoconductive cell and an amplifier stage to count objects passing along a conveyor belt.

8.7   With the aid of a diagram explain the operation of a circuit using a photoconductive cell which could be used as an industrial alarm system.
State with reasons what type of cell you would use and explain its action.

8.8   (a) Describe, with the aid of a sketch of a typical characteristic curve, the principle of operation and the construction of one type of photoconductive device.

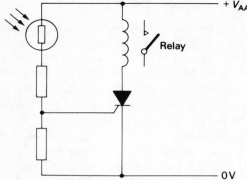

Fig. 8.11   Figure for problem 8.8.

(b) Explain the operation of the circuit in Fig. 8.11 when the incident illumination increases from zero to full brightness. Show how the circuit may be reset when the illumination level falls to a low value.

8.9   (a) Outline the principle of operation of a photovoltaic cell. (b) The characteristic of the photovoltaic cell in Fig. 8.12 for an illumination of 2500 lumens/m² is as follows

V (mV)	200	250	300
I (μA)	96	90	80

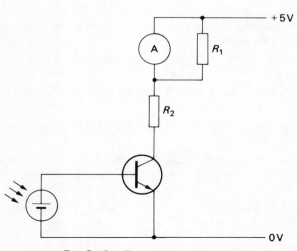

Fig. 8.12   Figure for problem 8.9.

The input characteristic of the junction transistor in the circuit is linear between the following points

V_{BE} (mV)	200	250
I_B (μA)	20	90

The common-emitter current gain of the amplifier is 150 over the working range of the circuit. Determine suitable values for R_1 and R_2 to enable the meter to give full scale deflection for an illumination of 2500 lumens/m^2. The meter gives f.s.d. for a current of 1 mA, when the p.d. across the meter is 75 mV. Assume that the voltage across the transistor when the cell is fully illuminated is 1 V.

9. A.C. amplifiers

9.1 Amplifier classification

Amplifiers are classified in many ways according to such factors as their frequency range, the method of interstage coupling used, the bias point at which the transistors or valves operate, and the aspect of the output signal which is of particular interest, e.g., the voltage, current, or power.

Circuits which amplify a wide band of frequencies are known as *untuned amplifiers* or *broadband amplifiers,* and those which are tuned to amplify a narrow band of frequencies are known as *tuned amplifiers* or *narrowband amplifiers.* The method of coupling between stages of amplification modifies the performance to some extent, the most common method being *a.c. coupling* or *alternating current coupling.* In this type of interconnection, low frequency components (including unidirectional or d.c. signals) are not transmitted to the following stage. Some amplifiers are *direct coupled,* so that they transmit every frequency down to unidirectional signals to the following stage. The latter type of amplifier is one form of *d.c. amplifier* or *direct current amplifier,* which also includes a range of circuits known as *chopper amplifiers.* In chopper amplifiers, the input signal is 'chopped' into a series of pulses by a device known as a 'chopper', which is either a semiconductor circuit or a synchronous relay, so that the signal is converted into an alternating signal. This is amplified by a.c. coupled amplifiers, and is reconverted into d.c. at the output by a process which is the inverse of 'chopping'.

The point on the characteristics to which electronic devices are biased is related to the amplifying function carried out by that stage. For the moment, we merely classify the operation in terms of the relationship between the input signal and the current flowing in the load circuit.

CLASS A   Current flows in the load during the whole period of the
            input signal cycle.

CLASS AB   Load current flows for more than one-half cycle, but less
than the full cycle of the input signal waveform.

CLASS B   Load current flows for one-half cycle of the input signal
waveform.

CLASS C   Current flows for less than one-half cycle of the input signal
waveform.

Typical input and output waveforms for the three classes of operation are
illustrated in Fig. 9.1.

Tuned and untuned voltage amplifiers, and low power audio-frequency amplifiers

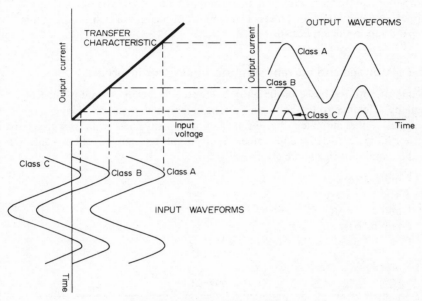

Fig. 9.1   Amplifier classification.

generally work in class A, while audio-frequency power amplifiers work in class
B, as do some tuned radio-frequency amplifiers. Oscillators and radio-frequency
amplifiers usually operate in class C.

Switching amplifiers and *pulse amplifiers* often form another grouping. These
amplifiers are largely concerned with transmitting signals which rapidly change
between two voltage or current levels, without delaying the signal or distorting
the waveform.

The *gain* of an amplifier is the ratio of the magnitude of the output signal to
that of the input signal. *Voltage amplifiers* increase the magnitude of the input
voltage signal, but are generally incapable of providing a significant amount of
output power. *Current amplifiers* and voltage amplifiers are generally bracketed
together so far as amplifier classification goes (it has already been shown that

current generator models and voltage generator models are interchangeable), the principal difference between them being the relative values of their output impedance. The operating efficiency of voltage amplifiers is not generally a major consideration, and greater attention is paid to keeping distortion to a minimum.

Power amplifiers are designed to provide an adequate signal power to drive output devices. The output power may range from a few watts to many megawatts, and the choice of amplifying device is very wide. Operating efficiency is a major consideration in such amplifiers, whereas distortion may not be an important factor. In high power control systems, the input signal to the power amplifier may be in the form of a continuous voltage, and the output may appear as a succession of pulses. The amount of distortion that is acceptable depends upon the application.

9.2   Voltage and current symbols in electronic circuits

A circuit notation based on BS 3363 is adopted in this book, and is illustrated here by reference to the collector current in a bipolar transistor. Upper case (capital) letters indicate either mean (d.c.) or r.m.s. values, and lower case (small) letters indicate instantaneous values. The symbols are summarized in Table 9.1, and examples of its use are given in Fig. 9.2.

I and i—current
V and v—voltage
E and e—emitter electrode
B and b—base electrode
C and c—collector electrode

Table 9.1

Symbol	Subscript	Description
i or v	e, b or c	Instantaneous value of the a.c. component
i or v	E, B or C	Instantaneous total value
I or V	e, b or c	(i) R.m.s. value of the a.c. component, or (ii) with the additional subscript (m) the peak value of the a.c. component
I or V	E, B or C	(i) the d.c. value, or (ii) with the additional subscript (AV) the total average, or the subscript (M) the total peak value

Where a voltage or current is given two subscripts, e.g., V_{BE}, the first subscript denotes the terminal at which the quantity is measured and the second subscript is the reference junction. Supply voltages are indicated by repeating the terminal subscript, i.e., V_{CC}, V_{BB}, V_{EE}, etc.

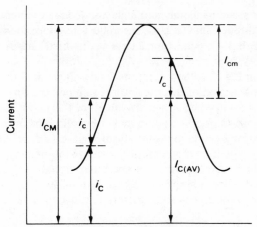

Fig. 9.2   Current symbols in electronic circuits.

9.3   A common-emitter class A voltage amplifier

In order that a circuit can amplify an alternating signal, the transistor must be *biased* so that it operates on the linear region of its characteristics. A basic common-emitter amplifier is shown in Fig. 9.3; in this circuit the base bias current is supplied via resistor R_B. The value of the base bias current is chosen so that the average value of the collector voltage is about one-half of the supply voltage, i.e., $V_{CC}/2$. The value of the collector voltage when the applied a.c. signal (V_1) is zero is known as the *quiescent* value of collector voltage, i.e., the collector voltage when the circuit is 'quiet'. The corresponding value of collector current is known as the quiescent collector current.

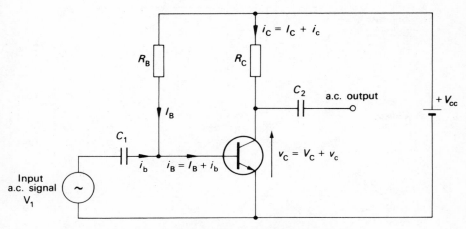

Fig. 9.3   A simple common-emitter amplifier.

The reason for selecting a quiescent collector voltage of about $V_{CC}/2$ is that it allows the a.c. imput signal to cause the collector voltage to swing down towards zero and up towards V_{CC}, permitting a large undistorted output voltage swing to be developed.

In the circuit in Fig. 9.3, the a.c. input signal is connected to the amplifier by capacitor C_1. The function of this capacitor is to block the flow of direct current from the bias circuit into the a.c. signal source; for this reason C_1 is described as a *blocking capacitor*. Capacitor C_1 also makes Fig. 9.3 into an *a.c. amplifier* since only alternating signals can be transmitted through it. In order that C_1 presents little impedance to the flow of alternating current at normal operating frequencies, its reactance at the lowest frequency of operation should be less than the input impedance of the transistor amplifier. A capacitor of 20–30 μF capacitance is adequate for general purpose work; electrolytic capacitors are usually used for

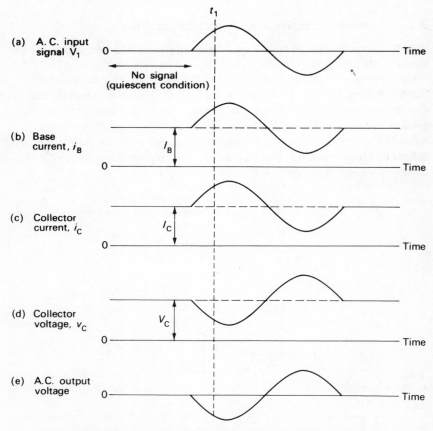

Fig. 9.4   Waveforms in the simple common-emitter amplifier.

these applications since they have the largest capacitance-to-volume ratio of all capacitors. Arising from the very low reactance of C_1, practically all the input a.c. voltage is applied to the transistor base region.

For similar reasons to those given above, capacitor C_2 is also described as a blocking capacitor since it blocks the flow of direct current from the amplifier into the external load circuit.

The operation of the amplifier in Fig. 9.3 is explained by considering the waveforms in the circuit when a sinusoidal input V_1 is applied to the circuit (see Fig. 9.4). Under quiescent conditions the values of the base current, collector current and collector voltage are I_B, I_C and V_C, respectively. At time t_1 in the positive half-cycle of the input cycle (Fig. 9.4 (a)), the total instantaneous base current i_B (curve (b)) is greater than I_B. Due to the current gain of the transistor, an increase in base current causes the collector current to increase, hence the waveform of i_C (see curve (c)) is in phase with that of i_B. The increase in the collector current at t_1 causes the p.d. across R_C to increase, and since the collector supply voltage V_{CC} is constant the net result is a reduction of the collector voltage v_C below the quiescent value (see curve (d)).

The collector voltage is seen to be the sum of two components, namely the quiescent (d.c.) component and an alternating component. The two components are separated by means of the blocking capacitor C_2; this capacitor blocks the flow of d.c. while presenting only a very low reactance to the flow of a.c. from the circuit. The a.c. component of the collector voltage (curve (e)) is seen to be antiphase to the input signal. For this reason the common-emitter amplifier in Fig. 9.3 is often described as a *phase-inverting amplifier*.

9.4 The d.c. load line or static load line

The performance of an amplifier can be predicted from a knowledge of the output (collector) characteristics and of the values of the circuit components. Applying Kirchhoff's second law to the collector circuit in Fig. 9.3 yields the equation

$$V_{CC} = v_C + i_C R_C$$

or

$$i_C = \left(\frac{-1}{R_C}\right) i_C + \frac{V_{CC}}{R_C} \qquad (9.1)$$

Equation (9.1) is known as the *d.c. load line equation*, and is the equation of a straight line of the form $y = mx + c$ where the slope of the graph (m) is given by $(-1/R_C)$ and the vertical intercept (c) is equal to V_{CC}/R_C. The load line is therefore a straight line which terminates at its upper end (when $v_C = 0$) at a collector current of V_{CC}/R_C, and at the lower end (when $i_C = 0$) at a value equal to the supply voltage V_{CC}; the slope of the load line is $-1/R_C$. An amplifier having a supply voltage of 9 V and a collector load of 1 kΩ has a load line which terminates at its upper end when $i_C = V_{CC}/R_C = 9$ V/1 kΩ = 9 mA, and at the lower end at $v_C = V_{CC} = 9$ V. The operating conditions of the amplifier are determined

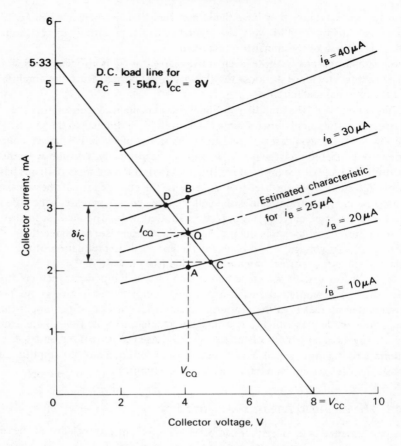

Fig. 9.5   Figure for example 9.1.

by superimposing the load line on the output characteristics of the transistor (see Fig. 9.5).

Equation (9.1) defines the operation of the amplifier with a pure resistive load, and *the operating point of the amplifier is always constrained to move along the load line*. It was stated earlier in this section that the quiescent collector voltage should be about $V_{CC}/2$; the quiescent point of the amplifier is therefore located *on the load line* at a collector voltage of about $V_{CC}/2$. In Fig. 9.5 the quiescent point is given by Q, and the quiescent value of the collector voltage and current, and the quiescent base current are 4·1 V, 2·6 mA and 25 μA, respectively.

Example 9.1: The characteristics of an n-p-n transistor are linear between the points listed in Table 9.2.

Table 9.2

Base current (μA)	Collector current (mA) for collector voltages of	
	2 V	10 V
10	0·9	1·7
20	1·8	2·8
30	2·8	4·2
40	3·9	5·5

The transistor is used in a circuit of the type in Fig. 9.3 with a collector resistor of 1·5 kΩ and a supply voltage of 8 V. Estimate, using a load line

(a) the total power dissipated in the circuit
(b) the quiescent collector power dissipation if the quiescent base current is 25 μA
(c) the current gain, h_{fe}, of the transistor at the quiescent point
(d) If a sinusoidal input current of 5 μA peak value is injected into the transistor base, estimate the peak-to-peak change in collector current.

Solution: The characteristics are plotted in Fig. 9.5, together with the estimated output characteristic for the quiescent base current of 25 μA. The d.c. load line terminates at V_{CC} = 8 V at its lower end, and at $i_C = V_{CC}/R_C$ = 8 V/1·5 kΩ = 5·33 mA at the upper end. The quiescent point Q, is given by the intersection of the load line and the output characteristic for i_B = 25 μA. From the graph V_{CQ} = 4·1 V, and I_{CQ} = 2·6 mA.

(a) The total power dissipated in the circuit is equal to the mean power drawn from the battery.

$$\text{Total power} = V_{CC}(I_{CQ} + I_{BQ}) = 8 \text{ V} \times (2\cdot6 + 0\cdot025) \text{ mA}$$
$$= 21 \text{ mW}.$$

(b) The quiescent collector power dissipation is

$$V_{CQ}I_{CQ} = 4\cdot1 \text{ V} \times 2\cdot6 \text{ mA} = 10\cdot66 \text{ mW}$$

(c) The value of h_{fe} of the transistor is estimated for a base current change of ±5 μA about the quiescent point Q. That is the collector current is assumed to change between points A and B on Fig. 9.5 (remember, h_{fe} is evaluated at a constant value of collector voltage).

$$h_{fe} = \frac{\text{change in } i_C}{\text{change in } i_B} \text{ at constant } v_C \, (v_C = V_{CQ} \text{ in this case})$$

$$= \frac{(3\cdot18 - 2\cdot06) \text{ mA}}{(30 - 20) \, \mu\text{A}} = 112$$

(d) When the transistor is used in an amplifier the operating point moves along the load line, and for a base current change of ±5 μA the operating point changes between points C and D on Fig. 9.5, hence

$$\text{peak-to-peak change in } i_C = \delta i_C = (3 \cdot 05 - 2 \cdot 15)\,\text{mA} = 0 \cdot 9\,\text{mA}.$$

Note: the effective *current gain* of the amplifier (given by the ratio of the change in i_C to the change in i_B) is 90, which is less that the value of h_{fe} of the transistor. Readers may like to explain why this should be so.

9.5   Current gain, voltage gain and power gain of a common-emitter amplifier

For a maximum value $i_{b(max)}$ of base current there is a maximum value $i_{c(max)}$ of collector current, and corresponding to $i_{b(min)}$ there is a minimum current $i_{c(min)}$ in the collector circuit. The *current gain* of the amplifier may be defined as follows

$$\text{Current gain } A_i = \frac{i_{c(max)} - i_{c(min)}}{i_{b(max)} - i_{b(min)}} \tag{9.2}$$

Taking values from the load line in example 9.1 gives $i_{c(max)} = 3 \cdot 05$ mA, $i_{c(min)} = 2 \cdot 15$ mA, $i_{b(max)} = 30\ \mu\text{A}$, $i_{b(min)} = 20\ \mu\text{A}$, hence

$$A_i = \frac{(3 \cdot 05 - 2 \cdot 15)\,\text{mA}}{(30 - 20)\,\mu\text{A}} = 90$$

The current gain can also be evaluated if the r.m.s. value of the collector current I_c and the r.m.s. value of the base current I_b are known, when $A_i = I_c/I_b$. The r.m.s. value of the current in the load, assuming sinusoidal collector current, is

$$I_c = \frac{i_{c(max)} - i_{c(min)}}{2\sqrt{2}}$$

$$= \frac{0 \cdot 9}{2 \cdot 828} = 0 \cdot 32\,\text{mA}$$

The corresponding r.m.s. value of base current, assuming a sinusoidal signal is

$$I_b = \frac{i_{b(max)} - i_{b(min)}}{2\sqrt{2}} = \frac{10}{2 \cdot 828} = 3 \cdot 55\ \mu\text{A}$$

The above r.m.s. values give a current gain of $A_i = I_c/I_b = 0 \cdot 32 \times 10^{-3}/3 \cdot 55 \times 10^{-6}$ $= 90$.

The *voltage gain* of the amplifier may be defined as follows

$$\text{Voltage gain, } A_v = - \left\{ \frac{v_{c(max)} - v_{c(min)}}{v_{b(max)} - v_{b(min)}} \right\} \tag{9.3}$$

where v_c and v_b refer to the collector voltage and the base voltage, respectively. The negative sign associated with the expresssion for voltage gain implies that the amplifier is phase inverting. The collector voltage values can be determined from the load line construction, and the base voltage values can be calculated from a knowledge of the input resistance, R_{in}, of the amplifier together with the base current values as f llows.

$$v_{b(max)} = i_{b(max)}R_{in}$$

$$v_{b(min)} = i_{b(min)}R_{in}$$

hence

$$A_v = -\left\{\frac{v_{c(max)} - v_{c(min)}}{v_{b(max)} - v_{b(min)}}\right\} = -\left\{\frac{i_{c(max)}R_C - i_{c(min)}R_C}{i_{b(max)}R_{in} - i_{b(min)}R_{in}}\right\}$$

$$= -\left\{\frac{i_{c(max)} - i_{c(min)}}{i_{b(max)} - i_{b(min)}}\right\}\frac{R_C}{R_{in}}$$

$$= -A_i\frac{R_C}{R_{in}} \tag{9.4}$$

Taking values from the circuit in example 9.1 (also see above for A_i), and if $R_{in} = 1$ kΩ then

$$A_v = -A_iR_C/R_{in} = -90 \times 1{\cdot}5 \times 10^3/10^3 = -135$$

The voltage gain can also be calculated from the r.m.s. value of the collector voltage, V_c, and the base voltage, V_b, as follows

$$A_v = -\frac{V_c}{V_b} \tag{9.5}$$

The *power gain* of a common-emitter amplifier is given by

$$\text{Power gain}, A_p = \frac{\text{r.m.s. power in the collector load}}{\text{r.m.s. power applied to the transistor input}}$$

$$= \frac{I_c^2 R_C}{I_b^2 R_{in}} \tag{9.6}$$

where I_c and I_b are the r.m.s. values of the collector and base current, respectively. Equation (9.6) may be written in the form

$$A_p = \left(\frac{I_c}{I_b}\right)^2 \frac{R_C}{R_{in}} = A_i^2 \frac{R_C}{R_{in}} \tag{9.7}$$

or it may be written in the form

$$A_p = \frac{I_c}{I_b} \times \frac{I_c R_C}{I_b R_{in}} = \frac{I_c}{I_b} \times \frac{V_c}{V_b} = A_i A_v \tag{9.8}$$

In eq. (9.8) the modulus of A_v is used, the negative sign associated with it being ignored. For the circuit in example 9.7 and using the values calculated above

$$A_p = A_i A_v = 90 \times 135 = 12\,150$$

9.6 The decibel

When dealing with electronic and electrical circuits it is often convenient to think in terms of the transmission of sinusoidal signals, rather than non-sinusoidal signals. As a result of the circuit constants, sinusoidal signals are subject either to *gain* or to *attenuation* and to a *phase-shift*.

Gain and attenuation are most conveniently expressed as a logarithmic ratio. Historically, the logarithmic ratio of two values of power is given in *bels* (after the scientist Alexander Graham Bell), as follows

$$\text{Power ratio} = \lg P_2/P_1 \text{ bels (B)} \tag{9.9}$$

where P_1 and P_2 are two values of power. If the two power levels are produced in resistors R_1 and R_2 by voltages V_1 and V_2, respectively, then

$$\text{Power ratio} = \lg \frac{V_2^2/R_2}{V_1^2/R_1} = \lg \left(\frac{V_2}{V_1}\right)^2 - \lg \left(\frac{R_2}{R_1}\right)$$

$$= 2\lg(V_2/V_1) - \lg(R_2/R_1) \text{ B} \tag{9.10}$$

V_2 and V_1 are often the respective voltages at the output and input of electronic equipment, and R_2 and R_1 are the respective load and input resistances. When applied to electronic circuits, it is frequently assumed that $R_2 = R_1$ and eq. (9.9) is written in the form

$$\text{Power ratio} = 2\lg(V_2/V_1) \text{ B} \tag{9.11}$$

The bel is an inconveniently large unit, and the *decibel* (1 dB = 0·1 B) is commonly used in electronics, when

$$\text{Power ratio} = 20\lg V_2/V_1 \text{ dB} \tag{9.12}$$

The use of the ratio is strictly only correct when V_1 and V_2 are developed across equal values of resistance. The definition of the decibel is distorted in its application to electronic circuits, since the two voltages may be developed across unequal values of resistance. Thus, an amplifier with an input signal of 0·1 V r.m.s., and an output signal of 10 V r.m.s. is said to have a voltage gain of 20 lg 10/0·1 = 40 dB, even if the input resistance is 1 kΩ and the load resistance is 100 kΩ.

Logarithmic ratios are also very useful in indicating when a *change* in the signal level has occurred. When no change has occurred, then $V_2 = V_1$, and the 'gain' is 20 lg 1 = 0 dB. When the gain in decibels has a positive value, then V_2 is greater than V_1; when the decibel gain has a negative value then V_2 is less than V_1, and the signal is said to be *attenuated*. The simplest method of computing the 'gain' in decibels of an attenuator is as follows:

$$20\lg V_2/V_1 = 20\lg(V_1/V_2)^{-1} = -20\lg V_1/V_2 \tag{9.13}$$

Thus, if $V_1 = 1$ V, and $V_2 = 0 \cdot 1$ V, the gain in dB is

$$20 \lg \frac{0 \cdot 1}{1} = -20 \lg \frac{1}{0 \cdot 1} = -20 \lg 10 = -20 \text{ dB}$$

A feature of logarithmic gain ratios is that the overall gain of cascaded amplifier and attenuator stages can be calculated simply by *adding* the logarithmic gain values together. For instance, if two voltage amplifiers with gains of 20 dB and 40 dB, respectively, are cascaded with a circuit giving 30 dB of attenuation, the overall gain is

$$20 + 40 - 30 = 30 \text{ dB}$$

An alternative method of expressing power ratios is given by the *neper* (after the Scottish farmer-mathematician John Napier). The power ratio in nepers is defined by the relationship

$$\text{Power ratio in neper} = \ln P_2/P_1$$

The neper is equal to $8 \cdot 686$ decibel.

9.6.1 Reference level

The decibel is merely a means of comparing two signal levels and no reference level is necessarily implied in the calculations. However, it is sometimes useful to quote a change in signal level by stating that it is X decibels above or below a reference level. There are two common examples of this; the first is in amplifier applications, in which the gain is substantially constant over a range of frequencies, but is reduced at other frequencies. Without implying the reference value of gain, it is permissible to say that the gain at a certain frequency is, say, 3 dB below the reference gain. The second example is in general telecommunications practice, where a reference level of 1 mW is often used. In this case a power level of 2 mW would be expressed as $10 \lg 2/1 = 3 \cdot 01$ dB.

9.7 The a.c. load line or dynamic load line

In many amplifiers the load is a resistor R_L which is connected between the output terminals of Fig. 9.3. In the quiescent state, the collector voltage is constant so that the blocking capacitor C_2 prevents d.c. from flowing into the load. The quiescent operating point of the amplifier is therefore fixed by the d.c. load and the quiescent base current in the manner described earlier.

When an a.c. signal is applied to the amplifier in Fig. 9.3, the reactance of C_2 to the signal frequency is very low, so that R_L is effectively connected to the collector of the transistor so far as a.c. is concerned. Hence the effective 'a.c. load' resistance R'_L, is equivalent to R_C in parallel with R_L. That is

$$R'_L = \frac{R_L R_C}{R_L + R_C} \tag{9.14}$$

In order to estimate the changes in the values of the collector voltage and current, a line known as the *a.c. load line* or *dynamic load line*, of slope $(-1/R'_L)$ and passing through the quiescent point on the d.c. load line is used (see Fig. 9.6).

Example 9.2: The transistor in the circuit in Fig. 9.7 has the following characteristics which are linear between the points given.

Base current	i_C (mA) for collector voltage of	
(μA)	1·0 V	8·5 V
40	1·9	2·65
60	2·9	3·95
80	3·95	5·2
100	4·95	6·45
120	5·9	7·7

The quiescent collector voltage is 4·5 V. Determine the quiescent value of the collector current and of the base current, and also estimate the value of the bias resistor R given that the quiescent base-emitter voltage is 0·6 V.

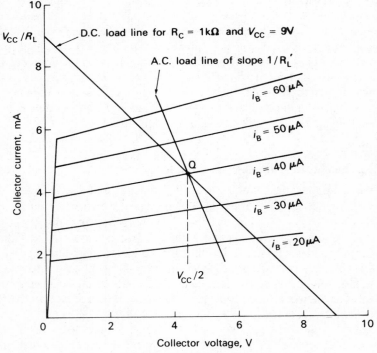

Fig. 9.6   d.c. and a.c. load lines.

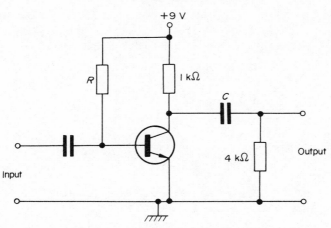

Fig. 9.7 Circuit for example 9.2.

Plot the d.c. and a.c. load lines on the output characteristics, and determine the r.m.s. value of the output voltage if the r.m.s. value of the a.c. component of the base current is $14 \cdot 14 \ \mu A$. Calculate also the value of h_{fe} of the transistor at the operating point. Capacitor C has a very low reactance at the operating frequency.

Solution: The output characteristics together with the d.c. load line are shown in Fig. 9.8. The quiescent point Q is given by the point on the d.c. load line where $v_C = 4 \cdot 5$ V. At point Q

$$\text{quiescent collector current} = 4 \cdot 5 \text{ mA}$$

$$\text{quiescent base current} = 80 \ \mu A$$

Since the only current in R is the quiescent base current, then

$$R = (V_{CC} - V_{BE})/\text{quiescent base current}$$
$$= (9 - 0 \cdot 6)/80 \times 10^{-6} = 105 \text{ k}\Omega$$

The a.c. load (R'_L) comprises the 1 kΩ collector load (R_C) in parallel with the 4 kΩ external load (R_L), hence

$$R'_L = (1 \times 4)/(1 + 4) = 0 \cdot 8 \text{ k}\Omega$$

The a.c. load line of slope $(-1/0 \cdot 8) = -1 \cdot 25$ mA/V is drawn through the Q-point on Fig. 9.8.

The peak-to-peak change in base current is $2\sqrt{2} \times 14 \cdot 14 \ \mu A = 40 \ \mu A$; that is the base current changes by $\pm 20 \ \mu A$ about the quiescent base current of $80 \ \mu A$. This change causes the transistor operating point to swing between points A and B on

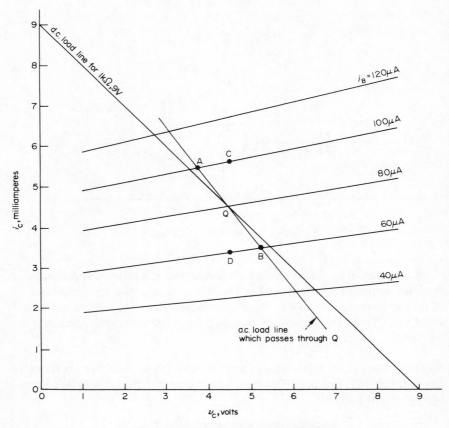

Fig. 9.8   Load lines for example 9.2.

the a.c. load line, giving a maximum collector voltage at point B of 5·3 V and a minimum collector voltage at point A of 3·7 V, hence

$$\text{peak-to-peak output voltage swing} = 5·3 - 3·7 = 1·6 \text{ V}$$

and

$$\text{r.m.s. output voltage} = 1·6/(2\sqrt{2}) = 0·57 \text{ V}$$

The value of h_{fe} at the Q-point is calculated using the values of collector current at points C and D, which are 5·6 mA and 3·35 mA, respectively.

$$h_{fe} = \frac{\text{change in collector current}}{\text{change in base current}} \text{ at constant collector voltage}$$

$$= (5·6 - 3·35) \text{ mA}/(100 - 60) \text{ } \mu\text{A} = 56·25$$

9.8 The small-signal equivalent circuit of the common-emitter amplifier

The small-signal a.c. equivalent circuit of the complete amplifier is drawn on the assumption that all d.c. sources either have zero resistance or that their resistance can be lumped with the value of some other resistance connected in series with them. That is, in Fig. 9.3, the internal resistance of V_{CC} can be lumped with R_C. This is illustrated in Fig. 9.9(a). The base bias supply in Fig. 9.3 is taken from the collector supply; to aid the understanding of the equivalent circuit, this is shown as a separate supply, V_{BB}, in Fig. 9.9 where $V_{BB} = V_{CC}$. From an a.c. viewpoint the internal resistance of V_{BB} is taken to be zero, so that R_B is effectively connected between the base and the emitter of the transistor. R_S in Fig. 9.9 is the internal resistance of the signal source. At normal operating frequencies the reactance of capacitor C (Fig. 9.9(a)) is very small when compared with the values of other components in the input circuit; capacitor C is replaced in the a.c. equivalent circuit by a short-circuit. At very low frequencies, when the capacitive reactance of C has a large value, it must be accounted for in calculations (see section 9.9). The basic a.c. equivalent circuit is then as shown in Fig. 9.9(b).

9.9 Calculation of component values for the common-emitter amplifier

When working as a Class A amplifier, the quiescent collector voltage is approximately $V_{CC}/2$. Since the quiescent collector current is I_C, then in Fig. 9.3

$$\text{p.d. across } R_C = V_{CC}/2 = R_C I_C$$

or

$$R_C = \frac{V_{CC}}{2I_C} \tag{9.15}$$

For example, if $V_{CC} = 9$ V and $I_C = 1$ mA, then $R_C = 9/(2 \times 1 \times 10^{-3}) = 4500\,\Omega$.

The p.d. across the base bias resistor is $V_{CC} - V_{BE}$, where V_{BE} is the forward bias between the base and the emitter. In a silicon transistor the value of V_{BE} is about 0·6 V. Since the quiescent base current is I_B, then

$$\text{p.d. across } R_B = V_{CC} - V_{BE} = I_B R_B$$

or

$$R_B = \frac{V_{CC} - V_{BE}}{I_B} = \frac{V_{CC} - V_{BE}}{I_C/h_{FE}} \tag{9.16}$$

where h_{FE} is the large-signal (d.c.) current gain of the transistor; the value of h_{FE} is obtained either by measurement or from data sheets. Suppose that its value is 100 and that $V_{BE} = 0·6$ V, then for the circuit considered

$$R_B = (9 - 0·6)/(10^{-3}/100) = 840\text{ k}\Omega$$

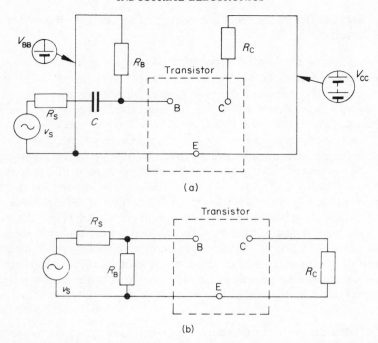

Fig. 9.9   Reduction of the a.c. circuit of the basic common-emitter amplifier.

The effective input resistance, R_{in}, presented by the amplifier to the signal source is the parallel combination of R_B and the input resistance of the transistor; the latter may be assumed to have the value of the parameter h_{ie}. The effective input resistance of the amplifier to small signals is therefore

$$R_{in} = R_B h_{ie}/(R_B + h_{ie}) \qquad (9.17)$$

With the value of R_B calculated above and taking h_{ie} to have a value of 1 kΩ, then

$$R_{in} = 840 \times 1/(840 + 1) \simeq 1 \text{ k}\Omega, \text{ that is } h_{ie}$$

At high frequencies, when the reactance of the input blocking capacitor (C_1 in Fig. 9.3) can be neglected, the input impedance of the amplifier is equal to R_{in}. At lower frequencies the reactance of C_1 introduces a voltage drop in the input circuit, and the following criteria is applied at the *lowest operating frequency*, f_L.

$$\text{Reactance of } C_1 \ll R_{in}$$

that is

$$\frac{1}{2\pi f_L C_1} \gg R_{in}$$

or

$$C_1 \gg \frac{1}{2\pi f_L R_{in}}$$ (9.18)

If f_L = 63·6 Hz and R_{in} = 1 kΩ, then

$$C_1 \gg 1/(2\pi \times 63·6 \times 1000) \text{ F} = 2·5 \text{ } \mu\text{F}$$

The value selected should be 25 μF or greater.

9.10 Stabilization of the operating point of a common-emitter amplifier

Variations in such factors as leakage current and transistor parameters can cause a shift in the quiescent point. The most common cause of short-term changes in these values is temperature variation.

The relative importance of these factors depends on the type of semi-conductor material used in the construction of the transistor. For instance, the variation in leakage current with temperature in a germanium transistor is far greater than in an equivalent silicon device, while the variation in h_{FE} with temperature in a silicon device is much greater than in a germanium transistor. In both types of semiconductor, v_{BE} reduces with increasing temperature. The effects are related to the thermal generation of electron-hole pairs, as follows. An increase in temperature results in additional electron-hole pairs appearing in the emitter junction, leading to increased conductivity in that region, and a reduction in v_{BE}. In the collector junction, the additional charge carriers result in an increase in leakage current.

The basic common-emitter circuit in Fig. 9.3 is found to be unsatisfactory from a *thermal stability* viewpoint for the following reasons. Under normal work-ing conditions at constant temperature, the steady current in the base circuit is approximately V_{BB}/R_B. A rise in ambient temperature results in the thermal generation of electron-hole pairs within the transistor, which has an equivalent effect to a rise in external base drive. This results in an increased collector current and a reduced collector voltage. The quiescent point thus moves along the load line with change in temperature. In the circuit in Fig. 9.3 no attempt is made to prevent this happening.

In a power amplifier circuit, this condition leads to an increase in internal power dissipation which can result in a further increase in junction temperature. If the heat generated rises at a greater rate than it can be dissipated, the effect becomes cumulative, leading to *thermal runaway*. As a result, the transistor may be damaged. Thermal runaway is of primary importance in power amplifier stages.

Some improvement of thermal stability is achieved by the circuit in Fig. 9.10(a). For the moment, we will ignore capacitor C_1. Making the assumption that v_{BE} is small compared with V_{CE}, the bias current is approximately

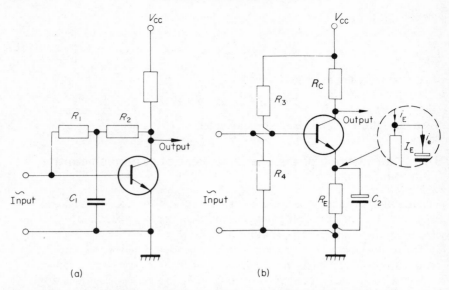

Fig. 9.10   Two circuits which provide thermal stability. Insert in (b) shows how the unidirectional component I_E and the a.c. component i_e of the total emitter current i_E divide in the emitter circuit.

$V_{CE}/(R_1 + R_2)$. As the ambient temperature rises it causes the quiescent collector voltage to fall in value, and with it the bias current. The reduction in base bias reduces the collector current, so that the change in collector voltage with temperature is less than it would otherwise be with the circuit in Fig. 9.3. Capacitor C_1 has a low reactance at the signal frequencies, and its function is to effectively earth the junction of R_1 and R_2 to the signal frequencies, so preventing alternating signals from being fed back to the base from the collector.

An even better circuit is shown in Fig. 9.10(b); a load line analysis is shown in Fig. 9.11(a). For the moment, we will ignore capacitor C_2. In this circuit, the base bias is provided by the resistor chain R_3R_4; an additional resistor R_E is included in the emitter circuit. Since part of the supply voltage is dropped across R_E, its value should be as small as possible so that the largest possible voltage can be developed across R_C. The value of R_E cannot be too small, however, otherwise the temperature stability of the circuit will suffer. A p.d. of about 1 V at the quiescent current is usually adequate.

Under normal operating conditions, the average potential at the base connection is maintained at a constant value over a wide temperature range by the resistive potential divider chain. As the ambient temperature rises the collector current rises, and with it the p.d. across R_E. Now,

$$v_{\mathbf{BE}} = V_{\mathbf{B}} - I_{\mathbf{E}} R_{\mathbf{E}}$$

where V_B is the potential of the base region with respect to the common line. Increase in temperature causes I_C (and I_E) to increase in value, and the increase in $I_E R_E$ with temperature causes v_{BE} to fall in value. This causes a reduction in base current, which compensates the collector current for the rise in temperature.

Variations in h_{FE} with temperature produce generally similar effects to those of variations in leakage current, and the circuits so far described reduce the effects of both. The change in v_{BE} with temperature is generally much smaller than the magnitude of the steady bias voltage applied to the circuit, and changes in v_{BE} are effectively swamped.

It was stated above that the value of R_E must be sufficiently large to provide adequate temperature compensation; however, R_E carries the steady

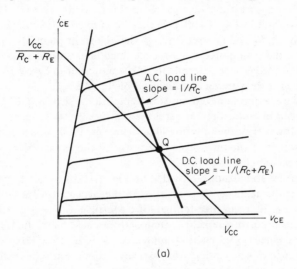

(a)

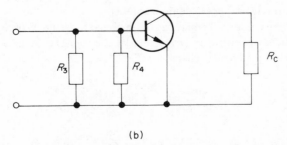

(b)

Fig. 9.11   (a) The Q-point lies on the d.c. load line, and the voltage gain is estimated from the a.c. load line; (b) shows a method of accounting for the bias network.

emitter current and dissipates power. To keep the power loss to a minimum, R_E should have a small value. The design of a circuit of this type is, at best, a compromise between thermal stability and other factors such as voltage gain and efficiency.

The total resistance in series with the transistor in Fig. 9.10(b) is $(R_C + R_E)$, and the so-called *d.c. load line* has a slope of $-1/(R_C + R_E)$. The operating point Q, Fig. 9.11(a), lies on this line. In order to prevent variation of the emitter potential when an input signal is applied, R_E is shunted by capacitor C_2 which has a reactance which is small at the lowest frequency of interest when compared with the resistance of R_E. The emitter capacitor effectively causes the varying component i_e of the emitter current i_E to bypass resistor R_E. So far as the varying component of the circuit current is concerned, the effective resistance in series with the transistor is R_C, since R_E is short-circuited by C_2. This is illustrated in the inset in Fig. 9.10(b). The *a.c. load line* or *dynamic load line* thus has a slope $-1/R_C$, and passes through the quiescent point Q in Fig. 9.11(a). The stage gain is then computed from the a.c. load line. Should a load resistor R_L be connected to the output terminals of the amplifier in Fig. 9.10(b), the effective a.c. load is the parallel combination of R_C and R_L.

A simplified a.c. equivalent circuit of the amplifier is shown in Fig. 9.11(b) R_E being replaced by a short-circuit. It is seen in Fig. 9.11(b) that both R_3 and R_4 effectively shunt the input circuit, so reducing the input impedance of the amplifier below that of the transistor. This is one of the less desirable features of this method of stabilization.

The temperature stabilization provided by Fig. 9.10(b) can be improved by incorporating temperature-sensitive resistors in the circuit. If R_4 is shunted by a resistor with a negative resistance-temperature coefficient, or R_E is replaced by one with a small positive resistance-temperature coefficient, then the base-emitter voltage changes rapidly with temperature to reduce the effects of temperature change on the circuit. Alternatively a diode could be included in series with R_4; as the ambient temperature rises the forward voltage drop across the diode falls, so reducing the base-emitter voltage to restore thermal stability. A silicon diode is normally used with a silicon transistor, and a germanium diode with a germanium transistor.

The effectiveness of the bias circuit in controlling the change in collector current with temperature is given either by the *stability factor S* or by the *thermal stability factor k,* where

$$S = \frac{\partial I_C}{\partial I_{CBO}} \quad \text{and} \quad k = \frac{\partial I_C}{\partial I_{CEO}} \tag{9.19}$$

hence,

$$S = h_{FE}k$$

The stability factor of the circuit in Fig. 9.10(b) can be evaluated from the equations of the circuit, and is given by

$$S = \frac{1 + R_E\left(\dfrac{1}{R_3} + \dfrac{1}{R_4}\right)}{\dfrac{1}{1 + h_{FE}} + R_E\left(\dfrac{1}{R_3} + \dfrac{1}{R_4}\right)}$$

For example, if $R_E = 1\ \text{k}\Omega$, $R_3 = 50\ \text{k}\Omega$, $R_4 = 5\ \text{k}\Omega$, and $h_{FE} = 99$, then $S = 5\cdot3$. A rule-of-thumb for estimating S is $S \simeq (1 + R_4/R_E)$.

In circuits with poor thermal stability, S has a high value, the worst circuit being that of Fig. 9.3, in which $S = 1 + h_{FE}$. Maximum thermal stability is achieved when S has unity value. Generally speaking, more care must be taken with circuits employing germanium transistors since the leakage current is significant at room temperature, and it doubles for each $8°\text{C}$ to $10°\text{C}$ temperature rise. In low power epitaxial silicon transistors, the leakage current is of the order of only $0\cdot01\ \mu\text{A}$ to $0\cdot1\ \mu\text{A}$ at room temperature. Even though the leakage current in silicon transistors increases at the same relative rate as in germanium transistors, it is of little importance in many applications. In silicon transistors, it is the variation of h_{FE} which is important and its value at $50°\text{C}$ is typically twice the value at $25°\text{C}$.

Example 9.3: A single-stage audio-frequency voltage amplifier uses an n-p-n transistor which works in class A. The base voltage of the transistor is $+1\cdot5\ \text{V}$ which is derived from a potential divider chain which is connected between the $+10\ \text{V}$ supply line and earth. The bias network comprises a $10\ \text{k}\Omega$ resistor between the base and the earth line, and a resistor R_3 between the base and the $10\ \text{V}$ line. If the quiescent collector current is $2\ \text{mA}$, and $h_{FE} = 50$, determine a suitable value for the resistor R_3.

If the quiescent value of the base-emitter voltage is $0\cdot6\ \text{V}$, estimate the ohmic value of a resistor R_E which must be connected in series with the emitter. This resistor is shunted by a capacitor C_E; determine its value if the lowest signal to be amplified has a frequency of $31\cdot8\ \text{Hz}$

Solution: Since $I_{CE} = 2\ \text{mA}$, and $h_{FE} = 50$, then

$$I_{BE} = 2/50 = 0\cdot04\ \text{mA} \qquad \text{or} \qquad 40\ \mu\text{A}$$

The current flowing in the $10\ \text{k}\Omega$ resistor is $1\cdot5\ \text{V}/10\ \text{k}\Omega = 0\cdot15\ \text{mA}$, hence, the current in R_3 is $0\cdot04 + 0\cdot15 = 0\cdot19\ \text{mA}$. The p.d. across R_3 is

$$V_{CC} - V_{BE} = 10 - 1\cdot5 = 8\cdot5\ \text{V},$$

hence,

$$R_3 = 8\cdot5/0\cdot19 = 44\cdot7\ \text{k}\Omega$$

Since $V_{BE} = 0.6$ V, the p.d. across the emitter resistor is $1.5 - 0.6 = 0.9$ V, and the quiescent emitter current is $I_{CE} + I_{BE} = 2 + 0.04 = 2.04$ mA.

Hence,

$$R_E = 0.9/2.04 = 0.441 \text{ k}\Omega \quad \text{or} \quad 441 \ \Omega$$

At the lowest frequency of interest, the reactance of C_E should be about one-tenth the value of the resistance of R_E, therefore,

$$C_E \geqslant 10/\omega R_E = 10/2\pi \times 31.8 \times 441 = 114 \ \mu\text{F}$$

9.11   JUGFET common-source amplifier circuits

JUGFETS are depletion-mode devices, and to bias a depletion-mode FET to its correct operating point for class A operation, it must be *biased-off*. That is, a reverse bias voltage must be applied between the gate and source. One bias circuit for an N-channel junction-gate depletion-mode FET is shown in Fig. 9.12(a). Here, the bias voltage is developed across R_{S1}, while C_S effectively shunts the varying component of the source current from R_{S1}. The bias voltage developed across R_{S1} is known as *self-bias* or *auto-bias*. Resistor R_G merely provides an ohmic connection between the common line and the gate to allow the bias voltage to be applied to the gate.

The gate-to-source voltage which is selected by the designer is dependent on the ultimate application of the amplifier. A bias of a few tenths of a volt is all that is necessary to provide amplification with minimum signal distortion, whereas the highest voltage gain can be obtained by applying a bias which approaches the pinchoff voltage of the FET. The effects of thermal changes are minimized by using a voltage which is between the two extremes.

Each type of FET has a 'family' of characteristics, and manufacturers supply typical 'minimum' and 'maximum' curves. For example, curve A in Fig. 9.12(b) is a typical 'maximum' *mutual curve* or *transconductance curve* for one type of JUGFET, whilst curve B represents a 'minimum' curve. The transconductance curves for all FETs of that type number will lie between curve A and curve B. When connected in the circuit in Fig. 9.12(a), the gate bias voltage and quiescent drain current are determined by the intersection of the *bias line* of slope $(-1/R_{S1})$ and the transconductance curve for the FET. With the conditions shown in Fig. 9.12(b), the quiescent drain current has a value which lies between I_{D1} and I_{D2}.

The point where the transconductance curve cuts the vertical axis (when $v_G = 0$) gives the *drain-source saturation current* I_{DSS}. The range of values of I_{DSS} for a given FET type is quoted by its manufacturer, and when designing a bias circuit for the circuit in Fig. 9.12(a) it is advisable to choose a nominal value of quiescent drain current which is less than the minimum value of I_{DSS}. If the latter value is $I_{DSS(min)}$, a suitable value of quiescent drain current would

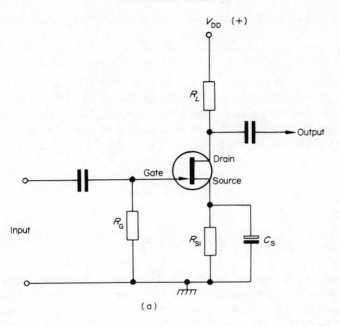

(a)

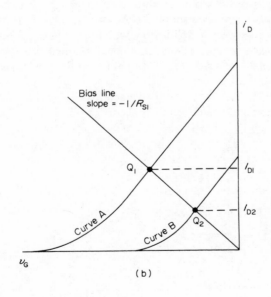

(b)

Fig. 9.12   A common-source amplifier using an n-channel JUGFET.

be about $0 \cdot 5 I_{DSS(min)}$. The value of R_{S1} is given by the equation

$$R_{S1} = \frac{\text{Required bias voltage}}{\text{Nominal value of quiescent drain current}} = \frac{V_{GS}}{0 \cdot 5 I_{DSS(min)}}$$

For example, if a gate-to-source bias voltage of $0 \cdot 6$ V is required and if $I_{DSS(min)} = 0 \cdot 9$ mA, then $R_{S1} = 0 \cdot 6/(0 \cdot 5 \times 0 \cdot 9 \times 10^{-3}) = 1333$ Ω.

The function of C_S is to provide a low reactance path for the flow of alternating current at the signal frequency. At the lowest signal frequency f_L, the reactance of C_S must be much less than the resistance of R_{S1}, hence

$$\frac{1}{2\pi f_L C_S} \ll R_{S1}$$

or

$$C_S \gg \frac{1}{2\pi f_L R_{S1}} \tag{9.20}$$

The spread of values of the quiescent drain current is rather large in Fig. 9.12(a), and is reduced by the circuit in Fig. 9.13(a) in which an additional voltage divider network is used. The bias resistor chain $R_1 R_2$ fixes the potential of the gate at V_{GG}, so that the bias line intersects the $i_D = 0$ axis at $v_G = V_{GG}$. The bias resistor in Fig. 9.13(a) has a higher value than R_{S1} in Fig. 9.12(a), so reducing the spread of quiescent drain current values to the range I'_{D1} to I'_{D2}. The circuit in Fig. 9.13(a) also minimizes the effects of the spread of parameter values when compared with the circuit in Fig. 9.12(a). Analysis of Figs. 9.12(a) and 9.13(a) shows that the latter circuit is better in terms of thermal stability.

A load line analysis of the JUGFET amplifier in Fig. 9.12(a) is illustrated in

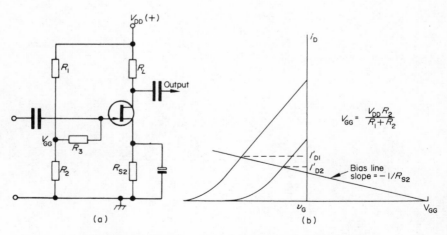

Fig. 9.13   An improved JUGFET amplifier circuit.

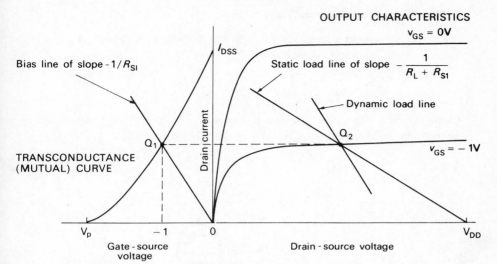

Fig. 9.14   Load line analysis of a JUGFET amplifier. The drain and gate voltage are not to the same scale.

Fig. 9.14. The value of R_{S1} is determined by the method outlined above, and the quiescent point Q_1, is given by the intersection of the bias line with the transconductance curve. The static (d.c.) load line having a slope of $(-1/(R_L + R_{S1}))$ is drawn from V_{DD} through the Q_2 point on the output characteristics. Changes in drain current and voltage are estimated from the dynamic (a.c.) load line which passes through Q_2.

9.11.1   Voltage gain of a JUGFET amplifier

From the work in chapter 4 (eq. (4.4)), the r.m.s. value of the drain current is given approximately by

$$I_d = g_m V_g$$

Since the amplifier is phase inverting, the r.m.s. value of the drain voltage is

$$V_d = -I_d R_L' = -g_m V_g R_L'$$

where R_L' is the effective *a.c. load* connected to the drain terminal; this consists of R_L in parallel with any external load connected via the output blocking capacitor. Hence

$$\text{Voltage gain, } A_v = \frac{V_d}{V_g} = -g_m R_L' \qquad (9.21)$$

If $g_m = 5$ mA/V and $R_L' = 5$ kΩ, then $A_v = -25$.

9.12 Class A valve amplifiers

Two class A amplifier circuits are shown in Fig. 9.15. In both circuits, the grid bias voltage is developed across R_K.

Hence,

$$V_{GK} = I_K R_K \quad \text{or} \quad R_K = V_{GK}/I_K$$

where V_{GK} is the quiescent grid bias voltage and I_K is the quiescent cathode current. As with the transistor, the valve is biased to the middle of the working

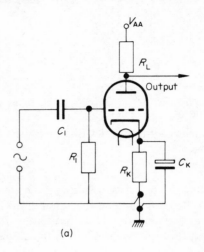

(a)

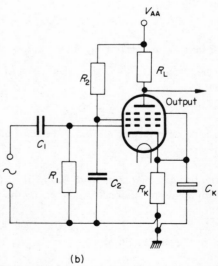

(b)

Fig. 9.15 (a) Common-cathode triode amplifier, (b) pentode amplifier.

range of the characteristics. The quiescent point lies on the d.c. load line of slope $-1/(R_L + R_K)$, the voltage gain being computed from information provided by the a.c. load line of slope $-1/R_L$ which passes through the quiescent point. The graphic construction is generally similar to that shown in Fig. 9.14.

Ambient temperature changes have little effect upon the operating point of valve circuits, and temperature stabilizing circuits are not required. Since the control grid and the cathode are not electrically connected, an external resistor R_1 is necessary to apply the bias voltage to the grid. Since the grid is always at a negative potential with respect to the cathode when the valve works in class A, the grid does not draw current and R_1 can have a high value. A 1 MΩ resistor is commonly used for this purpose. Owing to the high input impedance of the circuit, the capacitance of C_1 is usually only a fraction of a microfarad.

To ensure that a steady voltage is developed across R_K, it is shunted by capacitor C_K which has a reactance at the lowest frequency of interest which is much less than the resistance of R_K. As a rule-of-thumb guide, the reactance of C_K should be about one-tenth of the resistance of R_K at the lowest operating frequency. If this frequency is ω_L, then

$$C_K \geqslant \frac{10}{\omega_L R_K} \text{F}$$

In the circuit of Fig. 9.15(b), the screen grid potential is fixed by the values of V_{AA} and R_2; capacitor C_2 effectively short-circuits the screen-grid to ground so far as the signal frequency is concerned. One significant difference between the pentode and the triode is that in the pentode the steady cathode current is $(I_A + I_{G2})$, while it is I_A in the triode. In the pentode, the screen current may represent a significant proportion of the cathode current.

Example 9.4: A triode in an amplifier similar to the one shown in Fig. 9.15(a) passes a quiescent anode current of 8 mA when the grid bias is -4 V. Estimate suitable values for R_K and C_K if the lowest frequency of interest is 15·92 Hz. If the grid coupling resistor R_1 has a value of 1 MΩ, and the input capacitor C_1 reduces the gain at 15·92 Hz to 0·707 of its value at higher frequencies, estimate a suitable value for C_1.

Solution:

$$R_K = |V_{GK}|/I_{AK} = 4/8 = 0\cdot5 \text{ k}\Omega \quad \text{or} \quad 500 \ \Omega$$

$$C_K \geqslant 10/\omega R_K = 10/2\pi \times 15\cdot92 \times 500 \text{ F} \quad \text{or} \quad 20 \ \mu\text{F}$$

For C_1 to produce an attenuation of 0·707 at 15·92 Hz, then

$$R_1 = 1/\omega C_1$$

or

$$C_1 = 1/\omega R_1 = 1/2\pi \times 15\cdot92 \times 10^6 \text{ F} \quad \text{or} \quad 0\cdot01 \ \mu\text{F}$$

9.13   Effect of reactive loads

Imagine that a signal with a square waveform is applied to the input of the common emitter amplifier in Fig. 9.16(a), which has an inductive load. The initial base current and collector voltage are i_{B1} and v_{C1}, respectively.

When the base current is suddenly increased to i_{B2}, the inductance of the load causes the collector current to remain initially constant at i_{C1}, causing the collector voltage to fall to v_{C2}. This transition on the characteristics is shown by the lower horizontal line in Fig. 9.16(b). When the inductance has dissipated

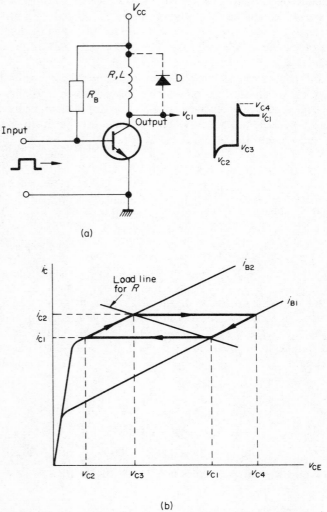

(a)

(b)

Fig. 9.16   The effect of an inductive load on the collector voltage waveform.

its excess stored energy, the collector voltage rises to v_{C3} along a constant base current characteristic. A reduction in input current to i_{B1} causes the collector voltage to suddenly rise to v_{C4} along a line of constant collector current, following which the collector voltage slowly decays to v_{C1} along a line of constant base current.

When the input signal changes in a negative direction, a positive-going voltage spike is generated at the collector. The peak value of this spike can exceed V_{CC}, and may even exceed the voltage rating of the transistor. In circuits of this type, transistors are often protected against overvoltage by shunting the load by diode D. It is not usually necessary to protect values in this way, since they can sustain large over-voltages without damage.

If the input signal has a sinusoidal waveshape, the excursion traced out on the characteristics is approximately elliptical in shape, the movement round the ellipse being in a clockwise direction.

With a capacitive-type load there is a tendency for current spikes to be generated, since the capacitor initially maintains a constant voltage between its terminals, resulting in a rush of charging or discharging current.

9.14 Simplified transistor analysis in terms of the *h*-parameters

The following analysis applies to any transistor configuration, e.g., common-emitter, common-base, or common-collector, since the general *h*-parameters h_i, h_r, h_f, and h_o are used. The gain, input impedance, etc., of any specific configuration are then obtained by inserting the appropriate *h*-parameters into the general equations. For instance, if the transistor is used in the common-emitter mode the parameters h_{ie}, h_{re}, h_{fe}, and h_{oe} are inserted in place of h_i, h_r, h_f, and h_o, respectively.

The r.m.s. values of the input voltage applied to the transistor and the output voltage from the transistor are V_1 and V_2, respectively, while I_1 and I_2 are the respective values of the input and output current. In the common-emitter configuration, the quantities V_1, V_2, I_1, and I_2 correspond to V_{be}, V_{ce}, I_{be}, and I_{ce}, respectively.

The general hybrid equations are (see also chapter 3)

$$V_1 = h_i I_1 + h_r V_2 \tag{9.21}$$

$$I_2 = h_f I_1 + h_o V_2 \tag{9.22}$$

Also

$$V_2 = -I_2 R_L \tag{9.23}$$

Where R_L is the load resistance connected to the collector of the transistor. In many applications the above equations may be simplified by making a few approximations. Firstly, in eq. (9.21) if $h_i I_1 \gg h_r V_2$, and in eq. (9.22) if $h_f I_1 \gg h_o V_2$, these equations become

$$V_1 = h_i I_1 \tag{9.24}$$

$$I_2 = h_f I_1 \tag{9.25}$$

From eq. (9.24) the input impedance of the amplifier is

$$R_{in} = V_1/I_1 \simeq h_i$$

from eq. (9.25)

$$A_i = I_2/I_1 \simeq h_f$$

and the voltage across the load is

$$V_2 = -I_2 R_L \simeq -h_f I_1 R_L$$

but

$$I_1 \simeq V_1/h_i$$

hence,

$$V_2 \simeq -\frac{h_f}{h_i} V_1 R_L$$

Note: h_f/h_i is the effective mutual conductance or transconductance of the transistor.

The voltage gain of the amplifier is

$$A_v = \frac{V_2}{V_1} \simeq -\frac{h_f}{h_i} R_L$$

The expression for power gain is

$$A_p = A_i{}^2 \frac{R_L}{R_{in}} \simeq h_f{}^2 \frac{R_L}{h_i}$$

Example 9.5: Compute the input impedance, the current gain, the voltage gain, and the power gain of a common-emitter amplifier which uses a transistor with $h_{ie} = 1500\ \Omega$, and $h_{fe} = 50$. The load resistance is 10 kΩ.

Solution:

$$R_{in} \simeq h_{ie} = 1500\ \Omega$$

$$A_i \simeq h_{fe} = 50$$

$$A_v \simeq -\frac{h_{fe}}{h_{ie}} R_L = -\frac{50}{1500} \times 10,000 = -333$$

$$A_p \simeq h_{fe}{}^2 \frac{R_L}{h_{ie}} = 50^2 \times \frac{10^4}{1500} = 16,700$$

9.15   Tuned voltage amplifiers

Where it is necessary to amplify either a single frequency or a narrow band of frequencies, amplifiers with tuned L-C loads are used. These circuits effectively reject frequencies other than those within the pass-band of the tuned circuit.

The simplest form of load is the parallel L-C circuit. If the inductor in the parallel circuit has resistance R, then the effective impedance at resonance (which is a pure resistance) is L/CR Ω, and is known as the *dynamic impedance* of the circuit. This arrangement ensures that a high impedance load is presented at resonance, and a low impedance at other frequencies. For example, if a 250 μH coil of resistance 8 Ω is tuned to a frequency of 0·5 MHz by a shunt capacitor, its dynamic impedance is 77 kΩ. The impedance of the circuit to a frequency of 0·45 MHz is only 3·7 kΩ.

To utilize the full gain offered by the high impedance load, either a transistor or a pentode should be used as the active device in the amplifier. In the case of transistor circuits, a step-down inductive coupling is necessary between the L-C circuit and the following stage to avoid loading effects due to the low input impedance.

9.16   Interstage coupling methods

The essential differences between a.c. coupling and direct coupling are shown in Fig. 9.17. The output from almost any amplifier consists of a quiescent voltage with a superimposed alternating component; it is the alternating component which generally carries the signal information. In a.c. amplifiers, the alternating component is separated from the d.c. component by the coupling network. In Fig. 9.17(a) this is achieved by an *R-C network*. It can equally well be done by a *transformer*. The capacitor C effectively blocks the d.c. component, so that only the a.c. component of the output signal causes a current to flow in resistor R. The voltage developed across R is then applied to the next stage for further amplification. In the context of Fig. 9.17, resistor R is the external load resistance of the amplifier which includes the input resistance of the following stage. For satisfactory operation, the reactance of capacitor C at the lowest frequency of interest must be much smaller than the resistance of R.

It can be shown that when $R = 1/\omega C$, the voltage across resistor R is 0·707 of the voltage applied to the R-C circuit. At the frequency at which this occurs, the R-C network introduces a reduction in voltage gain of 0·707 or 3 dB.

Example 9.6: If the input signal to a broadband amplifier is applied via a blocking capacitor, and the input impedance of the amplifier is 1 kΩ, calculate the capacitance of the capacitor if it introduces a reduction in gain of 3 dB below the mid-band gain at a frequency of 31·8 Hz.

Solution: For a 3 dB reduction,

$$R = 1/\omega C$$

or

$$C = 1/\omega R = 1/31·8 \times 2\pi \times 1000 = 5 \; \mu\text{F}$$

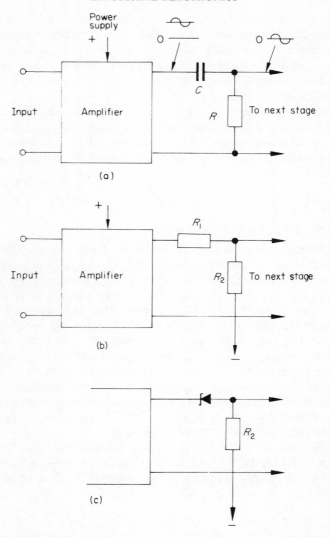

Fig. 9.17   (a) *R-C* interstage coupling; (b) and (c) show two methods of direct coupling between stages.

9.16.1   Direct coupling circuits

The basis of direct coupling circuits is shown in Fig. 9.17(b). The output of one stage is coupled to the next by the resistor chain $R_1 R_2$, which has its lower end taken to a negative supply rail (or a positive supply in the case of p-n-p transistor circuits). The function of the negative power supply is to balance out the quiescent output voltage of the amplifier. By this means, any variation in output voltage from the first stage, even a very slow change, is applied directly to the following stage. Thus, undesirable low frequency drift voltages are amplified as well as signal frequencies by subsequent stages. It is common practice in d.c. amplifiers to use low drift stages, e.g., a long-tailed pair amplifier (see chapter 11), at the input end to reduce the effects of drift.

A disadvantage of the resistive network in Fig. 9.17(b) is that the varying component of the output voltage is attenuated by the resistor chain. This reduces the overall gain of the stage. Some improvement is effected by replacing R_1 by a Zener diode, as shown in Fig. 9.17(c). The diode acts as a battery which opposes the d.c. component of the output voltage while allowing the a.c. component to pass with very little attenuation.

9.17   Multi-stage class A operation

A three-stage R-C coupled class A transistor amplifier is shown in Fig. 9.18(a). It contains three similar common-emitter stages, which are cascaded by R-C networks. Resistors R_1, R_2, and R_E provide base bias and temperature stabilization. It is common practice to develop about 1 V across the emitter resistor, the quiescent collector potential being approximately mid-way between the emitter potential and V_{CC}. At normal operating frequencies (i.e., mid-band frequencies), the reactance of the coupling capacitor is small enough to be neglected when compared with the input resistance of the driven stages. This being so, they are omitted from the small-signal a.c. equivalent circuit of the stage, shown in Fig. 9.18(b). In the figure, the equivalent circuit of the second stage is shown.

The input to Q2 is effectively shunted by R_1 and R_2, while its output is shunted by R_L, R_3, R_4 and R_{in} (the input resistance of the third stage).

Figure 9.18(c) illustrates the technique of graphical analysis as applied to this circuit. The quiescent point Q is selected at an appropriate point on the d.c. load line of slope $-1/(R_L + R_E)$. The a.c. load line has a slope of $-1/R_L'$, where R_L' is the value of the parallel combination R_L, R_3, R_4, and R_{in}. The output voltage swing can then be computed from a knowledge of the change in base current. A quantitative example is given in example 8.3 below.

Example 9.7: A transistor has the following h-parameters

$$h_{ie} = 1500 \ \Omega$$

$$h_{fe} = 50$$

Estimate the approximate value of the voltage gain of one stage of an amplifier using the circuit in Fig. 9.18 given that $R_L = 2 \ k\Omega$ and that the input resistance of the driven stage is 1 kΩ.

Solution: If the shunting effect of the bias circuit is ignored, the effective load resistance is R_L shunted by R_{in} of the driven stage, giving an effective load resistance of

$$2 \times 1/(2 + 1) \text{ k}\Omega = 667 \ \Omega$$

The current gain of the stage is $A_i \simeq h_{fe} = 50$, and the input resistance is approximately equal to h_{ie}. This gives an approximate voltage gain of

$$A_v = -50 \times 667/1500 = -22\cdot3$$

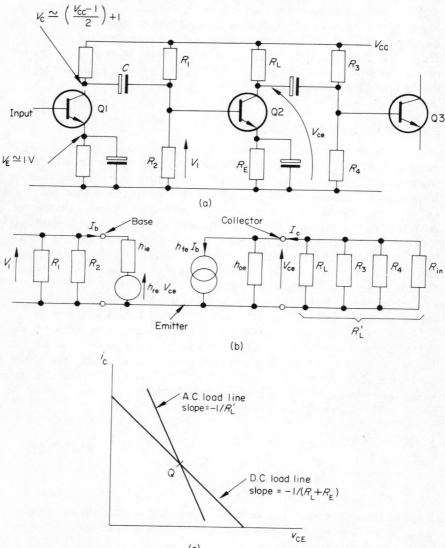

Fig. 9.18   (a) A three-stage R-C coupled amplifier, and (b) the small-signal equivalent circuit of the second stage. The application of the load line technique to determine the gain is shown in (c).

9.18   The transformer

The transformer, in its electronic context, is employed as an impedance trans-
forming device. That is to say, it is employed to modify the value of a load
resistance connected between its secondary terminals to a different value when
viewed from the primary side. Since we are dealing with flow of current in transformer windings, the following theory is applicable to a.c. signals.

In Fig. 9.19, the resistance coupled to the secondary winding of the transformer is given by

$$R_L = V_2/I_2$$

where V_2 and I_2 are the respective r.m.s. values of the secondary voltage and
current. In the figure, there are N times as many turns of wire on the primary

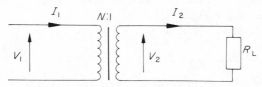

Fig. 9.19   An ideal transformer.

winding as there are on the secondary winding, hence the r.m.s. primary values
are

$$V_1 = NV_2 \qquad I_1 = I_2/N$$

Hence, the input impedance between the primary terminals is

$$R'_L = \frac{V_1}{I_1} = \frac{NV_2}{I_2/N} = N^2 \frac{V_2}{I_2} = N^2 R_L$$

That is to say, the transformer has converted the value of the load resistance R_L
connected between its secondary terminals into an apparent load value of $N^2 R_L$
between its primary terminals. The apparent value is known as the *reflected load
resistance*. Thus, if $N = 5$ and $R_L = 15\ \Omega$, then the a.c. input resistance between
the primary terminals is $5^2 \times 15 = 375\ \Omega$.

9.19   Conditions for maximum power transfer into a load

The output circuit of many electronic amplifiers can be simplified to the form
shown in Fig. 9.20, where E is the no-load output voltage, R_s is the output resistance, and R_L is the load resistance.

When $R_L = 0$, the voltage developed across it is zero, and the power consumed
in it must also be zero. At the other extreme, when $R_L = \infty$, the circuit current is
zero, and the power consumed in the load is again zero. At some point between
the two extremes lies a condition for maximum power consumption in the load.

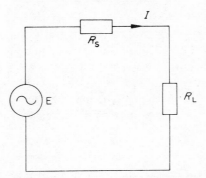

Fig. 9.20   The condition for maximum power transfer into R_L.

A knowledge of this condition is vital to the design of power amplifier stages.
    The circuit current in Fig. 9.20 is

$$I = E/(R_s + R_L)$$

and the power consumed in the load is

$$P_L = I^2 R_L = E^2 R_L/(R_s + R_L)^2 \qquad (9.26)$$

To determine analytically the value of R_L which consumes the maximum power,
it is necessary to differentiate eq. (9.26) with respect to R_L, and equate the result
to zero. This gives the relationship

$$R_L = R_s \qquad (9.27)$$

That is, maximum transfer to power into the load occurs when the load and
source resistances are equal in value. Under this condition, the load is said to be
matched to the source.
    If the load is coupled to the source by a transformer with a turns ratio of $N{:}1$,
maximum power transfer occurs when

$$R_s = N^2 R_L \qquad \text{or} \qquad N = \surd(R_s/R_L)$$

The value of N given above is known as the *optimum turns ratio* for maximum
power transfer.
    Transformers used in electronic circuits have power transfer efficiencies of the
order of 0·5 to 0·8 per unit (50 to 80 per cent). The losses in the transfer must
be provided by the primary circuit. To allow for the efficiency of the transformer, the reflected load resistance becomes $N^2 R_L \eta$, where η is the efficiency
of the transformer. The optimum turns ratio for an imperfect transformer is,
therefore, $\surd(R_s/R_L \eta)$.
    The condition for maximum power transfer should not be confused with the
condition for maximum voltage gain. Generally speaking, the voltage gain of an
amplifier operating under maximum power transfer conditions is one-half of the
maximum possible value.

It is an unfortunate fact of life that transformers used in practical circuits depart from the ideal by a considerable measure. In a practical transformer, there is a *core power loss,* which may be represented by a resistor shunting the primary winding. There are, also, *leakage fluxes* which link with one winding only, and do not contribute to the transmission of power. In addition, there is a shunt *capacitance* associated with each winding, and another capacitance between each pair of windings. The net result of these imperfections is a reduction in operating efficiency, and in the presence of resonant effects at high frequencies. In general, the quality of a transformer is reflected in its cost, and an expensive unit will give a better general performance than a cheaper unit. Even so, ideal conditions can never be achieved in transformers.

9.20   Bandwidth

The *bandwidth* or *pass-band* of an amplifier is the band of frequencies over which the power gain does not drop to a value less than an assigned fraction— usually one-half—of the 'mid-band' power gain (see Fig. 9.21). In tuned amplifiers, the reduction in power gain is expressed in terms of the gain at resonance. The bandwidth is derived from the amplifier *frequency response diagram* shown in the figure, in which gain (both power and voltage) is plotted to a base of frequency.

Curve A shows a response curve which is 'flat' down to d.c. or zero frequency, and is typical of a *d.c. amplifier.* At high frequency the gain begins to fall as a result of some frequency-dependent component in the circuit, e.g., stray capacitance which shunts the output. If the output power at frequency f_2 is one-half

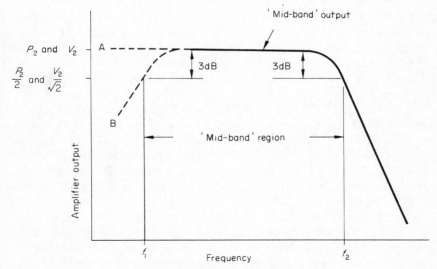

Fig. 9.21   Frequency response curve.

of the mid-band power output, then the comparative reduction in gain at f_2, expressed in logarithmic terms, is

$$\lg \frac{P_2}{0.5 P_2} = \lg 2 = 0.301 \text{ bel} = 3.01 \text{ dB}$$

For practical purposes this is taken to be 3 dB. The equivalent output voltage at f_2 is

$$\text{output voltage} = \sqrt{(\text{Output power} \times \text{Load resistance})}$$

$$= \sqrt{\left[\frac{P_2}{2} \times R \right]} = \sqrt{\left[\frac{1}{2} \left(\frac{V_2^2}{R} \right) R \right]}$$

$$= \frac{V_2}{\sqrt{2}} = 0.707 V_2 \tag{9.28}$$

Frequency f_2 is known variously as a *corner frequency*, a *cut-off frequency*, a *half-power point*, and a *break-point*.

In the case of characteristic A, the gain is constant down to d.c. The bandwidth of the d.c. amplifier is therefore $(f_2 - 0) = f_2$. A criterion for selecting circuits is the *gain-bandwidth product*, which is the product

Numerical value of gain × Bandwidth

If amplifier A has gain A_v, then the gain-bandwidth product is $A_v f_2$.

The magnitude of the linear slope of the high frequency end of the frequency response curve is related to the number of reactive elements in the circuit, and the way in which they are connected into the circuit. Generally speaking, the slope of the high frequency end of the response curve lies between 6 dB/octave and 12 dB/octave (20 dB/decade and 40 dB/decade), where one octave represents a frequency doubling (one decade is a tenfold increase in frequency). Thus, on the linearly falling part of the high frequency response, if the gain is 30 dB at 20 kHz, a slope of -6 dB/octave (-20 dB/decade) gives gain values of 24 dB, 18 dB, and 10 dB at frequencies of 40 kHz, 80 kHz, and 200 kHz, respectively.

Curve B is typical of an *a.c. amplifier*, in which the low frequency response falls off in much the same way as the high frequency response. Here, the lower corner frequency is f_1, and the bandwidth of the amplifier is $(f_2 - f_1)$. The gain-bandwidth product is $A_v(f_2 - f_1)$. In broadband a.c. amplifiers, f_1 may have a value of about 20 Hz and f_2 may be several megahertz, giving a bandwidth approximately equal to f_2. In tuned amplifiers, f_1 and f_2 may be close together, in which case both frequencies must be accounted for in calculations.

In many cases, it is necessary to cascade amplifier stages in order to achieve the desired gain or some other aspect of performance. Unfortunately, in many instances, this has the effect of reducing the bandwidth, as illustrated in the following. Suppose that an amplifier has an upper cut-off frequency of 1 MHz and a mid-band gain of 20 dB; if two such amplifiers are cascaded, the overall mid-band gain is 40 dB (assuming that one does not load the other), but at 1 MHz the gain is 3 + 3 = 6 dB below this value. The new corner frequency (i.e., when the total gain is 37 dB) occurs when each stage contributes a reduction of gain of 1·5 dB. This gives a bandwidth for the cascaded amplifier of about 0·6 MHz.

9.21 Waveform distortion

Under class A operating conditions the output signal waveform should be a faith-ful reproduction of the input signal waveform. When we speak of *waveform distortion,* we mean that the output signal waveform is not a true reproduction of the input signal. It is possible to recognize three basic forms of distortion, which may either exist separately or simultaneously. They are:

(a) Non-linear distortion or harmonic distortion.
(b) Amplitude-frequency distortion.
(c) Phase-frequency distortion or delay distortion.

Non-linear distortion or *harmonic distortion* occurs when the amplifier introduces additional harmonic component frequencies of the input signal. Illustrative examples of the effects of harmonic distortion are given in Fig. 9.22. The introduction of a third harmonic term which is in phase with the funda-mental signal distorts the waveform in the manner shown in Fig. 9.22(a), the resultant waveform being the sum of the two harmonic components. The harmonics so introduced are generated by the non-linear characteristics of the amplifying device used or of the circuit used.

The way in which the phase-shift between the fundamental and the harmonic term can modify the waveform is illustrated in Fig. 9.22(b). Here, a second harmonic signal is introduced, the harmonic signal lagging behind the funda-

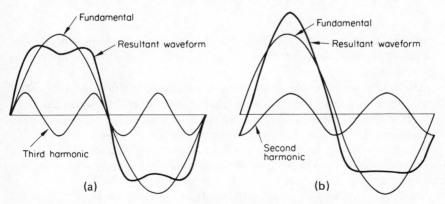

Fig. 9.22 Distortion introduced by (a) a third harmonic, and (b) a second harmonic.

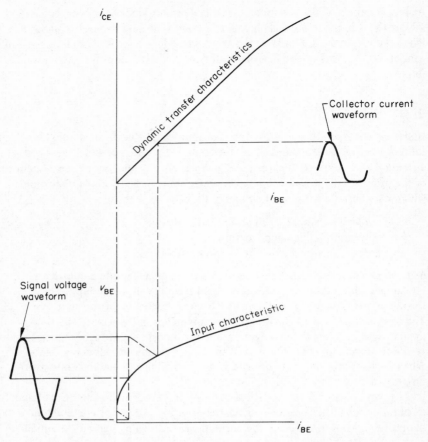

Fig. 9.23   Harmonic distortion is introduced by non-linear effects.

mental by an angle equal to 90 degrees of the harmonic waveform. Since this is
a second harmonic, the angle of lag is equivalent to 45 degrees of the fundamental waveform.

One way in which harmonic distortion is introduced is illustrated in Fig. 9.23.
Owing to the non-linearity of the input characteristic of the transistor, the
collector current falls to zero for part of the cycle, causing the collector current
waveform to be non-sinusoidal in the negative half-cycle of the input waveform.
The collector current waveform in Fig. 9.23 is seen to be generally similar to the
resultant waveform in Fig. 9.22(b), resulting in the introduction of a large second
harmonic term in the output.

Any *complex waveform*, such as the resultant waveforms in Fig. 9.22, can be
shown to consist of a fundamental sinusoid, together with a number of
harmonics. When the input signal to the amplifier is itself a complex waveform,

the non-linear characteristic of the amplifier can also result in *intermodulation distortion*. That is, frequencies which are the sum and difference of all the harmonic frequencies present at the input may be generated. This is used to advantage in communications equipment.

Amplitude-frequency distortion or *amplitude distortion* occurs when the component frequencies of a complex waveform are not amplified by equal amounts. For example, an amplifier with the frequency response diagram shown in Fig. 9.21 gives greater amplification to a signal frequency in the mid-band range (between f_1 and f_2), than it does to a signal frequency which is either greater than f_2 or less than f_1. Over the mid-band frequency range, the amplitude-frequency distortion is zero.

Phase-frequency distortion or *delay distortion* arises when all the component frequencies of a complex wave are not delayed by an equal time interval. Ideal amplifiers either give zero phase-shift (zero delay) to all frequencies, or give a phase-shift to each component frequency which is proportional to the frequency. In the former case, there is no delay, and the output waveform is undistorted. In the latter case, all harmonic components are delayed by an equal time interval, and the complex wave is delayed as a single unit, giving zero phase distortion.

Problems

9.1 Discuss the methods used to classify amplifiers; are other methods of classification possible?

9.2 Explain the essential differences between: (a) class A and class B operation, (b) d.c. coupled and a.c. coupled amplifiers, (c) voltage amplifiers and power amplifiers.

9.3 The output characteristics of a transistor connected in the common-emitter mode are linear between the following points:

v_{CE} (V)	2	25	
i_C (mA)	4·5	5·5	when $i_B = 50\,\mu A$
i_C (mA)	14·0	16·0	when $i_B = 150\,\mu A$
i_C (mA)	23·5	26·5	when $i_B = 250\,\mu A$

Draw the characteristics and construct the load line for a collector load of 1 kΩ and a collector supply voltage of 30 V.

If the peak-to-peak sinusoidal current swing in the base circuit is 200 μA, about a mean value of 150 μA, estimate:

(a) the r.m.s. value of the a.c. component of collector current.
(b) the r.m.s. value of the voltage developed across the load.
(c) the r.m.s. value of the a.c. power developed in the load, and
(d) the values of h_{fe} and h_{oe} at the quiescent point.

9.4 The output characteristics of an n-p-n transistor connected in the common-emitter configuration are linear between the following points:

v_{CE} (V)	10	40	
i_C (mA)	4·5	5·0	when i_B = 20 μA
i_C (mA)	9·4	11·6	when i_B = 40 μA
i_C (mA)	14·5	17·0	when i_B = 60 μA
i_C (mA)	19·4	26·5	when i_B = 80 μA
i_C (mA)	25·0	40·0	when i_B = 100 μA
i_C (mA)	31·0	52·0	when i_B = 120 μA

The leakage current is negligible. Plot the static transfer characteristics of the transistor relating the collector current to the base current for collector voltages of (a) 10 V, (b) 20 V, (c) 40 V. Estimate the current gain at each value of v_{CE}.

The transistor is to be used with a load resistor of 1 kΩ and a collector supply voltage of 40 V. Draw the dynamic transfer characteristic of the amplifier and estimate its current gain.

9.5 Estimate the component values to be used in a common-emitter amplifier of the type shown in Fig. 9.3 if the collector supply voltage is 6 V and the maximum allowable collector current is 2 mA. The quiescent collector current is to be 1 mA and the value of h_{FE} is 50.

9.6 If the small-signal current gain of the amplifier in question 9.5 is 45, compute the voltage gain and the power gain of the stage if the input impedance is 1 kΩ.

9.7 If a 600 Ω load is connected to the amplifier in question 9.6, calculate the new overall voltage gain.

Note: The effective value of load resistance is now R_L in parallel with 600 Ω.

9.8 Give three basic configurations of the transistor amplifier. What precautions are necessary to reduce the effect of temperature variation on the d.c. working point of each circuit?

Explain in detail the operation of a typical stabilizing circuit and show how it modifies the input and output impedance of the amplifier.

How can the effect of the feedback be restricted to direct current and very low frequencies?

9.9 Define the thermal stability factor of a transistor amplifier in terms of (a) I_{CBO} and (b) I_{CEO}. Show how the two are related.

9.10 Given the following details, estimate the values of circuit components in an amplifier of the type in Fig. 9.10(b). The collector supply voltage is 20 V, the quiescent collector current is 2 mA, and the quiescent collector-emitter voltage and base-emitter voltage are 5·5 V and 0·25 V, respectively. The value of h_{FE} at the operating point is 100. In order to provide adequate thermal stability, R_E = 1 kΩ. The lowest frequency of interest is 31·8 Hz.

9.11 Explain why temperature stabilization is less important in the design considerations of common-base amplifiers than it is in grounded-emitter amplifiers.

9.12 Describe the techniques necessary to achieve the correct operating point in valves and transistors (including FETs). Comment on whether or not it is necessary to stabilize against temperature change in each case.

9.13 Explain the meaning of the terms p-n-p and n-p-n as applied to transistors. What is the essential difference in the circuits appropriate to these two types of transistors?

The characteristics of a transistor in the grounded base connections are, for small signals, represented by the following equations:

$$V_e = h_{ib}I_e + h_{rb}V_c$$
$$I_c = h_{fb}I_e + h_{ob}V_c$$

In a particular transistor, $h_{fb} = 0.97$, $h_{ob} = 5\mu S$, $h_{ib} = 20\ \Omega$, $h_{rb} = 0.0005$. If this transistor is used in the grounded base connection with a load resistor of 50 kΩ in the collector circuit, calculate (a) the voltage amplification, (b) the input resistance.

9.14 The output characteristics for a transistor connected in the common-base configuration are as follows:

v_{CB}(V)	0	−10	−20	
i_C (mA)	−57	−57·5	−58	when $i_E = -60$ mA
i_C (mA)	−38	−38·5	−39	when $i_E = -40$ mA
i_C (mA)	−19	−19·5	−19·75	when $i_E = -20$ mA

Draw the characteristics, and construct a load line for a load of 330 Ω and a collector supply voltage of −20 V.

If the quiescent emitter current is −40 mA and a sinusoidal current of 20 sin ωt is injected into the emitter, estimate (i) the r.m.s. output voltage, and (ii) the r.m.s. output power.

9.15 The following table contains information relating to a triode:

Anode current	Anode voltage when bias is		
	Zero	−4 volts	−8 volts
10 mA	100	180	260
3 mA	40	120	200

Plot the anode characteristics (assumed to be linear).

The triode is to be used in class A, with a resistive load of 25 kΩ with a supply voltage of 300 V. A fixed bias of −4 V is provided.

Draw, on the static characteristics, a load line representing these conditions and hence determine:

(i) the mean anode current and voltage.
(ii) the a.c. output voltage if the magnitude of the sinusoidal input signal is 2·83 volts r.m.s.
(iii) the stage gain.
(iv) the output power.

9.16 Explain briefly why it is necessary to stabilize a grounded emitter transistor against changes in temperature.

A transistor in a circuit similar to that in Fig. 9.10(b) has a leakage current of 200 μA and $h_{fe} = 50$. If the current through resistor R_3 is ten times the base current, calculate the values of R_3 and R_4 to the nearest kilohm (presume V_{BE} to be negligible).

If the leakage current increases by 1 mA calculate the increase in collector current.

9.17 The input power P_1 applied to a circuit is 10 mW. If the output power P_2 is (a) 10 W, (b) 1 W, (c) 100 mW, (d) 10 mW, (e) 1 mW, (f) 1 μW, calculate the power gain in decibels in each case.

9.18 The voltage gains of a number of cascaded amplifiers and attenuators, expressed in decibels, are 22 dB, $-6\cdot2$ dB, $-10\cdot1$ dB, and $4\cdot5$ dB. Compute the overall gain in decibels.

9.19 If a voltage of 10 mV is applied to the network in question 9.18, calculate the output voltage.

9.20 If the voltage gain of the network in question 9.18 is reduced by a further 20 dB, calculate the overall gain in decibels. What then is the output voltage with an input of 50 mV?

9.21 Express in decibels a power of 10 W with reference to standard power levels of (a) 1 mW, (b) 100 mW, (c) 1 W, and (d) 100 W.

9.22 A constant input voltage of 25 mV r.m.s. of variable frequency is fed to an amplifier, and as the frequency is changed the output voltages recorded in the table are obtained.

Frequency (Hz)	50	100	250	500	1 k	2·5 k	5 k	10 k	20 k
Output (V r.m.s.)	0·07	0·22	0·59	0·75	0·78	0·71	0·30	0·27	0·11

Assuming the input and output impedances of the amplifier to be the same, plot on log-linear graph paper the output voltage in decibels against frequency. State the two frequencies between which the output is constant within ± 2 dB.

The output from the amplifier is then fed to a second amplifier having the same characteristic as the first. Plot the overall characteristic for the combination and again state the two frequencies between which the overall gain is constant to within ± 2 dB. What will be the output voltage from the combination at 6 kHz?

9.23 Compare qualitatively common-base and common-emitter amplifiers in respect of (a) input and output resistances, (b) cut-off frequency, and (c) suitability for being cascaded.

Explain in general terms how the differences arise. Explain what is meant by the term 'alpha cut-off frequency'.

9.24 An ideal transformer has an input voltage of 200 V and an output voltage of 50 V. If the load is a pure resistance of 50 Ω, calculate the values of the primary current and the secondary current. Calculate also the input power to and the output power from the transformer. What is the turns ratio of the transformer?

9.25 Draw to scale the phasor diagram of the transformer in question 9.24. Show on the diagram the effect of the no-load current of a practical transformer.

9.26 A load of resistance 10 Ω is connected to the secondary of an ideal transformer with a voltage step-down ratio of 15. Compute the effective a.c. resistance presented to the primary winding.

9.27 Define the decibel.

Two amplifiers, having the gain/frequency responses given in the table below, are connected in tandem with a 10 dB resistive attenuator. Calculate and plot the overall gain of the combination, expressed in decibels, assuming that all input and output impedances are equal.

Frequency (kHz)	60	66	72	78	84	90	96	102	108
Voltage gain (Amp. 1)	29·8	34·5	38·0	38·9	38·5	38·0	38·0	34·7	29·0
Voltage gain (Amp. 2)	28·2	37·2	37·6	36·7	36·5	36·7	38·7	39·1	29·8

9.28 Draw a circuit diagram of a two stage transistor audio-frequency amplifier and explain its operation. Explain the precautions taken to stabilize against the effects of temperature variation.

9.29 A single stage, common-source, class A amplifier has a 47 kΩ resistive load. If the mutual conductance of the FET is 1 mS, draw the small-signal equivalent circuit of the amplifier (a) if the drain resistance, r_d, can be neglected, (b) if the drain resistance cannot be neglected. Calculate the voltage gain in case (a), and also in case (b) for r_d = 100 kΩ.

Sketch a practical circuit for the amplifier, and explain how auto bias is achieved.

9.30 An n-channel JUGFET has the following characteristics which are linear between the points given.

V_{GS} (volts)	Drain current (mA) at V_{DS} of	
	10 V	30 V
−1·0	9·3	9·6
−1·5	7·2	7·5
−2·0	5·2	5·5
−3·0	1·1	1·2
−4·0	0·2	0·2

It is to be used in a single-stage, class A, common-source amplifier with a resistive load. The supply voltage is 30 V.

(a) From the characteristics estimate (i) the drain resistance, r_d, for a gate-source voltage of −2 V, (ii) the mutual conductance of the FET for V_{DS} = 20 V when the FET gate voltage is changed from −1 V to −3 V; (b) if the quiescent point of the amplifier is V_{GS} = −2 V, V_{DS} = 20 V, construct the d.c. load line and use it to estimate the voltage gain of the amplifier (assume that the gate voltage changes between −1 V and −3 V); (c) What is the value of the drain load resistor?

9.31 (a) Define the decibel and give reasons for its use in electronics. (b) The input and output power levels expressed in decibels (relative to a reference power level) of three separate circuits are given below. State (with reasons) the possible nature of each network.

Circuit	Input	Output
A	0 dB	15 dB
B	15 dB	5 dB
C	10 dB	10 dB

(c) If networks A and B are connected in cascade, what would be the ratio of the power output to power input expressed (i) in decibels, (ii) numerically?

10. Power amplifiers

10.1   Class A power amplifiers

In class A audio frequency amplifiers, the load can either be connected directly in the collector circuit or it can be transformer-coupled to it. The latter method enables the load to be matched to the amplifier in order to realize the maximum power gain, while keeping the d.c. power loss small because of the small resistance of the transformer primary winding.

Since we are concerned here with delivering the maximum a.c. power into the load, consistent with consuming the least possible d.c. power, a factor of interest is the *conversion efficiency* η of the amplifier. This is defined as the ratio of the r.m.s. value of the alternating power delivered into the load to the average power drawn from the collector (or anode) supply source. An illustrative example of the conversion efficiency is given later in this section.

A circuit diagram of a class A transistor power amplifier is shown in Fig. 10.1. In the figure, the driving stage is represented by a constant current generator. Transformer T1 provides impedance matching between the output of the driver stage and the input of the amplifier. Base bias and temperature stability are provided by resistors R_1, R_2, R_E, and thermistor R_3. Capacitor C provides a low impedance path for the flow of signal currents in the base-emitter loop. The ratio of T2 is chosen on a basis of maximum power transfer. Since the quiescent current of a class A power amplifier is high, the base current is proportionally high, and the ohmic values of the bias circuit resistors are much lower than in an equivalent class A voltage amplifier. Accordingly, the value of R_E may only be 0·5 Ω, and that of the parallel combination R_2 and R_3 only 10 Ω. So that capacitor C has a low reactance when compared with these values, the capacitance of C is very high, and a value of 1000 μF is not uncommon.

The maximum theoretical value of the conversion efficiency is deduced from the output characteristic in Fig. 10.2. Under zero-signal conditions, the effective resistance in the collector circuit is that of the primary winding of the trans-

158

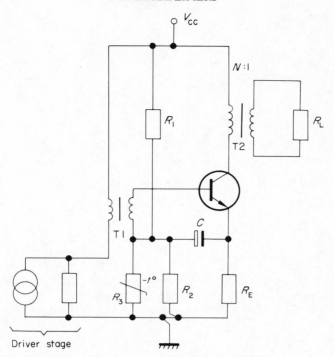

Fig. 10.1   A class A power amplifier.

former. This has a very small value, and is assumed to be zero in the figure. Thus, the d.c. load line is a vertical line rising from V_{CC}. If the transformer winding resistance is R_p, the d.c. load line has a slope of $-1/R_p$ terminating at V_{CC} on the v_{CE} axis. The quiescent point Q is set by the base bias circuit, and lies very near to the maximum average power dissipation curve $P_{C(max)}$. Since the transistor is worked on its power limit, the collector region of the transistor is normally connected to the case of the transistor, which is secured to a heat sink. In valves, the internal heat losses are dissipated by conduction and radiation, and internal temperatures are limited by the point at which occluded gases are released.

When the collector current is reduced below the quiescent value I_C (as a result of a change in i_{BE}), the collapse of the flux in the transformer core causes the instantaneous collector voltage to rise above V_{CC}. The only restriction imposed upon the maximum collector voltage $V_{C(max)}$ is the breakdown voltage of the transistor. $V_{C(max)}$ is usually limited to a few volts below this value. In valves, the maximum anode voltage is restricted only by the quality of the insulation.

Given the operating conditions shown in Fig. 10.2, with the Q-point on the $P_{C(max)}$ hyperbola, the maximum collector voltage is $V_{C(max)} = 2V_{CC}$, which may be verified by drawing a tangent to the $P_{C(max)}$ curve at point Q. That is,

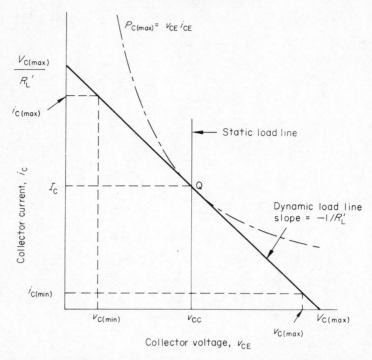

Fig. 10.2   Determination of the efficiency of a class A amplifier.

the maximum possible collector voltage is twice the supply voltage. If saturation effects can be ignored, the minimum collector voltage is zero, giving a maximum possible collector current of

$$\frac{V_{C(max)}}{R'_L} = 2I_C$$

where R'_L is the reflected value of the load resistance. Owing to the non-linear nature of the characteristics, it is necessary to constrain the voltage and current swings, otherwise excessive harmonic distortion is introduced. Suppose that the maximum and minimum values of collector voltage are $v_{C(max)}$ and $v_{C(min)}$, respectively, and the respective values for collector current are $i_{C(max)}$ and $i_{C(min)}$, then the r.m.s. collector voltage is

$$V_{ce} = \frac{v_{C(max)} - v_{C(min)}}{2\sqrt{2}} \qquad (10.1)$$

and the r.m.s. collector current is

$$I_{ce} = \frac{i_{C(max)} - i_{C(min)}}{2\sqrt{2}} \qquad (10.2)$$

Since the load is resistive, the r.m.s. power P_{ac} delivered into the load is

$$P_{ac} = V_{ce}I_{ce} = \frac{(v_{C(max)} - v_{C(min)})(i_{C(max)} - i_{C(min)})}{8}$$

The average power P_{dc} drawn from the supply is

$$P_{dc} = V_{CC}I_C \tag{10.3}$$

Hence, the conversion efficiency for a class A power amplifier is

$$\eta = \frac{P_{ac}}{P_{dc}} = \frac{(v_{C(max)} - v_{C(min)})(i_{C(max)} - i_{C(min)})}{8V_{CC}I_C} \tag{10.4}$$

The maximum possible theoretical efficiency can be predicted by assuming that the whole of the voltage and current swing is available, when

$$v_{C(max)} = 2V_{CC} \quad v_{C(min)} = 0$$

$$i_{C(max)} = 2I_C \quad i_{C(min)} = 0$$

when

$$\eta_{max} = \frac{2V_{CC}2I_C}{8V_{CC}I_C} = 0\cdot5 \text{ per unit or 50 per cent}$$

This figure can be approached in transistor stages, since the minimum possible voltage is $V_{CE(sat)}$ for the transistor, which is of the order of $0\cdot2$ V to $0\cdot7$ V. Unfortunately, efficiencies of this magnitude can only be obtained at the expense of an increase in harmonic distortion.

In the case of valves, the anode voltage and current swing are limited to much smaller proportions of the theoretical values. Suppose that the maximum voltage swing is only $1\cdot4\,V_{CC}$ and the maximum current swing is $1\cdot4I_C$, then the conversion efficiency is $1\cdot4^2\,V_{CC}I_C/8V_{CC}I_C = 0\cdot245$ per unit or $24\cdot5$ per cent.

In a bipolar transistor amplifier, the power gain is useful in describing its operation, since a finite input power is required to develop an output power. In FET and valve amplifiers, the input power is zero (unless grid current is allowed to flow), and the power gain is infinity. A convenient figure of merit for FET and valve amplifiers is the *power sensitivity*, defined by the equation

$$\text{Power sensitivity} = \frac{\text{Signal power output}}{V_g^2}$$

where V_g is the r.m.s. value of the input signal voltage. The term in the denominator is derived from the fact that the input power is related to the square of the applied voltage. Thus, if $P_{ac} = 10$ W, and $V_g = 10$ V, then the power sensitivity is $10/10^2 = 0\cdot1$ W/V^2.

Example 10.1: A common-emitter class A transistor power amplifier uses a transistor with $h_{FE} = 60$. The load has a resistance of $81\cdot6$ Ω, which is transformer-coupled to collector circuit. If the peak values of the collector voltage and current are 30 V and 35 mA, respectively, and the corresponding minimum values are 5 V and 1 mA, determine:

(a) The approximate value of the quiescent current.
(b) The quiescent base current.
(c) P_{dc}.
(d) P_{ac}.
(e) The conversion efficiency.
(f) The turns ratio of the transformer.

Solution: (a) The quiescent collector current is approximately half-way between the maximum and minimum values of collector current.

$$I_C = \left(\frac{35 - 1}{2}\right) + 1 = 18 \text{ mA}$$

Similarly,

$$V_C = \left(\frac{30 - 5}{2}\right) + 5 = 17\cdot5 \text{ V}$$

Since the load is transformer coupled, then $V_{CC} \simeq 17\cdot5$ V

(b). $I_B = I_C/h_{FE} = 18/60 = 0\cdot3$ mA

(c). $P_{dc} = V_{CC}I_C = 17\cdot5 \times 18 = 315$ mW

(d). $V_{ce} = (30 - 5)/2\sqrt{2} = 8\cdot84$ V

$$I_c = (35 - 1)/2\sqrt{2} = 12 \text{ mA}$$

$$P_{ac} = 8\cdot84 \times 12 = 106 \text{ mW}$$

(e). $\eta = 106/315 = 0\cdot337$ per unit or $33\cdot7\%$

(f). The a.c. resistance in the collector circuit is determined from the slope of the load line. Thus,

$$-\frac{1}{R'_L} = \frac{35 - 1}{5 - 30} = -\frac{34}{25} \text{ mS}$$

Therefore,

$$R'_L = 25/34 \text{ k}\Omega = 0\cdot735 \text{ k}\Omega \text{ or } 735 \ \Omega$$

Now,

$$R'_L = N^2 R_L$$

hence,

$$N = \sqrt{(R'_L/R_L)} = \sqrt{(735/81\cdot6)} = 3:1$$

10.2 Sources of distortion in the common-emitter amplifier

The main sources of distortion in the common-emitter amplifier are the non-linear regions of the input and output characteristics.

Consider the characteristics in Fig. 10.3, which are typical of a low frequency power transistor. It is clear that, unless the input signal is small, distortion of the output waveform will result from the curvature of either or both of the characteristics. In the figure, two types of signal source are considered—a *voltage source* and a *current source*. It has already been shown that the two are fundamentally different in nature, since a pure voltage source has zero output impedance, and a pure current source has an infinitely large output impedance, In both instances, the quiescent point Q on the input characteristic is chosen to give a base current of 30 mA and a collector current of 1·65 A.

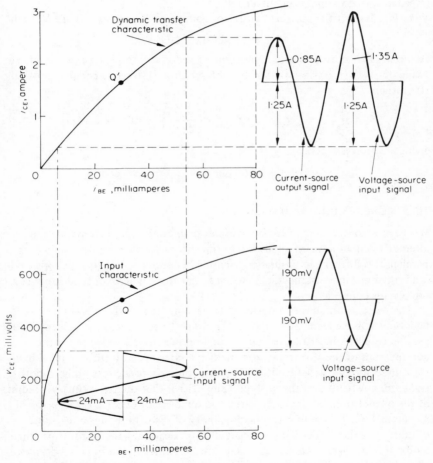

Fig. 10.3 Distortion can be introduced by using 'ideal' signal sources.

Considering firstly the voltage source input signal, the peak input voltage of 190 mV takes i_{CE} to 3 A, an upward swing of $(3 - 1 \cdot 65) = 1 \cdot 35$ A. The negative voltage swing of 190 mV takes i_{CE} to 0·4 A, or a negative-going swing of $(1 \cdot 65 - 0 \cdot 4) = 1 \cdot 25$ A. It is seen that, in this case, there is a flattening of the negative peak of the collector current waveform.

Upon the application of a signal from a current source which provides a peak current of 24 mA, the peak positive collector current has a value of 2·5 A, and the minimum value is 0·4 A. This gives a positive-going collector current swing of 0·85 A, and a negative-going swing of 1·25 A, resulting in a flattening of the positive half-cycle of the collector current waveform.

It is clear that, for minimum distortion, the impedance of the signal source must be a compromise between the two types. Thus, the turns ratio of T1 in Fig. 10.1 is chosen to present the amplifier with a signal source of the correct impedance to give minimum distortion.

In Fig. 10.3, if the quiescent collector voltage of the transistor is 12 V, then

$$P_{dc} = 12 \times 1 \cdot 65 = 19 \cdot 8 \text{ W}$$

Assuming that optimum source resistance gives a peak-to-peak collector current swing of 2·4 A (e.g., from 0·45 A to 2·85 A) into an effective collector load of 10 Ω, then

$$P_{ac} = V_{ce} I_{ce} = I_{ce}^2 R'_L = \left(\frac{2 \cdot 4}{2\sqrt{2}} \right)^2 \times 10 = 7 \cdot 2 \text{ W}$$

giving a conversion efficiency of

$$\eta = 7 \cdot 2/19 \cdot 8 = 0 \cdot 364 \text{ per unit or } 36 \cdot 4 \text{ per cent}$$

10.3　Class A push-pull operation

Where more power is required by the load than can be supplied by one transistor, alternative circuits are adopted. If two transistors are connected directly in parallel, it is difficult to ensure load sharing between the two. Parallel operation is adopted in some instances, e.g., voltage regulators, where other techniques are not always convenient.

The most common method used in signal amplifiers is the *push-pull* connection; the basic circuit is shown in Fig. 10.4. This circuit has an advantage over parallel-connected circuits, in that even harmonics are cancelled out if the current gains of the two transistors are of the same order. In the circuit shown, the quiescent point is set by V_{BB}; V_{CC} is a common collector supply to both transistors. A feature of the push-pull amplifier is that the two primary windings of the output transformer carry current in opposite directions, giving zero net magnetization. This minimizes the possibility of distortion due to magnetic saturation of the iron circuit, resulting in a physically smaller transformer than is required for a *single-ended* class A stage. An amplifier is said to be single-ended when it employs only one transistor (or valve), as, for example, Fig. 10.1.

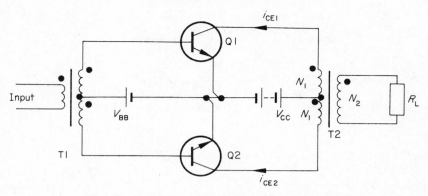

Fig. 10.4   A class A push-pull amplifier circuit.

The transformers in Fig. 10.4 are marked with dots according to the *dot notation* for induced e.m.f.s. In this notation, if the instantaneous polarity of any terminal marked with a dot is positive, then the induced e.m.f.s in all other windings on the same transformer are such as to make the ends of the windings marked with dots of like instantaneous potential, i.e., positive. Thus, if the upper terminal of the primary of T1 in Fig. 10.4 becomes positive relative to the lower terminal, it induces an instantaneous positive potential at the upper ends of both secondary windings. Hence, a positive-going signal applied to the upper primary terminal of T1 causes the collector current of Q1 to increase, while that in Q2 decreases. A negative-going input signal reverses the effects on the collector currents.

The operation of the circuit in Fig. 10.4 with a sinusoidal input signal is illustrated in Fig. 10.5. The characteristics shown are the *dynamic mutual characteristics*, which give the relationship between the base-emitter voltage and the collector current of the transistor for given values of V_{CC} and R_L; the characteristics are deduced from a knowledge of the input characteristics, the source resistance, and the dynamic transfer characteristic. The bias point chosen on the characteristics results in the introduction of harmonic distortion (mainly second harmonic distortion) in the collector current waveforms. As will be seen from an inspection of the dot notation applied to the output transformer T2, the current flowing in the load is proportional to $(i_{CE1} - i_{CE2})$. When the two current waveforms are subtracted from one another the resultant waveform is practically sinusoidal, which is due to the fact that the second harmonic terms in the separate waveforms are in opposition to one another. This is verified by the simplified analysis which follows. Suppose that the collector current of transistor Q1 is represented by the expression

$$i_{C1} = I_C + I_1 \sin \omega t + I_2 \sin 2\omega t + I_3 \sin 3\omega t + \cdots \qquad (10.5)$$

Where I_C is the quiescent current, I_1 is the peak value of the fundamental harmonic component, I_2 is the peak value of the second harmonic component,

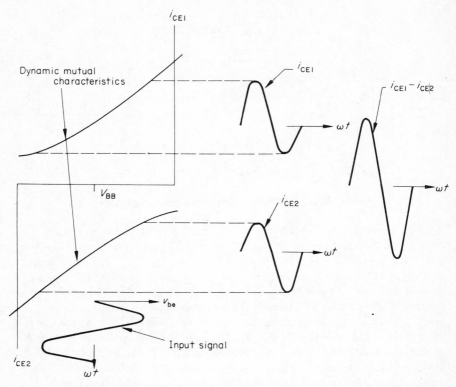

Fig. 10.5   Collector current waveforms in a class A push-pull amplifier.

etc. The expression for i_{C2} is generally similar to the above, but having ωt replaced by $(\omega t + 180°)$ due to the phase-inversion of the base voltage signal by T1.

$$i_{C2} = I_C + I_1 \sin(\omega t + 180°) + I_2 \sin 2(\omega t + 180°)$$

$$+ I_3 \sin 3(\omega t + 180°) + \cdots$$

$$= I_C - I_1 \sin \omega t + I_2 \sin 2\omega t - I_3 \sin 3\omega t + \cdots \qquad (10.6)$$

Subtracting eq. (10.6) from eq. (10.5) gives

$$i_{C1} - i_{C2} = 2(I_1 \sin \omega t + I_3 \sin 3\omega t + \cdots) \qquad (10.7)$$

The d.c. components cancel as do the even harmonic terms, leaving the fundamental and odd harmonics, i.e., the 3rd, 5th, 7th harmonics, etc. When operating in class A the amplitude of odd harmonics is normally small enough to be ignored, and

$$i_{C1} - i_{C2} \simeq 2I_1 \sin \omega t$$

If the current gains of the two transistors are not equal, the even harmonic terms do not cancel out and some distortion is introduced.

10.4   Bias arrangements in push-pull circuits

A single-battery version of Fig. 10.4 can be evolved if the bias voltage is developed across a resistor in the emitter lead, similar to Fig. 10.8. Waveforms with one peak more flattened than the other have been shown to contain second harmonics, so that i_{C1} and i_{C2} contain a proportion of second harmonic current. Since the resistor in the emitter lead carries the sum of the two collector currents, then

$$i_{C1} + i_{C2} = 2(I_C + I_2 \sin 2\omega t + I_4 \sin 4\omega t + \cdots)$$

Under Class A operating conditions, the harmonic distortion is relatively small, and the emitter current is approximately $2I_C$. From this, it would appear that it is possible to use an unbypassed resistor in the emitter lead, but there is a snag. The phase relationships of the even-order harmonics with the input signal are such that they generate *positive feedback conditions* (see chapter 13), which can lead to unstable operating conditions. For this reason, it is usual to bypass the emitter resistor with a capacitor. In many transistor amplifiers, an independent bias supply is provided.

10.5   Class B and class C operation

In *Class B* operation, the transistor or valve is biased so that collector (or anode) conduction occurs during one-half cycle of the input signal, as illustrated in Fig. 10.6. Owing to the curvature of the mutual characteristic, waveform distortion is introduced at the commencement and completion of the half-cycle.

There is, also, an additional class of operation known as *class AB,* in which collector (or anode) current flows for more than 180 degrees of the input cycle, but less than the whole of it. Class AB operation is generally a compromise between increased efficiency when compared with class A, and reduced harmonic distortion when compared with class B. In thermionic valve circuits, this class is further divided into two sub-classes AB1 and AB2. In class AB1, grid current does not flow, but in class AB2 it is permitted.

When operating in class C, the bias applied to the circuit is greater than that in class B, so that collector (or anode) current flows for less than one half-cycle, as shown in Fig. 10.6. In the figure, collector current flows over the range θ_1 to θ_2. Class C amplifiers are commonly used to drive tuned circuits which develop an oscillatory voltage between their terminals. It is only necessary in such circuits to provide a pulse of energy during each cycle, in order to supply the power losses of the circuit. The pulse of current supplied by the transistor (or valve) operating in class C fulfils this function.

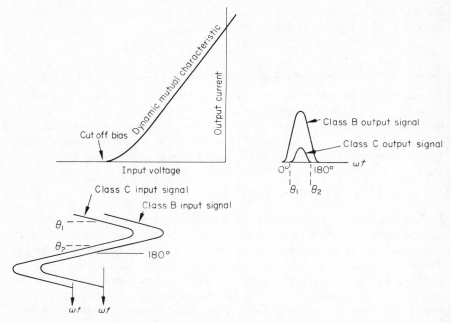

Fig. 10.6   Collector current waveforms in class B and class C circuits.

As the amplifier classification changes from class A to class C a progressively greater conversion efficiency is achieved. Thus, a class AB stage is more efficient than a class A stage, a class B stage is more efficient than a class AB stage, and so on.

10.6   Class B push-pull operation

The principal disadvantage of class A working is the high quiescent power loss. The conversion efficiency is improved by class B working, but some form of push-pull circuit must be employed to overcome the problem of the harmonics which are generated in this mode of operation.

The circuit configuration of a class B push-pull stage is generally similar to that of the class A stage shown in Fig. 10.4. Ideally, the base bias of a class B stage is zero, but this has the unfortunate effect of introducing another form of distortion known as *crossover distortion*, which is illustrated in Fig. 10.7(a). In the region of zero collector current on the dynamic mutual characteristic of the transistor, the curve flattens and causes waveform distortion. The net effect is that odd harmonics of the signal frequency are introduced into the output waveform. This effect can be minimized by applying a small forward bias to the transistors, modifying the characteristics as shown in Fig. 10.7(b). The overall characteristic of the amplifier is then approximately linear.

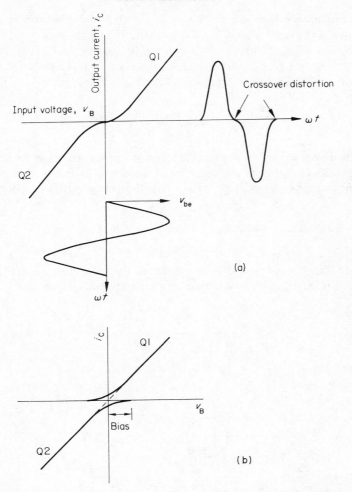

Fig. 10.7   (a) Crossover distortion is introduced by the curvature of the dynamic characteristic. One method of counteracting this defect is shown in (b).

It is advisable in push-pull circuits to choose two transistors which have closely matched characteristics, otherwise one half of the output waveform will have a larger peak value than the other due to the difference in amplification. This leads to an increase in distortion.

A typical class B transistor push-pull amplifier circuit is shown in Fig. 10.8. Resistors R_1, R_2, and R_E are chosen to provide the correct bias conditions and temperature stability. Resistor R_E normally has a very small value, often as low as a fraction of an ohm. Capacitor C is a harmonic bypass capacitor. A diode can, conveniently, be incorporated in series with R_2 to improve thermal stability.

The maximum conversion efficiency of a class B push-pull stage is estimated as follows. If the peak value of i_{C1} is I_{CM}, then the peak value of i_{C2} is $-I_{CM}$, and the r.m.s. value of the effective current in the primary of T2 (Fig. 10.8) is $I_{CM}/\sqrt{2}$. Since the peak excursion of the collector voltage is equal to V_{CC}, the r.m.s. value of the voltage change across T2 is $V_{CC}/\sqrt{2}$, so that the r.m.s. power developed is

$$P_{ac} = \frac{V_{CC} I_{CM}}{\sqrt{2}\sqrt{2}} = \frac{V_{CC} I_{CM}}{2} \qquad (10.8)$$

Since the power supply must provide a series of half-sine pulses of current to the two transistors in turn, the average value of the supply current is $2I_{CM}/\pi$; and since the average supply voltage is V_{CC}, then the average power supplied is

$$P_{dc} = 2V_{CC} I_{CM}/\pi \qquad (10.9)$$

giving a maximum theoretical conversion efficiency of

$$\eta = P_{ac}/P_{dc} = \pi/4 = 0.785 \text{ per unit or } 78.5 \text{ per cent}$$

Owing to the effect of saturation in transistors, the full voltage swing of V_{CC} cannot be realized, and the maximum efficiency in practice is about 75 per cent.

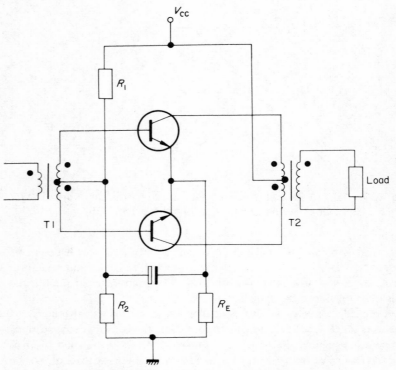

Fig. 10.8   A class B push-pull amplifier.

10.7   Class B driver stages

Class B push-pull stages require complementary input signals to the two transistors for correct operation. The simplest method is to use a single-ended class A stage to energize the primary winding of the input transformer in Fig. 10.8. Alternatively, a long-tailed pair amplifier (see section 11.2) can be used to provide complementary signals.

The circuit in Fig. 10.9 is also used as a phase-splitter. The transistor is operated in Class A, so that the emitter potential is always within about 0·2 V to 0·7 V of the base potential. Thus, output 2 is in phase with the input signal,

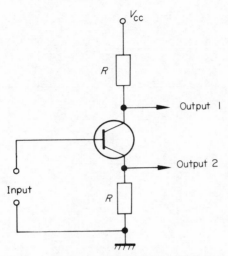

Fig. 10.9   A single-transistor phase-splitting amplifier.

while output 1 is antiphase to it. If the resistors in the emitter and collector loads are of equal value, then the voltage gains between the input and each of the two outputs are equal. One snag with this circuit is that the output impedance at the emitter output is much lower than the output impedance at the collector output, with the result that the application of similar loads to each output terminal can give different output voltages.

10.8   Transformerless class B output stages

Wherever possible, amplifiers are designed to eliminate the need for transformers, since they are both costly and bulky and can introduce distortion. Two basic versions of transformerless power output stages are shown in Fig. 10.10; the biasing arrangements are omitted for clarity.

The circuit in Fig. 10.10(a) uses an n-p-n transistor and a p-n-p transistor having similar characteristics. A pair of transistors of this kind are described as a

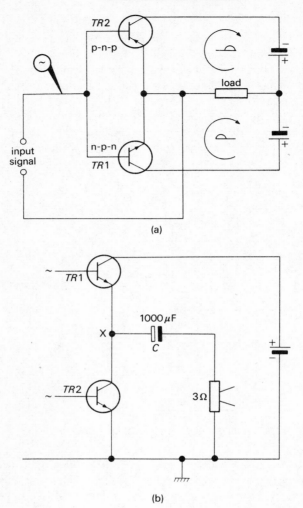

Fig. 10.10   Basic circuits for transformerless audio frequency power output
stages.

complementary pair, and the circuit is described as a *complementary symmetric
push-pull amplifier.* A common input signal is applied to both transistors, one
only conducting during each half-cycle of the input waveform. During the
positive half-cycle, the n-p-n transistor (TR1) conducts and current flows through
the load from left to right. In the negative half-cycle of the input waveform, TR2
conducts and the direction of the current flow through the load is reversed.

An alternative version of the circuit using only one power supply together
with two transistors of the same type is shown in Fig. 10.10(b). The transistors

are biased so that they operate in class AB, with the potential of point X being about one-half of the supply voltage. Transistors TR1 and TR2 are supplied by signals of opposite phase; a positive-going signal causes TR1 to conduct more heavily and TR2 to conduct less heavily, and vice versa during the negative half-cycle. The change in voltage at point X is transmitted via the blocking capacitor C to the load.

If the supply voltage is E, then the maximum possible peak-to-peak voltage swing of point X is equal to E. With a sinusoidal signal, the maximum r.m.s. voltage which can be developed across the load is $E/2\sqrt{2}$ V, and the peak power dissipated in a load of resistance R is $E^2/8R$ W.

Problems

10.1 What is meant by the terms *class A* and *class B* when applied to transistor amplifiers?

Explain, with the aid of diagrams, the operation of a push-pull amplifier and list possible reasons for its use.

Show how the bias is obtained for (a) class A operation and (b) class B operation.

10.2 (a) Explain what is meant by phase (phase/frequency) distortion and frequency (amplitude/frequency) distortion in the output of an amplifier.

Illustrate your answer with either graphs or waveform diagrams.

What are the possible causes of these forms of distortion in a voltage amplifier and how may they be kept to a minimum?

(b) State why an a.f. power amplifier is usually transformer-coupled to its load and explain how the transformer may introduce distortion.

10.3 State the essential differences between voltage and power amplifiers with reference to:

(a) type and value of load,
(b) the class of operation (A, B, or C),
(c) input and output impedances,
(d) typical frequency response curves.

Give, complete with circuit connection diagram, a typical application of each type of amplifier.

10.4 A p-n-p power transistor has the following linear characteristics

i_B (mA)	i_C (A) for a collector voltage of	
	2·5	17·5 V
10	0·67	0·70
30	1·45	1·65
50	2·33	2·64

For a collector voltage of 8 V, estimate the value of the common-emitter current gain for the transistor and hence calculate the value of the common-base current gain.

The transistor is to be used as a common-emitter type amplifier having a collector load resistance of 6 Ω. If under no-signal conditions the base current is 30 mA and the collector voltage is 8 V, draw a suitable load line and estimate

(a) the collector supply voltage required,
(b) the current gain of the amplifier,
(c) the voltage gain of the amplifier assuming that the input resistance is 5 Ω.

10.5 The common-emitter characteristics of an n-p-n power transistor are linear between the following points.

v_{CE} (V)	4	30	
i_C (A)	0·05	0·1	at i_B = 0
i_C (A)	0·6	0·75	at i_B = 10 mA
i_C (A)	1·2	1·4	at i_B = 20 mA
i_C (A)	1·8	2·05	at i_B = 30 mA
i_C (A)	2·45	2·75	at i_B = 40 mA
i_C (A)	3·1	3·45	at i_B = 50 mA

The transistor is used in a common-emitter, single-ended class A amplifier with an ideal 5:1 step-down transformer and a 0·3 Ω load. The quiescent point is determined by the current in a resistor connected between the base of the transistor and the collector supply voltage.

If the collector dissipation is not to exceed 25 W, determine graphically a suitable point which will allow maximum undistorted output power to be developed. Determine also the collector supply voltage and the value of the bias resistor. State the maximum and minimum values of collector voltage swing.

10.6 In a class A, transformer-coupled power amplifier, the collector current alternates between 3 mA and 110 mA and its quiescent value is 58 mA. The load resistance is 13 Ω, and when referred to the primary winding is 325 Ω; the supply voltage is 20 V. Estimate, stating any assumptions (a) the transformer turns ratio, (b) the a.c. power output, (c) the minimum power rating of the transistor, (d) the d.c. power supplied to the circuit (neglect the base circuit power).

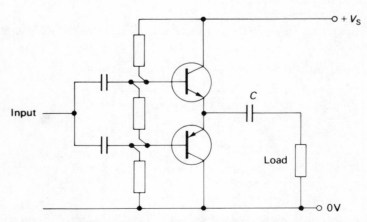

Fig. 10.11   Figure for problem 10.7.

10.7 (a) Explain the operation of the transformerless power output stage in Fig. 10.11. Describe the complete path of the load current in each half-cycle of the load current.

(b) If the load in Fig. 10.11 has a resistance of 8 Ω, determine a suitable value for capacitor C when the circuit is used as an audio frequency power amplifier. Estimate also the maximum r.m.s. value of sinusoidal power that may be developed in the load if the supply voltage is 20 V.

11. D.C. amplifiers

11.1 Drift in d.c. amplifiers

The principal feature of interest in direct coupled amplifiers is their ability to amplify signals ranging from d.c. to a frequency of many megahertz. They find a wide range of applications in the more specialized fields of electronics, including measuring instruments, automatic control systems, voltage regulators, cathode-ray oscilloscopes, and analogue computers.

Unfortunately, d.c. amplifiers are subject to a phenomenon known as *drift*, which is a slow variation of the output voltage or current of the amplifier when the input signal is maintained at a constant level. This imposes a limitation upon the permissible voltage gain of some designs of amplifier. Drift is caused by a shift in the operating point on the characteristics of the amplifying device, due to several factors including variations in

(a) The parameters of the device used.
(b) The supply voltage.
(c) The heater voltage (in valves).

In bipolar transistor circuits, it is principally the temperature-dependent parameters which are involved. These are the current gain, the base-emitter voltage, and the leakage current. Both (b) and (c) above are due to mains voltage variation, and their effects can be minimized by using stabilized power supplies.

Drift is particularly troublesome when the magnitude of the input signal is small and its frequency is very low; in this case, the drift and input signal effects may be indistinguishable from one another.

The temperature dependence of the gain of semiconductor d.c. amplifiers can be reduced by utilizing the temperature-dependent effects of other semiconductor devices, e.g., thermistors and diodes to compensate for the original changes. Thus, by replacing the resistor in the collector of a common-emitter amplifier by a thermistor, its effective resistance falls with rising temperature. If the thermis-

176

tor is correctly selected, it compensates for the increase in current gain of the transistor with temperature.

A circuit in which the effects of drift are minimized is the *long-tailed pair amplifier*, described in section 11.2.

11.2   Emitter-coupled amplifiers

In the emitter-coupled amplifier, Fig. 11.1, the emitters are connected together and taken via a common resistor to a negative potential V_{b2}, as shown. When both input signals are zero, the potential of the emitter connection will adjust itself to become slightly negative. With equal values of collector load resistors and balanced input signals, then $I_1 = I_2$ and $V_o = V_o'$. The output signal from these circuits is usually taken as the *differential signal* (the signal difference) between the two collectors; its value is zero under the conditions considered. Any variation in the collector supply voltage causes the collector currents of both transistors to change by equal amounts, and the differential output voltage remains unchanged. Any drift effects due to temperature variation or supply voltage variation thus causes little change in the differential output voltage.

If the two input signals v_1 and v_2 are equal in magnitude and are in phase with one another, then the two collector voltages change by equal amounts, and the

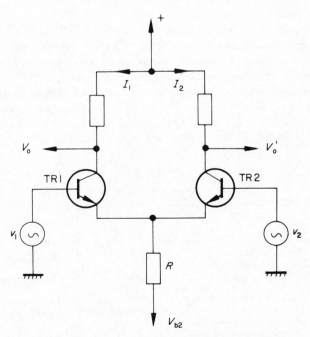

Fig. 11.1   An emitter-coupled amplifier or long-tailed pair.

differential output voltage is again zero. When the input signals are in phase with one another, they are known as *common-mode signals* since both signals have the same polarity with respect to the common line; since the circuit in Fig. 11.1 gives practically zero differential output signal for common-mode input signals, it is said to have a high *common-mode rejection* figure. This is very desirable in d.c. amplifiers, where electrical noise often appears as a common-mode signal.

If one of the two input signals is zero, say v_2, and signal v_1 becomes positive with respect to earth, it has the effect of increasing the current through TR1. This has two simultaneous effects. Firstly, it causes the collector potential of TR1 to fall, and secondly the emitter potential rises. The increase in the emitter potential reduces the bias voltage applied to the base of TR2, resulting in a reduction of current through TR2. Thus, as V_o is reduced, V_o' increases, giving a differential output between the two anodes. Thus, the circuit amplifies the difference in the two input signals. For this reason, it is known as a *difference amplifier* or *differential amplifier*. The magnitude of the output signal is further increased if the differential input voltage is increased. One method of achieving this end is to energize TR1 with a signal which is antiphase to the signal applied to TR2.

In circuits where a large voltage gain is required, differential amplifier stages can be cascaded so that outputs V_o and V_o' are used as the inputs to a second differential amplifier (see section 11.3).

The operation of the differential amplifier may, alternatively, be explained by the following argument. If the magnitude of the negative supply voltage is large, and resistor R has a large value, then the emitter resistor acts as a constant-current source which limits the sum of the two emitter currents to V_{b2}/R. In this event, an increase in the differential mode input voltage causes an increase in current through one transistor, and an equal reduction in current in the other transistor since the sum $I_1 + I_2$ remains constant. The common-emitter resistor R gives rise to an alternative name for the circuit—the *long-tailed pair*. Circuits using FETs to replace the bipolar transistors in Fig. 11.1 are popular where a high input impedance is desirable (see Table 11.1); examples include

Table 11.1

Important parameters of two types of op-amp

	FET-input op-amp	741 op-amp
Supply voltages	±6 V to ± 18 V	±3 V to ±18 V
Maximum differential input voltage	30 V	30 V
Output voltage swing	±10 V	±13 V
Low frequency voltage gain	100 000	100 000
Resistance between the two input terminals	$10^{14} \Omega$	$2 \times 10^5 \Omega$

measuring instruments and oscilloscopes. These amplifiers are known as *source-coupled amplifiers*.

To minimize the effects of temperature variation in semiconductor versions, it is preferable to use dual transistors in the same canister, which can be mounted on a heat sink if necessary.

The small-signal gain of the long-tailed pair amplifier is determined as follows. The instantaneous potential of the common-emitter connection is approximately equal to the average value of the two input signals. That is

$$v_e = \tfrac{1}{2}(v_1 + v_2)$$

Now, the instantaneous base-emitter voltage applied to each transistor is equal to the difference between the input voltage and v_e, hence,

$$v_{be1} = v_1 - v_e = v_1 - \tfrac{1}{2}(v_1 + v_2) = \tfrac{1}{2}(v_1 - v_2)$$

$$v_{be2} = v_2 - v_e = v_2 - \tfrac{1}{2}(v_1 + v_2) = -\tfrac{1}{2}(v_1 - v_2) = -v_{be1}$$

If the mutual conductance of the transistors is $g_m\,(\simeq h_{fe}/h_{ie})$, then,

$$i_{c1} \simeq g_m v_{be1} \quad \text{and} \quad i_{c2} \simeq g_m v_{be2} = -i_{ce1}$$

Assuming balanced loading conditions, with each transistor having a collector load of R_L, then the changes in the collector potentials are

$$v_{ce1} = i_{c1} R_L = \tfrac{1}{2} g_m (v_1 - v_2) R_L$$

$$v_{ce2} = i_{c2} R_L = -\tfrac{1}{2} g_m (v_1 - v_2) R_L = -v_{ce2}$$

and the differential output voltage is

$$v_{ce1} - v_{ce2} = g_m R_L (v_1 - v_2)$$

and the magnitude of the stage gain is

$$g_m R_L = \frac{h_{fe}}{h_{ie}} R_L$$

The theory given above is based on the assumption that the devices used in the amplifier have transistor-like characteristics.

The transistors TR1 and TR2 in Fig. 11.1 may be replaced by valves, when the circuit is known as a *cathode-coupled* amplifier.

Example 11.1: An emitter-coupled transistor amplifier using n-p-n transistors has a +10 V collector supply and a −8 V emitter supply. If the emitter resistor has a value of 2 kΩ, and the quiescent collector voltage of the transistor with zero input signal is to be about +5 V, estimate suitable values for the collector resistors. If the transistors used have h_{fe} = 50, h_{ie} = 1 kΩ, estimate the magnitude of the voltage gain.

Solution: With zero input signal, the potential of the emitter connection is approximately zero, and the current in the emitter resistor is approximately

$$I_E = 8 \text{ V}/2 \text{ k}\Omega = 4 \text{ mA}$$

Since this current divides between the two transistors, the collector current of each is 2 mA. This current causes a p.d. of 5 V in the collector resistor, hence

$$R_L = 5 \text{ V}/2 \text{ mA} = 2{\cdot}5 \text{ k}\Omega$$

and the magnitude of the differential gain is

$$g_m R_L \simeq \frac{h_{fe}}{h_{ie}} R_L = \frac{50}{1} \times 2{\cdot}5 = 125$$

11.3 Operational amplifiers

An operational amplifier, frequently referred to as an *op-amp*, is simply a direct-coupled amplifier which has a very high value of voltage gain.

A block diagram of a typical op-amp is shown in Fig. 11.2. Op-amps have two input terminals marked '−' and '+', respectively; these 'polarity' signs refer to the phase relationship existing between the input signals and the output signal as follows. When a voltage V_N is applied to the '−' terminal (the *inverting input*), the output signal is antiphase to V_N. When a voltage V_P is applied to the '+' terminal (the *non-inverting input*), the output signal is in phase with V_P. Inputs

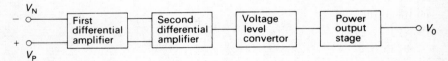

Fig. 11.2   Block diagram of an operational amplifier.

V_P and V_N in Fig. 11.2 refer to inputs v_2 and v_1, respectively in Fig. 11.1. The reader should appreciate at this point that the '+' sign on input V_P does not impose any restriction on the polarity of the input signal, since a signal of either positive or negative polarity can be applied. This comment also applies to the inverting ('−') input terminal.

The two output signals developed at the collectors of the transistors in the first differential amplifier are used as input signals to the second differential amplifier. The voltage level convertor amplifier shifts the voltage level at one output of the second differential amplifier to a value at which zero differential input voltage (that is when $V_P - V_N = 0$) gives zero output voltage ($V_0 = 0$). The power amplifier stage is of the emitter follower type (see chapter 13), and has a very low output resistance.

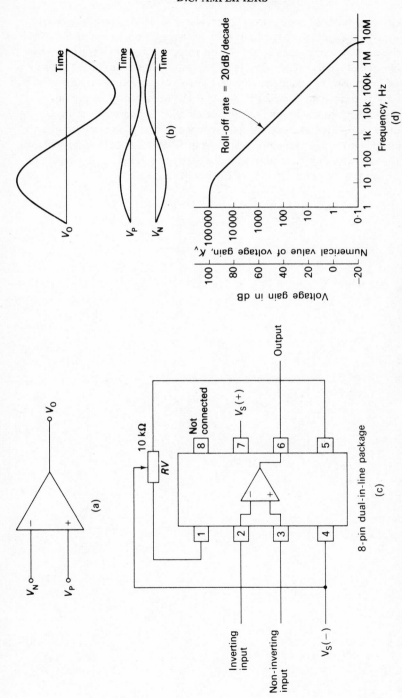

Fig. 11.3   (a) Op-amp circuit symbol, (b) output waveform for sinusoidal inputs, (c) 741 op-amp in an 8-pin DIL pack, (d) frequency response curve of the 741 op-amp.

The circuit symbol of the op-amp is shown in Fig. 11.3(a), and the phase relationships between the input and output voltages are illustrated in Fig. 11.3(b). One of the most popular types is the 741 op-amp, and a plan view of an 8-pin dual-in-line (DIL) package containing this op-amp is shown in Fig. 11.3(c); pins 4 and 7 are used for the negative and positive power supplies, respectively. Resistor RV is connected externally (its use is not mandatory) to provide a means of manually compensating for any small *offset voltage* appearing at the output of the amplifier when both input signals are zero. The more important parameters of two types of op-amp are given in Table 11.1; the reader will note the significant difference in input resistance between the FET-input type and the 741 op-amp which uses bipolar transistors throughout.

12. Noise in electronic circuits

.

12.1 Types of noise

Noise is defined as all spurious signals, random or otherwise, that are no part of
the input information. Noise is generally regarded as being either *narrowband*
(artificial or man-made) or *broadband* (natural noise). Narrowband noise is of
low frequency origin, typically in the range 10 Hz to 1 kHz, and is often
harmonically related to the power supply frequency, e.g., mains 'hum'. This type
of noise can be minimized or even eliminated by the use of suppressor circuits.
Broadband noise comprises signals above a frequency of about 1 kHz, and is
generated by the movement of electrons. The effects of this type of noise
cannot be completely eliminated, only minimized.

12.2 Reduction of induced voltages

The most effective way to reduce voltages induced in circuits from unwanted
external signals is to shield the circuit by enclosing it in a metal box. The box
places the contents in a uniform field, so that the effects of low frequency
radiations are minimized. If the box is made of iron, it provides a degree of
magnetic shielding. High frequency shielding is provided if the box is made
from a good conductor such as aluminium or copper.

12.3 Evaluation of noise

Noise voltages produced by natural effects are due to the movement of charge
carriers within components. Since the noise voltage may have both positive
and negative fluctuations, the 'noisiness' of a circuit is expressed either in terms
of the *mean square noise voltage* or in terms of the *noise power*. A criterion of
the performance of an electronic circuit is given by the ratio of the signal power
delivered to the load to the noise power delivered. This ratio (usually expressed

in decibels) may have a value from 25 dB to over 60 dB, the lower value referring to a less acceptable system.

12.4   Bipolar junction transistor noise

As an example of the noise produced by electronic components, Fig. 12.1 shows a typical noise response of a bipolar transistor.

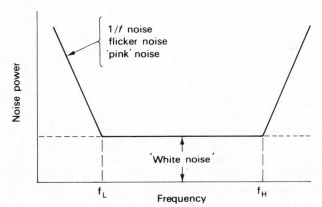

Fig. 12.1   Noise power curve for a bipolar transistor.

12.4.1   White noise

This consists of the components of noise which are independent of frequency (they exist at all frequencies up to about 10^{13} Hz). By its analogy with white light, which is broadband in nature, this noise is described as white noise. It is due to a number of components including *thermal noise* or *Johnson noise* (after the scientist who first described it), *shot noise* and *partition noise*. Thermal noise or Johnson noise is due to the continual interchange of energy between charge carriers in the crystal structure, resulting in variations in charge density. This effect varies with temperature, and manifests itself as a noise voltage between the terminals of the component. Shot noise is due to the random nature of current; the rate of which charge carriers arrive at the collector of a transistor varies very rapidly, and as each charge carrier arrives it gives up its charge and generates a 'spike' in the collector current waveform. Partition noise is another version of shot noise and is thought in bipolar transistors to be due to recombination of charge carriers in the base region; this effect also occurs in valves, and is due to the division of electrons between positively charged electrodes (for this reason multi-electrode valves are inherently noisy).

12.4.2 $\dfrac{1}{f}$ noise, flicker noise or pink noise

At frequencies below f_L in Fig. 12.1 (below about 1 kHz) the noise power increases with reducing frequency; for this reason it is described as *1/f noise*. One source of this noise is ripple (or *flicker*) from rectifiers. Since the noise is spread over a narrow bandwidth it is known as coloured noise (as distinct from white noise) and is frequently referred to as *pink noise*. A great deal of this noise in transistors is due to the effects of surface leakage current.

12.4.3 High frequency effects

At frequencies above f_H in Fig. 12.1, the signal power gain of the transistor reduces. This causes a relative increase in noise power.

12.5 Noise in FETs

These devices are inherently less noisy than bipolar transistors, the main sources of noise being (a) thermal noise in the conducting channel, (b) shot noise due to gate leakage current, and (c) 1/f noise arising from surface leakage. The value of f_L (Fig. 12.1) can be as low as 100 Hz.

12.6 Valve noise

The noise sources in valves include those listed in section 12.4 for bipolar transistors. Additionally, there is another noise source known as *microphony* which results from vibration of the electrodes when the valve is subjected to mechanical shock; this type of noise can be reduced by mounting the valve in a resilient holder, and by acoustically shielding the valve.

12.7 Signal-to-noise power ratio

This ratio is given by

$$\text{Signal-to-noise power ratio, } \frac{S}{N} = \frac{\text{signal power}}{\text{noise power}} \tag{12.1}$$

Since $P = V^2/R$, substituting this into eq. (12.1) for the case where both values of power are developed in a common value of resistance R

$$\frac{S}{N} = \frac{v_s^2/R}{v_n^2/R} = \left(\frac{v_s}{v_n}\right)^2 \tag{12.2}$$

where v_s and v_n are the respective values of signal and noise voltage. Equation (12.2) is usually expressed in decibels as follows

$$\left(\frac{S}{N}\right)_{dB} = 10 \log_{10}\left(\frac{v_s}{v_n}\right)^2 = 20 \log_{10}\left(\frac{v_s}{v_n}\right) dB \qquad (12.3)$$

In the above, v_s/v_n is known as the *signal-to-noise voltage ratio*.

12.8   Noise figure

The noise figure for a circuit is given by

$$\text{Noise figure, } F = \frac{\text{signal-to-noise-power ratio at the input}}{\text{signal-to-noise power ratio at the output}}$$

$$= \frac{(v_{si}/v_{ni})^2}{(v_{so}/v_{no})^2} \qquad (12.4)$$

The noise figure is expressed in decibels as follows

$$F_{dB} = 20 \log_{10}\left(\frac{v_{si}/v_{ni}}{v_{so}/v_{no}}\right) dB \qquad (12.5)$$

Problems

12.1   Describe the sources of noise in:
  (a) thermionic valves,
  (b) transistors,
and mention, where appropriate, how these vary with frequency.

12.2   Explain the reasons for, and distinguish between, white noise and $1/f$ noise.

13. Feedback amplifier theory

13.1 The objects and methods of application of feedback

Up to this point in the book, basic amplifier circuits, sometimes known as *open-loop* amplifiers, have been considered. They are known as open-loop amplifiers because the output signal is not monitored and used to control the amplifier. A change in conditions, say a sudden demand for load current, results in the output voltage being reduced. In open-loop amplifiers, no attempt is made to compensate for changes in circuit conditions or in load conditions, e.g., changes in load resistance, supply voltage, component values and parameters, etc.

If the output is monitored, and the information is fed back to the input, correcting action can be taken. Amplifiers using some method of information feedback are known as *feedback amplifiers* or *closed-loop amplifiers,* since the feedback loop is closed. Generally speaking, feedback is applied only where it is beneficial and can improve some of the qualities of the circuit. In some cases, however, feedback has undesirable effects, adversely affecting the performance of the circuit.

In many amplifiers, either a part or all of the output signal is fed back and included as a part of the input signal. If the signal is fed back deliberately, then the results can be predicted by circuit theory. If the output signal is fed back as a result of parasitic components, e.g., by leakage capacitance, then the results are not easily predictable.

If the signal fed back is in phase with the input signal, it is referred to as *positive feedback* or *regenerative feedback*; if it is antiphase to the input signal, it is known as *negative feedback* or *degenerative feedback. Series feedback* is applied when the output signal, or a part of it, is connected in series with the input signal. In *shunt feedback,* the input and output signals are converted into electric currents by applying the voltage signals to resistances or impedances; the sum (or difference) of the two currents is used to develop a voltage across a

187

further impedance (which may be the input impedance of the amplifier), which is then amplified.

Voltage feedback is said to be applied when the signal fed back is proportional to the output voltage of the amplifier. When the signal fed back is proportional to the output current, *current feedback* is applied. Generally speaking, the principal properties affected by feedback are the *input impedance,* the *output impedance,* and the *gain.* Other properties, such as *distortion, bandwidth,* etc. are also affected.

Hybrid feedback circuits, combining both current and voltage feedback are used in practice to give the correct combination of gain, input impedance, output

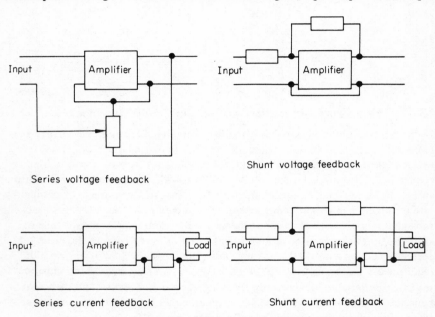

Series voltage feedback

Shunt voltage feedback

Series current feedback

Shunt current feedback

Fig. 13.1   Basic feedback amplifier configurations.

impedance, bandwidth, etc. In general, positive feedback results in the opposite effects to those achieved by negative feedback.

The block diagrams of several basic forms of feedback circuit are shown in Fig. 13.1.

13.2   Series positive voltage feedback

The block diagram of a series positive voltage feedback amplifier is shown in Fig. 13.2. The amplifier, of gain A_v, is non-phase-inverting, that is to say the output signal is in phase with the input signal. A proportion βV_2 of the output signal is fed back and added in series with the input signal. The *feedback network* or *β-network,* in this case a potentiometer, has a transfer ratio β which

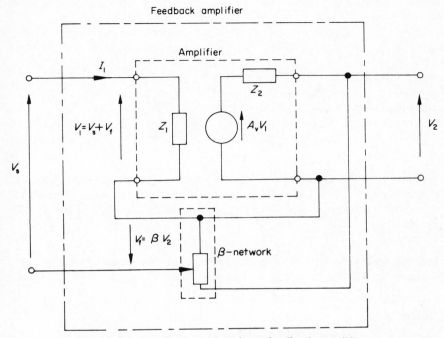

Fig. 13.2   A series positive voltage feedback amplifier.

has a value less than, or equal to, unity. With the connections shown, the signal fed back is in phase with the input signal, and overall positive feedback is applied.

In order to distinguish the complete circuit in Fig. 13.2 from the *amplifier* itself, the complete network (including the amplifier) is described as a *feedback amplifier* or *closed-loop amplifier,* since the 'loop' around the amplifier between input and output is complete or closed.

With the configuration in Fig. 13.2, it is impossible to earth one of the input terminals and one of the output terminals simultaneously, since this would result in the output of the β-network becoming short-circuited, rendering the feedback circuit inoperative.

In Fig. 13.2, the output voltage is

or

$$\left.\begin{aligned} V_2 &= A_\mathrm{v} V_1 \\[2mm] V_1 &= \frac{V_2}{A_\mathrm{v}} \end{aligned}\right\} \qquad (13.1)$$

where V_1 is the net voltage applied to the amplifier terminals. Also, from Fig. 13.2

$$V_1 = V_\mathrm{s} + \beta V_2 \qquad (13.2)$$

hence, from eqs. (13.1) and (13.2)

$$\frac{V_2}{A_v} = V_s + \beta V_2$$

or

$$V_2 = \frac{A_v V_s}{1 - A_v \beta}$$

The closed-loop no-load gain of the feedback amplifier A_{vf} is, therefore

$$A_{vf} = \frac{V_2}{V_s} = \frac{A_v}{1 - A_v \beta} \qquad (13.3)$$

The product $A_v \beta$ is known as the *loop gain*, and A_v is known as the *forward gain*. It will be seen from the following example that series positive voltage feedback effectively increases the gain of the feedback amplifier above that of the amplifier itself.

Example 13.1: Calculate the loop gain and the closed-loop gain of an amplifier similar to that in Fig. 13.2, if $A_v = 10$ and $\beta = 0.09$.

Solution:
   Loop gain = $A_v \beta$ = 10 x 0·09 = 0·9
   Closed-loop gain = $A_{vf} = A_v/(1 - A_v \beta)$ = 10/(1 − 0·9)
                    = 100

That is, the gain of the closed-loop amplifier is ten times greater than that of the amplifier itself.

The physical reason for the increase in the gain is as follows. When series positive voltage feedback is applied, the net input voltage V_1 applied to the amplifier is greater than the signal voltage V_s applied to the closed-loop amplifier, since a voltage βV_2 is added to V_s before being applied to the amplifier. Signal V_1 is then amplified A_v times, giving an output voltage which is significantly greater than would be the case if V_s was alone amplified. In example 13.1, if the feedback network was disconnected the gain would be 10, and, for an output of 1 V, the input signal applied to the amplifier would be 0·1 V. When positive series voltage feedback is applied, an output of 1 V from the closed-loop amplifier results in 0·09 V being fed back by the β-network. The signal voltage in this case is the difference between 0·1 V and 0·09 V, i.e., 0·01 V. That is, a signal voltage of 0·01 V gives an output of 1 V, corresponding to a gain of 1 V/0·01 V = 100.

The net input voltage V_1 is computed by eliminating V_2 between eqs. (13.1) and (13.2), giving

$$V_1 = \frac{V_s}{1 - A_v \beta} \qquad (13.4)$$

There are clearly limitations to the theory developed here, since if the product $A_v\beta = 1$, then from eqs. (13.3) and (13.4),

$$A_{vf} = A_v/(1-1) = \infty$$

and

$$V_1 = V_s/(1-1) = \infty$$

This condition arises in the amplifier in problem 13.1 if the forward gain A_v is increased to $A_v = 1/\beta = 11\cdot111$ (or if β is increased to $\beta = 1/A_v = 1/10 = 0\cdot1$). This condition is said to be *unstable*, since sufficient output signal is fed back through the β-network to sustain the output voltage, with no input signal applied to the closed-loop amplifier. The problem of instability is discussed more fully in section 13.9.

13.3 Series negative voltage feedback

If the amplifier in Fig. 13.2 is replaced by a phase-inverting amplifier having gain $-A_v$, other connections remaining unchanged, the closed-loop gain is evaluated by replacing A_v by $-A_v$ in eq. (13.3), giving

$$A_{vf} = \frac{-A_v}{1-(-A_v)\beta} = \frac{-A_v}{1 + A_v\beta} \qquad (13.5)$$

Thus, if $-A_v = -100$, and $\beta = 0\cdot09$, the amplifier gain is, from eq. (13.5),

$$A_{vf} = \frac{-100}{1-(-100 \times 0\cdot09)} = -10$$

The principal features of eq. (13.5) are

(a) The output voltage is antiphase to the input voltage V_s, indicated by the negative sign in the numerator.
(b) The gain of the closed-loop amplifier is less than the gain of the amplifier itself, since the denominator has a value greater than unity.

Feature (b) is explained as follows. An increase in the amplifier input voltage by an amount $+V_1$ results in an output voltage of $-V_2$. The voltage fed back by the β-network is $\beta(-V_2) = -\beta V_2$. Since the connections to the input circuit are as shown in Fig. 13.2, the amplifier input voltage is

$$V_1 = V_s + (-\beta V_2) = V_s - \beta V_2$$

Comparing this equation with the equivalent expression for the positive feedback case, eq. (13.2), it is seen that V_1 is reduced when negative feedback is applied. Since the output voltage is $-A_v V_1$, the overall gain is reduced. This argument is supported by the following example.

If an amplifier has a gain of -1000, an input V_1 of 1 mV supports an output of -1 V. If the amplifier is used as a part of a negative series voltage feedback amplifier with a feedback coefficient of $\beta = 0{\cdot}1$, the voltage fed back to the input is $0{\cdot}1 \times (-1) = -0{\cdot}1$ V.

Now

$$V_1 = V_s + \beta V_2 = V_s - 0{\cdot}1$$

or

$$V_s = 0{\cdot}001 + 0{\cdot}1 = 0{\cdot}101 \text{ V}$$

This gives an overall gain for the feedback amplifier of

$$A_{vf} = V_2/V_s = -1/0{\cdot}101 = -9{\cdot}901$$

As a result of the application of negative feedback, the input voltage to the amplifier has to be increased in order to maintain the same output voltage, resulting in an overall reduction of gain. Using eq. (13.5)

$$A_{vf} = -1000/(1 - [-1000 \times 0{\cdot}1]) = -9{\cdot}901$$

If, in eq. (13.5), the loop gain $A_v\beta$ has a value which is much greater than unity, then

$$A_{vf} \simeq -A_v/-(-A_v)\beta = -1/\beta$$

That is, the closed-loop gain is set by the β-network, and is independent of the actual value of the amplifier gain. In the above illustrative example $-A_v\beta = 100$, which is much greater than unity, and the approximation given above can be used. This gives a gain of $A_{vf} = -1/0{\cdot}1 = -10$, which is in error by only 1 per cent.

An alternative method of applying series negative voltage feedback is to use a non-phase-inverting amplifier, and a phase-inverting β-network. This technique is readily applicable to systems in which the input and output are electrically isolated from one another, e.g., control systems, and electronic circuits using isolating transformers in the feedback path. The equation for the gain of these amplifiers is obtained by replacing β in eq. (13.3) by $-\beta$, giving

$$A_{vf} = A_v/(1 + A_v\beta) \qquad\qquad (13.6)$$

The resulting closed-loop amplifier is non-phase-inverting with a gain less than A_v.

A study of the principal properties of series negative voltage feedback amplifiers follows.

13.3.1   Stabilization of gain

In the absence of feedback, a change in the amplifier gain, as a result of some internal change, results in a proportional change in the output voltage. In the feedback amplifier, this change of output is fed back to the input, causing V_1 to change. As a direct result of this the output voltage is brought back to a level which is nearly equal to its original value.

Example 13.2: Calculate the per-unit change in the closed-loop gain of a series negative voltage feedback amplifier, with $\beta = 0{\cdot}1$, when the amplifier gain falls from -1000 to -500.

Solution: When the gain is -1000

$$A_{vf} = -1000/(1 - [-1000 \times 0 \cdot 1]) = -9 \cdot 901$$

and when -500,

$$A_{vf} = -500/(1 - [-500 \times 0 \cdot 1]) = -9 \cdot 805$$

and the per-unit reduction in A_{vf}, when A_v changes by $0 \cdot 5$ per-unit, is

$$(9 \cdot 901 - 9 \cdot 805)/9 \cdot 901 = 0 \cdot 0097 \text{ per unit or } 0 \cdot 97 \text{ per cent}$$

A physical explanation of this phenomenon is obtained by utilizing the results of eq. (13.4). Suppose that the input voltage to the feedback amplifier in example 13.2 is maintained at 1 V. The amplifier input voltage, for $A_v = -1000$, is

$$V_1 = 1/(1 - [-1000 \times 0 \cdot 1]) = 0 \cdot 009901 \text{ V or } 9 \cdot 901 \text{ mV}$$

and the amplifier output voltage is

$$V_2 = -1000 \times 9 \cdot 901 \times 10^{-3} = -9 \cdot 901 \text{ V}$$

When the gain is reduced to -500, the amplifier input voltage rises to

$$V_1 = 1/(1 - [-500 \times 0 \cdot 1]) = 0 \cdot 01961 \text{ V or } 19 \cdot 61 \text{ mV}$$

giving an output voltage of

$$V_2 = -500 \times 19 \cdot 61 \times 10^{-3} = -9 \cdot 805 \text{ V}$$

Thus, in order to compensate for the 50 per cent reduction in amplifier gain, V_1 practically doubles to give an overall gain for the feedback amplifier which is not significantly different from that which existed before the amplifier gain was reduced.

Alternatively, an expression for the change in closed-loop gain can be deduced by differentiating eq. (13.3) with respect to A_v, which gives the per-unit change in gain as $(dA_v/A_v)/(1 - A_v\beta)$, where dA_v/A_v is the per-unit change in gain A_v. In example 13.2, this yields $-0 \cdot 5/(1 - [-1000 \times 0 \cdot 1]) = -0 \cdot 00495$, a reduction of $0 \cdot 495$ per cent. This should be compared with the figure of $0 \cdot 97$ per cent in example 13.2. The reason for the difference in the two solutions is that the equation developed here is valid for small changes in A_v (up to, say, 5 per cent), and it does not give accurate results for large changes in gain.

13.3.2   Input impedance Z_{1f}

Practically all electronic devices have a finite input impedance, its value being high in the cases of thermionic and field effect devices, and relatively low in bipolar transistors. The input impedance of the circuit is modified by feedback, the actual change being dependent on the form of feedback used, and the way in which it is applied. In series negative voltage feedback amplifiers, the net input voltage V_1 applied to the amplifier is less than the signal voltage V_s, and the current drawn from the signal source is thereby reduced. This gives the effect of an increase in input impedance above that of the amplifier itself.

For example, if an amplifier has a gain of -100 and an input impedance of 1 kΩ, a 10 mV signal applied to the amplifier results in an output voltage of -1 V and an input current of 10 mV/1 kΩ = 10 μA. If a feedback network with $\beta = 0\cdot09$ is used with the above amplifier, the voltage fed back is $-1 \times 0\cdot09 = -0\cdot09$ V, and the signal voltage V_s required to maintain the output of 1 V is

$$V_s = V_1 - \beta V_2 = 0\cdot01 - (0\cdot09 \times -1) = 0\cdot1 \text{ V}$$

Under feedback conditions, the voltage applied to the amplifier terminals (V_1) remains at 10 mV, the current drawn from the signal source remains at 10 μA. The apparent input impedance, seen from the signal source, is

$$Z_{1f} = V_s/10 \times 10^{-6} = 0\cdot1/10^{-5} = 10^4 \ \Omega \text{ or } 10 \text{ k}\Omega$$

that is, an apparent increase in input impedance by a factor of 10, from 1 kΩ to 10 kΩ.

The theoretical input impedance is

$$Z_{1f} = Z_1(1 - A_v\beta) \tag{13.7}$$

and in the above example this yields $Z_{1f} = 1(1 - [-100 \times 0\cdot09])$ kΩ = 10 kΩ. In positive feedback amplifiers, when the product $A_v\beta$ has a positive value, the input impedance is reduced below that of Z_1.

13.3.3 Effect of loading the feedback amplifier

When current is drawn from the amplifier, the output voltage is reduced as a result of the p.d. in the output impedance Z_2 of the amplifier. The initial effect is an apparent reduction in voltage gain, and the general effects of load current on the feedback amplifier are broadly those resulting from a reduction of gain. However, negative feedback tends to compensate for reduction in gain, and the effects of loading on a negative feedback amplifier are generally less than in the case where no feedback is applied.

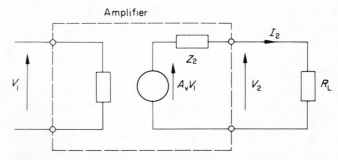

Fig. 13.3   A method of determining the effect of loading.

The effects of loading may be analysed with the aid of Fig. 13.3.
By potential divider action, $V_2 = A_v V_1 R_L/(Z_2 + R_L)$. The gain of the amplifier
itself, when loaded, is therefore

$$A_{vl} = V_2/V_1 = A_v R_L/(Z_2 + R_L) \qquad (13.8)$$

The effective constants of a voltage feedback amplifier when it is loaded are
obtained by substituting the value of A_{vl} in place of A_v in the appropriate no-load
equations. Thus,

$$A_{vf} = \frac{A_{vl}}{1 - A_{vl}\beta)} = \frac{A_v \dfrac{R_L}{Z_2 + R_L}}{1 - A_v \dfrac{R_L}{Z_2 + R_L}\beta} = \frac{A_v R_L}{Z_2 + R_L - A_v \beta R_L}$$

$$= \frac{A_v R_L}{Z_2 + R_L(1 - A_v \beta)} \qquad (13.9)$$

In addition, the load applied to the amplifier has a significant effect upon the
input impedance of the amplifier. Any variation in the load current causes the
output voltage to change, and with it the voltage which is fed back. For reasons
which have already been given, this causes V_1 to alter, causing the current drawn
from the signal source to change. This results in a change in the input impedance
of the closed-loop amplifier. In the case of a negative feedback amplifier, a
reduction of output voltage causes V_1 to increase, resulting in an increased input
current, and a reduction in input impedance.

An expression for the input impedance of the feedback amplifier when it is
loaded is developed by substituting eq. (13.8) into eq. (13.7), when

$$Z_{1f} = Z_1(1 - A_{vl}\beta) = \frac{Z_1(Z_2 + R_L[1 - A_v\beta])}{Z_1 + Z_2} \qquad (13.10)$$

To illustrate the effects of eqs. (13.9) and (13.10), consider the case of an amplifier
with a gain of -100, $\beta = 0.09$, $Z_2 = 1$ kΩ, $Z_1 = 1$ kΩ, and $R_L = 4$ kΩ. The results
of eqs. (13.9) and (13.10) and those for an unloaded amplifier (when $R_L = \infty$) are
given below.

	Unloaded amplifier	Loaded amplifier
Voltage gain	-10	-9.1
Input impedance (kΩ)	10	5.5

So far, the effects of the β-network itself have been neglected. This network
constitutes a load which is permanently connected to the amplifier, and it cannot
always be ignored. The effects of the β-network are generally the same as those
of an external load resistor.

13.3.4   Output impedance Z_{2f}

It has already been shown that the output voltage of a negative series voltage
feedback amplifier remains substantially constant over a very wide range of
loading conditions. That is, the output impedance of the feedback amplifier is
small when compared with that of the amplifier itself.

The effective output impedance of the closed-loop amplifier is given by

$$Z_{2f} = \frac{V_{2I}}{I_{2I}} = \frac{Z_2}{1 - A_v\beta \dfrac{Z_1}{Z_1 + R_s}} = \frac{Z_2(Z_1 + R_s)}{R_s + Z_1(1 - A_v\beta)} \qquad (13.11)$$

In the case of an amplifier with Z_1 = 1 kΩ, Z_2 = 1 kΩ, $-A_v$ = -100, β = 0·09,
and R_s = 1 kΩ, the closed-loop output impedance is 182 Ω, which is much lower
than the 1 kΩ value for the amplifier itself.

The minimum value of output impedance is achieved when the source
resistance R_s is zero, when

$$Z_{2f} = \frac{Z_2}{1 - A_v\beta} \qquad (13.12)$$

13.3.5   Noise in feedback amplifiers

Spurious signals, known as *noise* signals, appear at the output of amplifiers in
addition to the wanted signals (see also chapter 12). Noise signals are either
generated in circuit components, or they may be induced from neighbouring
signal sources such as the alternating mains supply.

If the noise originates at an early stage in the amplifier, e.g., in the first stage,
negative feedback has no significant effect in reducing it, since the noise signal
and the wanted signal are amplified equally. If the noise is generated at a late
stage in the amplifier, the wanted signal receives more amplification than the
noise, and the signal-to-noise ratio is improved by negative feedback. To keep
the noise level at its lowest value, great care must be taken in designing the
early stages of feedback amplifiers. A detailed analysis is beyond the scope
of this book, but it is given elsewhere*.

13.3.6   Effect of feedback on distortion

It was shown in chapter 10 that non-linear characteristics can result in the introduction of harmonic distortion in the output waveform from an amplifier. The
harmonics generated by this means fall within the definition of noise, given in
section 13.3.5. Thus, if an amplifier of gain A_v has an input signal V_1, and the
'noise' signal or harmonic distortion introduced by the circuit is V_n, then the

* Morris, N. M., *Control Engineering*, McGraw-Hill (1974).

output voltage in the absence of feedback is given by

$$V_2 = A_v V_1 + V_n$$

giving a signal-to-noise ratio at the output of $A_v V_1/V_n$. When feedback is applied in accordance with Fig. 13.2, the expression for output voltage becomes

$$V_2 = \frac{A_v}{1 - A_v \beta} V_s + \frac{V_n}{1 - A_v \beta}$$

giving a signal-to-noise ratio at the output of $A_v V_s/V_n$.

To maintain the same value of V_2 both with feedback and without it, V_s is much larger than V_1 when negative feedback is applied. Thus, if the two values of signal-to-noise ratio are compared at the same value of output signal, it is seen that the signal-to-noise ratio is improved by negative feedback in the ratio of V_s/V_1. From eq. (13.4), this is seen to be a factor of $(1 - A_v\beta)$.

It can also be shown that negative voltage feedback also has the effect of reducing the phase distortion in amplifiers.

13.3.7   Effect of feedback on bandwidth

A typical gain-frequency curve for an a.c. amplifier is shown in Fig. 13.4 (upper curve). The reduction in gain at high frequency occurs, usually, as a result of the change in the reactance of stray capacitors which shunt the output of the amplifier. At high frequency, the reactance of these capacitors falls to a low value, effectively short-circuiting the load. The reduction in gain at low frequencies is a direct consequence of the coupling methods used in a.c. amplifiers.

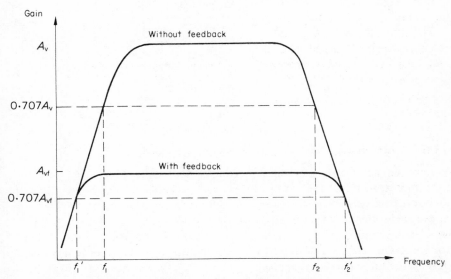

Fig. 13.4   Frequency response curve of an a.c. amplifier both before and after feedback is applied.

The bandwidth of the amplifier in the absence of feedback is $f_2 - f_1$, and its mid-band gain is A_v, giving an open-loop gain-bandwidth product of $A_v(f_2 - f_1)$. When series negative voltage feedback is applied, the cut-off frequencies become f_1' and f_2', respectively, where $f_1' = f_1/(1 - A_v\beta)$ and $f_2' = f_2(1 - A_v\beta)$*. The gain also falls to $A_{vf} (=A_v/[1 - A_v\beta])$. The closed-loop gain-bandwidth product is $V_{vf}(f_2' - f_1')$. Provided that the bandwidth is reasonably large, then the two gain-bandwidth products are found to be approximately equal. That is

$$A_v(f_2 - f_1) \simeq A_{vf}(f_2' - f_1') \qquad (13.13)$$

For example, if the gain of the amplifier is reduced by a factor of ten by the application of negative voltage feedback, then the bandwidth is increased tenfold.

13.4   The effects of series positive voltage feedback

Since a detailed treatment of the effects of negative feedback has been given above, it is not necessary to treat the equivalent positive feedback cases in depth. In general, the effects of positive feedback are opposite to those of negative feedback, and a summary of the more important results of the two forms of feedback are given in Table 13.1.

Table 13.1

A summary of the more important effects of series voltage feedback

	Form of feedback used	
	Negative	Positive
Gain	Reduced	Increased
Input impedance	Increased	Reduced
Output impedance	Reduced	Increased
Bandwidth	Increased	Reduced

13.5   Voltage summation using a resistive network

Voltage summation can be achieved by converting voltages into currents, and then summating the currents. The voltage developed across a resistor carrying the sum of the currents is then proportional to the sum of the voltages. This technique is utilized in the circuit in Fig. 13.5, where V_s would normally be the signal voltage source, V_2 the output voltage of the amplifier, and V_1 the input voltage to the amplifier. R_1 and R_f are resistors, and Z_1 is the input impedance of the circuit to which V_1 is applied.

* See Morris, N. M., *Control Engineering*, McGraw-Hill (1974).

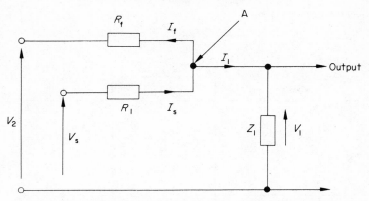

Fig. 13.5 Voltage summation using a resistive network.

Applying Kirchhoff's first law to the *summing junction* A in Fig. 13.5 yields

$$I_1 + I_f = I_s$$

or

$$\frac{V_1}{Z_1} + \frac{V_1 - V_2}{R_f} = \frac{V_s - V_1}{R_1}$$

or

$$V_1\left(\frac{1}{Z_1} + \frac{1}{R_f} + \frac{1}{R_1}\right) = \frac{V_2}{R_f} + \frac{V_s}{R_1}$$

If we let

$$Y = \frac{1}{Z_1} + \frac{1}{R_f} + \frac{1}{R_1},$$

then

$$V_1 = \frac{V_2}{R_f Y} + \frac{V_s}{R_1 Y} \qquad (13.14)$$

13.6 Shunt voltage negative feedback amplifiers

In the opening paragraphs of this chapter, it was stated that shunt feedback is applied by converting the input and output signals into currents, which are summated to form the amplifier input signal. This is achieved using the resistive network in Fig. 13.5, and its method of application to amplifiers is shown in Fig. 13.6.

A simplified explanation of the application of this method of feedback is as follows. The voltage V_1 developed at the input to the amplifier is $I_1 Z_1$, and since

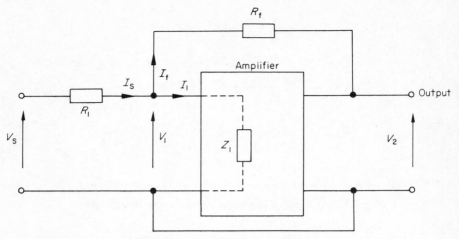

Fig. 13.6   Shunt voltage feedback.

$I_1 = (I_s - I_f)$ then $V_1 = Z_1(I_s - I_f)$. That is to say, the amplifier input voltage is proportional to the difference between the input current I_s and the current I_f in the feedback path. In turn, these are related to the input and output voltages, respectively, so that overall voltage feedback is applied around the amplifier.

13.6.1   Voltage gain A_{vf}

A detailed analysis of this type of circuit is more complex than for the series voltage feedback case, and a simplified analysis is given here. The basic assumptions made here are (1) the gain of the amplifier is large and it has a negative value, and (2) the input impedance is very large. The first assumption may be valid in almost any type of amplifier, but the second is not always true in the case of bipolar transistor circuits.

Now,

$$V_1 = -V_2/A_v \qquad (13.15)$$

and if A_v is very large then V_1 is very small, e.g., if $V_2 = -10$ V, and $A_v = -10^6$ (as it may be in operational amplifiers), then $V_1 = 10 \ \mu V$. In basic calculations, therefore, we may assume that $V_1 \simeq 0$. For this reason, the junction of the summing resistors is referred to as a *virtual earth*. Hence, in Fig. 13.6,

$$I_s = I_f \quad \text{or} \quad \frac{V_s}{R_1} = -\frac{V_2}{R_f} \qquad (13.16)$$

$$A_{vf} = V_2/V_s = -R_f/R_1 \qquad (13.17)$$

For example, if $R_f = 1$ MΩ and $R_s = 0.1$ MΩ, then $A_{vf} = -10$.

A detailed analysis yields an expression for gain of

$$A_{vf} = \frac{A_v}{R_1 Y} \bigg/ \left(1 - \frac{A_v}{R_1 Y}\right) \qquad (13.18)$$

$$= A_{vs}/(1 - A_{vs}\beta_s) \qquad (13.19)$$

where Y is defined in section 13.5. In eq. (13.19) A_{vs} is the forward gain $(=A_v/R_1 Y)$ of the shunt feedback amplifier, and β_s $(=R_1/R_f)$ is its effective feedback factor. The similarity between eqs. (13.19) and (13.3) should be noted. The effect of loading can be dealt with in much the same way as for the series feedback case.

Amplifiers of this type are sometimes known as *see-saw amplifiers,* since the input and output voltages appear to pivot about the virtual earth point.

13.6.2   Input impedance Z_{1f} of the shunt feedback amplifier

Assuming that the summing junction is a virtual earth, the input resistance is seen to be approximately equal to R_1. A detailed analysis yields the expression

$$Z_{1f} = R_1 + Z_1 R_f/(R_f + Z_1[1 - A_v]) \qquad (13.20)$$

13.6.3   Output impedance Z_{2f} of the shunt feedback amplifier

To a first approximation, the output impedance is the parallel combination of Z_2 and R_f (since R_f is 'earthed' at one end by the virtual earth).

$$Z_{2f} \simeq Z_2 R_f/(Z_2 + R_f) \qquad (13.21)$$

Example 13.3: Determine the voltage gain, the input impedance, and the output impedance of a shunt voltage feedback amplifier in which $R_1 = 10\ k\Omega$, $R_f = 200\ k\Omega$, gain $= -200$, $R_s = 1\ k\Omega$, $Z_1 = 1\ k\Omega$, and $Z_2 = 20\ k\Omega$.

Solution:

$$A_{vf} = -R_f/R_1 - 200/10 = -20$$

(the true gain is -9.5, due largely to the low value of Z_1)

$$Z_{1f} \simeq R_1 = 10\ k\Omega$$

(to be compared with the more accurate value of $10.5\ k\Omega$)

$$Z_{2f} = 20 \times 200/(20 + 200) = 18.2\ k\Omega$$

(the true value is $17.9\ k\Omega$).

13.7   Series current negative feedback

In a current feedback amplifier, the signal fed back is proportional to the output current. As with any feedback amplifier, it is the signal which is fed back that is maintained at a constant level, and in this case the output current is maintained at a value set by the input voltage signal. As a consequence of this, the series current feedback amplifier has a very high output impedance, a fact which is verified in section 13.7.4.

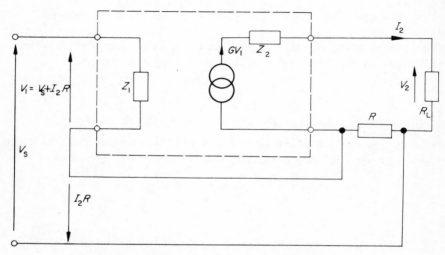

Fig. 13.7   A series positive current feedback amplifier.

Figure 13.7 shows a block diagram of a series current positive feedback amplifier. The current flowing in the output circuit develops a voltage $I_2 R$ across resistor R, which is added in series with the input signal V_s. The net voltage applied to the amplifier input is

$$V_1 = V_s + I_2 R \qquad (13.22)$$

Since the forward gain or *transconductance* of the amplifier is G A/V, then the current generated by the internal generator within the amplifier is GV_1 A.

13.7.1   No-load transconductance G_f

No-load conditions correspond to the case where the power delivered to the load is zero. A current amplifier theoretically continues to deliver current to the load so long as an input signal is applied. Thus, no-load conditions in a current amplifier correspond to the case where the voltage developed across the load is zero, i.e., when $R_L = 0$. Since the resistance of resistor R is usually much less than the value of Z_2, the following relationship holds good

$$I_2 = GV_1 \quad \text{or} \quad V_1 = I_2/G$$

Eliminating V_1 between the above expression and eq. (13.22) yields the no-load closed-loop transconductance G_f

$$G_f = \frac{I_2}{V_s} = \frac{G}{1 - GR} \tag{13.23}$$

If this equation is compared with equivalent equations for the two voltage feedback cases, eqs. (13.3) and (13.19), it is seen that the 'β' value for Fig. 13.7 is equal to R, and has the dimensions of resistance.

In the *negative feedback case,* using an amplifier of gain $-G$, if the product GR has a value much greater than unity, then

$$G_f = \frac{-G}{GR} = \frac{-1}{R}$$

That is,

$$\frac{I_2}{V_s} = \frac{-1}{R} \quad \text{or} \quad I_2 = -V_s/R \tag{13.24}$$

By this means, the output current is dependent on the input voltage and the feedback resistor R, and is independent of the transconductance of the amplifier.

13.7.2 No-load impedance Z_{1f}

The no-load input impedance is calculated with $R_L = 0$. The current drawn from the signal source is

$$I_s = \frac{V_1}{Z_1} = \frac{V_s + I_2 R}{Z_1}$$

Eliminating I_2 between the above equation and eq. (13.23) yields the input impedance

$$Z_{1f} = \frac{V_s}{I_s} = Z_1(1 - GR) \tag{13.25}$$

If positive feedback is applied (i.e., the product GR has a positive value), then Z_{1f} is less than Z_1; with negative feedback Z_{1f} is greater than Z_1.

13.7.3   Effect of an external load on current feedback amplifiers

When the load resistor has a finite value, the load current falls below the theoretical value of GV_1, reducing the effective gain of the amplifier. This modifies the closed-loop constants as follows:

$$G_f = G_l/(1 - G_l R) \quad \text{and} \quad Z_{1f} = Z_1(1 - G_l R)$$

where

$$G_l = GZ_2/(Z_2 + R_L + R)$$

13.7.4   Output impedance Z_{2f}

The output impedance is calculated by the same method used hitherto, that is the system is energized at its output terminals, and the signal source is replaced by its internal impedance. This gives an expression for the output impedance of the form

$$Z_{2f} = Z_2 + R - \frac{GRZ_1Z_2}{R_s + Z_1} \tag{13.26}$$

which may be simplified if $Z_2 \gg R$ and $Z_1 \gg R_s$, when

$$Z_{2f} \simeq Z_2(1 - GR) \tag{13.27}$$

If positive current feedback is employed (i.e., the product GR has a positive value), then Z_{2f} has a value which is less than Z_2. By altering the value of the product GR, the output impedance can be made zero, or even negative. In the latter case, an increased value of load resistance results in an increased load current. If negative feedback is employed, Z_{2f} is greater than Z_2.

Example 13.4: Calculate the closed-loop transconductance or gain of an amplifier similar to that in Fig. 9.7 if $G = -50$ mA/V, $Z_1 = 10$ kΩ, $Z_2 = 50$ kΩ, $R_L = 2$ kΩ, $R = 1$ kΩ, and $R_s = 5$ Ω. What is the magnitude of V_s to ensure a load current of 10 mA?

Solution: The load modifies the amplifier gain to

$$G_l = -50 \times 50/(50 + 2 + 1) = -47 \cdot 2 \text{ mA/V}$$

Hence,

$$G_f = -47 \cdot 2/(1 - [-47 \cdot 2 \times 1]) = -0 \cdot 98 \text{ mA/V}$$

(The value given by the no-load equation (eq. (13.23)) is 1 mA/V.)

$$Z_{1f} = 10(1 - [-47 \cdot 2 \times 1]) = 482 \text{ k}\Omega$$

(Equation (13.25) gives value of 510 kΩ.)

The output impedance, from eq. (13.26), is

$$Z_{2f} = 50 + 1 - \frac{-50 \times 1 \times 10 \times 50}{0.005 + 10} = 2551 \text{ k}\Omega$$

(the result from the approximate equation, eq. (13.27), is 2550 kΩ).

Since the closed-loop gain is -0.98 mA/V, the source voltage to maintain an output current of 10 mA into a load of 2 kΩ is

$$V_s = \frac{10}{-0.98} = -10.2 \text{ V}$$

Since the output impedance of this circuit is greater than 2·5 MΩ, the load current will be substantially constant at 10 mA over a range of load resistance values from zero to about 200 kΩ.

13.7.5 Application of current feedback to a voltage amplifier

In some applications it is desirable to apply current feedback to a voltage amplifier. The block diagram remains as in Fig. 13.7, but the output from the circuit is V_2 (the voltage across R_L) and not I_2. Since series current feedback is applied, then $V_s \simeq - I_2 R$. Now $V_2 = I_2 R_L$, so that $I_2 = V_2/R_L$, hence $V_s = - V_2 R/R_L$. The voltage gain is, therefore,

$$A_{vf} = V_2/V_s = -R_L/R$$

13.8 Measurement of system constants

It is frequently necessary to measure such constants as gain, input impedance, output impedance, and bandwidth. These constants can be measured by relatively simple methods using only an oscillator, a high impedance voltmeter and resistors, preferably in the form of a calibrated decade resistance box.

The voltage gain at any frequency is measured simply by determining the ratio of the output voltage to the source voltage at that frequency. The bandwidth is the band of frequencies between the points at which the gain falls to 0·707 of the mid-band gain (see Fig. 13.4).

To determine the input impedance, it is first necessary to measure the voltage gain of the stage in the manner described above. Let its value be A_{v1}. A resistance R_1 is then connected in series with the input of the amplifier, and the gain is again measured. Let its value be A_{v2}. In the latter case, the voltage applied to the amplifier terminals is

$$V_{sf} = \frac{Z_1}{Z_1 + R_1} V_s$$

where Z_1 is the input impedance of the amplifier. The output voltage from the amplifier is

$$V_2 = A_{v1} V_{sf} = A_{v1} \frac{Z_1}{Z_1 + R_1} V_s$$

hence,

$$A_{v2} = A_{v1} \frac{Z_1}{Z_1 + R_1}$$

therefore,

$$Z_1 = \frac{R_1}{\dfrac{A_{v1}}{A_{v2}} - 1}$$

If, for example $A_{v1}/A_{v2} = 1 \cdot 1, R_1 = 1 \text{ k}\Omega$, then $Z_1 = 10 \text{ k}\Omega$.

The output impedance can be measured by determining the gain with a load resistor R_2 connected between its output terminals. Let its value be A_{v3}. If the gain in the absence of R_2 is A_{v1}, then the additional load reduces the output voltage to

$$V_2 = A_{v1} V_s \frac{R_2}{R_2 + Z_2}$$

where V_s is the input signal voltage applied to the amplifier, and Z_2 is the output impedance of the amplifier.

Hence,

$$A_{v3} = \frac{V_2}{V_s} = A_{v1} \frac{R_2}{R_2 + Z_2}$$

therefore,

$$Z_2 = R_2 \left(\frac{A_{v1}}{A_{v3}} - 1 \right)$$

In an actual circuit, if $A_{v1}/A_{v3} = 1 \cdot 1$ and $R_2 = 50 \text{ k}\Omega$, then $Z_2 = 5 \text{ k}\Omega$. These techniques can be applied to amplifiers both with, and without, feedback applied.

13.9 Stability of feedback amplifiers

It was stated in section 13.2 that unstable operation could occur in feedback amplifiers under certain conditions. To deduce the general conditions for instability, the equations for the no-load gain of the positive feedback amplifiers discussed in this chapter are rewritten here

$$A_{vf} = A_v/(1 - A_v \beta) \tag{13.3}$$

$$A_{vf} = A_{vs}/(1 - A_{vs}\beta_s) \tag{13.19}$$

$$G_f = G/(1 - GR) \tag{13.23}$$

An inspection shows, in each case, that the closed-loop gain becomes infinity when the loop gain ($A_v\beta$ or GR) is unity. This constitutes an unstable operating state, since an output can exist when $V_s = 0$.

The equivalent equations for negative feedback circuits, using phase-inverting amplifiers, are

$$A_{vf} = -A_v/(1 + A_v\beta)$$

$$A_{vf} = -A_{vs}/(1 + A_{vs}\beta_s)$$

$$G_f = -G/(1 + GR)$$

Instability occurs in these amplifiers when the loop gain is -1. The conditions for instability for both positive and negative feedback amplifiers are seen to be the same, if the sign of A_v (or G) is borne in mind.

Instability thus occurs when the loop gain is unity and the loop phase-shift is zero, simultaneously.

If the loop gain is less than unity when the loop phase-shift is zero, then the closed-loop amplifier is stable, but if the loop gain is equal to, or greater than, unity then the closed-loop amplifier is unstable, and the output is oscillatory.

The general procedure to determine the stability of a feedback amplifier is as follows. Firstly, the feedback loop is broken or opened at one point, a convenient point for this operation being at the input to the amplifier. The normal signal source V_s (see Fig. 13.2) is removed and replaced by its internal resistance. A signal V_x is then injected into the amplifier, and the magnitude and phase-shift of the signal after it has been amplified around the loop are measured. This test is then repeated over a range of frequencies. If the magnitude of the signal after it has passed round the loop is V_y, and its phase-shift with respect to V_x is ϕ, then the loop gain is

$$A_v\beta = \frac{V_y}{V_x} \angle \phi$$

The locus of $A_v\beta$, as it changes with frequency, is then plotted on polar graph paper, and the resulting curve is known as a *Nyquist plot*. Alternatively, if the gain and phase-shift are plotted separately to a base of frequency, the combined graphs are known as *Bode diagrams*. If, at some frequency ω_p, the loop gain is greater than unity when the loop phase-shift is zero, then the amplifier will be unstable when the loop is closed and the output voltage will oscillate at that frequency. Frequency ω_p is known as the *phase crossover frequency*. If the loop gain is less than unity at the phase crossover frequency, then the loop may be closed and the amplifier will operate in a stable manner.

Circuits which depend for their operation on unstable conditions existing are known as *oscillators*, which are dealt with in chapter 15. The detailed theory of frequency response tests, together with the application of Nyquist and Bode diagrams, is beyond the scope of this book, and is available elsewhere*.

13.10 Simplified valve and transistor equations

In this section, we deduce simplified equations relating valve and transistor parameters to the terms A_v, G, Z_1, and Z_2 used in this chapter.

For the valve, the input impedance is very high and is assumed to be infinity. Its output impedance is equal to r_a, and its voltage gain is equal to $-\mu$ (the negative sign implies phase-inversion). Using the voltage-to-current generator conversion for the valve

$$G = \frac{\text{Voltage gain}}{\text{Output impedance}} = \frac{-\mu}{r_a} = -g_m$$

In the case of the bipolar transistor, it is convenient to deduce the constants in terms of the general h-parameters h_i, h_r, h_f, and h_o. The resulting equations can then be used in any of the transistor configurations. Also, to simplify the computations, the reverse parameter h_r is neglected. The input current is given by $I_1 = V_1/h_i$, hence $Z_1 = h_i$. Similarly the output impedance is $1/h_o$; since the internal current generator develops a current of $-h_f I_1 = -h_f V_1/h_i$, the effective transconductance of the transistor is $-h_f/h_i$. When converted into its constant voltage equivalent, the value of A_v for the transistor is found to be $-h_f/h_i h_o$. The results are summarized in Table 13.2.

Table 13.2

	Valve	Transistor	FET
Z_1	∞	h_i	∞
Z_2	r_a	$\dfrac{1}{h_o}$	r_d
A_v	$-\mu$	$\dfrac{-h_f}{h_i h_o}$	$-r_d g_m$
G	$-g_m$	$\dfrac{-h_f}{h_i}$	$-g_m$

Problems

13.1 Show from first principles that:
  (a) Series negative voltage feedback reduces the output impedance of an amplifier.
  (b) Series negative current feedback increases the output impedance of an amplifier.

* See Morris, N. M., *Control Engineering*, McGraw-Hill (1974).

13.2 If the gain of an amplifier without feedback is represented by A_v, derive an expression for the gain when a fraction β of the output voltage is fed back in opposition to the input.

In an amplifier with a constant input of 1 volt the output falls from 50 to 25 volts when feedback is applied. Calculate the fraction of the output which is fed back. If due to ageing, the amplifier gain fell to 40, find the percentage reduction in stage gain:

  (i) without feedback
  (ii) with the feedback connection.

13.3 An amplifier has a voltage amplification A_v and a fraction, β, of its output is fed back in opposition to its input. If $\beta = 0\cdot1$ and $A_v = 100$, calculate the change in the gain of the system if A_v falls 6 dB due to ageing. Thence, or otherwise, give one advantage arising from the introduction of negative feedback. What other advantages result?

13.4 If the gain of an amplifier stage without feedback is represented by A_v, derive an expression for the gain when a fraction β of the output voltage is fed back in opposition to the input.

An amplifier has a gain of 1000 without feedback. Calculate the gain when 0·9 per cent of negative feedback is applied. If due to ageing, the gain without feedback falls to 800, calculate the percentage reduction in gain

  (a) Without feedback.
  (b) With feedback.

Comment on the significance of the results of (a) and (b), and state two other advantages of negative feedback.

13.5 Show that series negative voltage feedback (a) stabilizes the no-load gain of an amplifier against change in the amplifier gain, (b) reduces the output impedance, and (c) increases the input impedance of the amplifier.

If the gain of the amplifier is 45 and it has input and output impedances of 200 and 0·5 Ω, respectively, in the absence of feedback calculate the input and output impedance if 20 per cent of the output voltage is fed back. What is the percentage change in the no-load closed-loop gain if the forward gain of the amplifier is changed by 5 per cent?

13.6 An amplifier has a constant signal input of 2 V and an output of 40 V when series negative voltage feedback is applied. The output increases to 60 V when the feedback signal is removed. Calculate the fraction of the output signal that is fed back.

If the amplifier gain fell to 20, calculate the percentage reduction in gain, (i) without feedback, and (ii) with the feedback connection.

13.7 Discuss the effects of negative and positive series current feedback on the steady-state output impedance of amplifiers.

A d.c. amplifier with an output impedance of 1 kΩ supplies a current of 3 mA at a terminal voltage of 7 V when the input to the amplifier is 0·2 V. Calculate the effective output impedance if this amplifier is used in a closed-loop amplifier of the type shown in Fig. 13.7 when using (a) negative current feedback, and (b) positive current feedback if $Z_2 = 1$ kΩ and $R = 10$ Ω. The input impedance of the amplifier is infinite.

If overall negative voltage feedback is then applied in conjunction with positive current feedback, determine the value of β (the amount of voltage feedback used) to reduce the net output impedance to 50 Ω.

13.8 An amplifier has a gain of 60 dB without feedback and 30 dB when feedback is applied. If the gain without feedback changes to 55 dB calculate the new gain with feedback.

14. Negative feedback amplifiers

14.1 Basic types of feedback amplifier

Practical examples of the way in which negative feedback is applied to transistor circuits are illustrated in Fig. 14.1. The block diagrams in Fig. 13.1 correspond to the circuits in Fig. 14.1. The bias arrangements for the circuits in Fig. 14.1 have been omitted for clarity. In Fig. 14.1(a), the output voltage V_O is developed across the resistor in the emitter line. The whole of this voltage is fed back in series opposition to the input signal V_{in}, so that 100 per cent *series negative voltage feedback* is applied. This circuit is known as an *emitter follower*, and is described in detail later in this chapter. In the circuit in Fig. 14.1(b), the output voltage is applied to one end of the feedback resistor R_f and the current through this resistor is added to the current drawn from the input source V_{in} at junction S. The phase relationship between V_{in} and V_O in this circuit is such that *shunt negative voltage feedback* is applied to the amplifier.

The circuit in Fig. 14.1(c) differs from that in Fig. 14.1(a) in that the load resistance R_L is connected in series with the collector line. Resistor R in the emitter lead has a value which is generally much lower than that of R_L, and the value of the voltage across R is proportional to the current flowing in the load resistor R_L. The phase relationships of the voltages in the circuit are such that the p.d. across R reduces the value of V_1 below that of V_{in}. Since the p.d. across R is effectively in series with the input signal, then this circuit has *series negative current feedback* applied to it. An analysis of this circuit shows that the magnitude of the voltage gain is approximately equal to R_L/R; if $R_L = 6 \cdot 8$ kΩ and $R = 470$ Ω, then the magnitude of the voltage gain of Fig. 14.1(c) is about $14 \cdot 5$.

The circuit in Fig. 14.1(d), in which *shunt negative current feedback* is applied, is more complex than the other circuits because it involves two stages of amplification. In this circuit, the load resistance R_L is in the collector circuit of *TR*2. Resistor R in the emitter circuit of *TR*2 carries a current

210

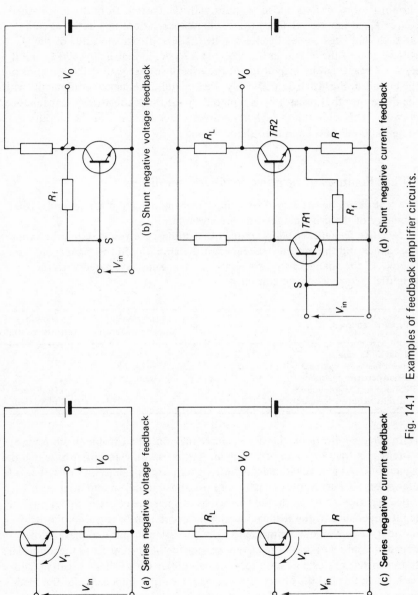

Fig. 14.1 Examples of feedback amplifier circuits.

which is nearly equal in value to the load current. The voltage developed across this resistor is applied to one end of the feedback resistor R_f; the current flowing in R_f is added in shunt with the current from the input signal source V_{in} at junction S. Once more, the phase relationships in the circuit are such that negative feedback is applied. The approximate value of the voltage gain of the circuit in Fig. 14.1(d) is R_f/R, so that if $R = 470 \ \Omega$ and if $R_f = 4\cdot7 \ k\Omega$, then the magnitude of the overall voltage gain is 10. Versions of the circuit in Fig. 14.1(d) are widely used in audio frequency equipment, with the difference that resistor R_f is replaced by a complex resistance–capacitance network. This allows the frequency response characteristic of the amplifier to be 'tailored' to the required shape.

14.2   Features of negative feedback amplifiers

The features of negative feedback amplifiers are many and varied, and a brief summary of the principal features are given here.

Negative feedback affects, among other things, the voltage gain, the input impedance and the output impedance of the amplifier in the manner shown below. All the changes listed are relative to the value associated with the amplifier *before* feedback is applied.

Type of feedback	Effect on the gain	Effect on the input resistance	Effect on the output resistance
Negative feedback	Reduced		
Shunt negative feedback		Reduced	
Series negative feedback		Increased	
Voltage negative feedback			Reduced
Current negative feedback			Increased

In some applications, the signal source may only be capable of supplying a current of a fraction of a microampere. In this case, the amplifier to which the signal source is connected must have a high input impedance in order that it draws very little current. Clearly, from the above table, an amplifier with series negative feedback should be used as this has the effect of increasing the input impedance of the feedback amplifier above that of the amplifier itself. In other cases, the load connected to the amplifier output may have a low impedance and will draw a relatively large value of current from the amplifier. In this instance, it is necessary to use an amplifier with voltage negative feedback, since this has the effect of reducing the output impedance of the feedback amplifier below that of the amplifier itself. Hence, a feedback amplifier with series negative voltage feedback applied has the properties of a higher input impedance and a lower output impedance than that of the basic amplifier used within the circuit. An amplifier of this kind was illustrated in Fig. 14.1(a).

Negative feedback also improves the gain stability of the amplifier against variations occurring within the circuit; this was illustrated in section 13.3. It also increases the bandwidth of the feedback amplifier above that of the basic amplifier. It can be shown that the gain–bandwidth product of a feedback amplifier remains constant, irrespective of the amount of feedback applied (see also section 13.3.7). If the amount of feedback applied causes the numerical gain to reduce by a factor of ten, it also increases the bandwidth of the amplifier by ten times.

Negative feedback can also reduce the amount of distortion in the output signal, providing that it was not too excessive before the feedback was applied.

14.3 Emitter follower and cathode follower circuits

These are perhaps the simplest to understand of all of the feedback amplifier circuits. Examples of practical circuits for a.c. applications are shown in Fig. 14.2. The bias current for the emitter follower, Fig. 14.2(a), is bled from the power supply via R_B; this ensures that a steady potential appears at the emitter under no-signal conditions.

If the potential of the base region with respect to the common line is v_B, then

$$v_B = V_2 + v_{BE}$$

where v_{BE} is the total instantaneous base-emitter voltage, which normally has a value between 0.2 V and 0.8 V. Since v_{BE} is generally small compared with V_2, then

$$V_2 \simeq v_B$$

That is to say, the output voltage 'follows' variations in the input signal, hence the name emitter follower. Since the net input voltage v_{BE} to the amplifying device is the difference between the input and output signal voltages, the emitter follower is a series negative voltage feedback amplifier with 100 per cent feedback ($\beta = 1.0$). Emitter followers and cathode followers are also known as *common-collector amplifiers* and *common-anode amplifiers* respectively.

In the cathode follower, v_{GK} is small compared with V_2, and the cathode potential 'follows' the grid potential. This argument also shows that output voltage is in phase with the input signal, since an increase in the input voltage V_s causes v_B (in the transistor circuit) and V_2 to increase by approximately the same amount.

In the cathode follower, Fig. 14.2(b), the bias voltage is obtained by dividing the cathode resistor R_K into two parts, the grid being returned to the common connection by R_g, which usually has a value of several megohms. The function of this form of connection is to provide a very high input resistance, and to ensure that the grid remains at a negative potential with respect to the cathode at all times.

Two other features of importance in these circuits are their high input impedance and low output impedance. The former results from the fact that the output voltage is practically equal in magnitude to the input voltage; negative feedback reduces the net input voltage to the active device to a small value, so that only a small current flows from the signal source. Suppose that

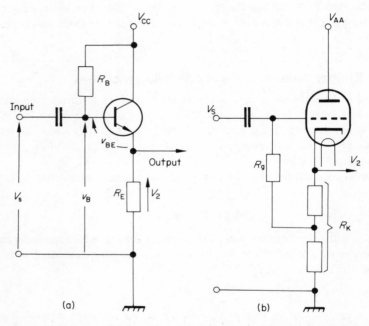

Fig. 14.2   (a) An emitter follower circuit, and (b) a cathode follower circuit.

the small-signal gain of an emitter follower is 0·95 and that the input impedance of the transistor is 1 kΩ. An input signal of 1 V gives rise to an output of 0·95 V, hence the signal voltage applied to the transistor is 0·05 V. The signal current flowing into the transistor base is, therefore, 0·05 V/1 kΩ = 50 μA, which is drawn from the input signal source. Since the actual input voltage is 1 V, the apparent input impedance of the circuit is 1 V/50 μA = 20 kΩ, which is much greater than the input impedance of the transistor.

The low output impedance results from the use of 100 per cent negative feedback, as follows. If the loading conditions are suddenly changed, say the load resistance is reduced, the output voltage tends to change—a reduction in this case. This causes the net input voltage ($V_s - V_2$) applied to the active device (transistor or valve) to change (an increase in the case of a bipolar transistor and a reduction in the case of a valve). This in turn causes the current flowing through the load to increase, so that the output voltage rises to a value which is nearly equal to the original value. Since the output voltage remains substantially constant over a wide range of loading conditions, the output impedance appears to have a low value.

To summarize, the principal features of interest are:

(a) The gain is approximately unity.
(b) The amplifier is non-phase inverting.
(c) The input impedance is high.
(d) The output impedance is low.

The above features make the emitter follower and cathode follower useful as *unity gain buffer amplifiers*; they are described as buffer amplifiers since they impose very little electrical load on the input signal source, yet have a sufficiently low value of output impedance to be able to 'drive' current into a relatively low impedance load, such as a transmission line. The name *voltage followers* is sometimes given to the general family of circuits having these characteristics.
A simplified analysis of the emitter follower is now given in which it is assumed that the input impedance of the transistor is equal to h_{ie}, that $h_{fe} \gg 1$, and that $R_E h_{fe}/h_{ie} \gg 1$.

Voltage gain

$$I_e = (h_{fe} + 1)I_b \simeq h_{fe}I_b$$

$$V_2 = R_E I_e \simeq R_E h_{fe}I_b \simeq R_E h_{fe}(V_s - V_2)/h_{ie}$$

Collecting terms

$$A_{vf} = \frac{V_2}{V_s} = \frac{R_E h_{fe}/h_{ie}}{1 + R_E h_{fe}/h_{ie}} \simeq 1 \tag{14.1}$$

Input impedance
From the work on voltage gain, $(V_s - V_2) \simeq V_2 h_{ie}/R_E h_{fe}$

$$Z_{1f} = \frac{V_s}{I_b} \simeq \frac{V_s}{(V_s - V_2)/h_{ie}} \simeq \frac{V_s}{V_2 h_{ie}/h_{ie} R_E h_{fe}} = R_E h_{fe}\frac{V_s}{V_2}$$

$$\simeq R_E h_{fe} \tag{14.2}$$

Output impedance
The open-circuit output voltage from the amplifier is

$$V_{oc} \simeq V_s$$

If the output terminals are short-circuited, then $V_2 = 0$ and the signal fed back is zero; in this mode of operation V_s is applied directly to the amplifier, and the base current is

$$I_{b(sc)} \simeq V_s/h_{ie}$$

and the current flowing in the emitter short-circuit is

$$I_{sc} = h_{fe}I_{b(sc)} = h_{fe}V_s/h_{ie}$$

Hence

$$Z_{2f} = V_{oc}/I_{sc} = V_s/(h_{fe}V_s/h_{ie}) = h_{ie}/h_{re} \qquad (14.3)$$

Thus if $h_{ie} = 1$ kΩ, $h_{fe} = 50$, $R_E = 1$ kΩ, then $A_{vf} = 0.98$, $Z_{1f} = 50$ kΩ and $Z_{2f} = 20$ Ω.

The current gain is given by

$$A_{if} = I_e/I_b = (1 + h_{fe})I_b/I_b = 1 + h_{fe} \qquad (14.4)$$

Example 14.1: A transistor whose h-parameters are given below, is used in an emitter follower with an emitter load of 5 kΩ. Evaluate the voltage gain, the current gain, the input resistance and the output resistance of the stage.

$$h_{ie} = 1500 \ \Omega$$
$$h_{fe} = 60$$

Solution:

$$A_{vf} = (R_E h_{fe}/h_{ie})/(1 + R_E h_{fe}/h_{ie})$$
$$= (5000 \times 60/1500)/(1 + 5000 \times 60/1500) \simeq 1$$

Current gain, $A_{if} = 1 + h_{fe} = 1 + 60 = 61$

Input resistance, $Z_{1f} = R_E h_{fe} = 5000 \times 60 \ \Omega = 300$ kΩ

Output resistance, $Z_{2f} = h_{ie}/h_{fe} = 1500/60 = 25 \ \Omega$

14.4 The source follower

Another form of voltage follower, the *source follower*, is shown in Fig. 14.3. An important feature of this circuit is that its input impedance is even higher than that of the emitter follower; an input impedance of many megohms can easily be obtained. This feature follows from the fact that an FET is used as the active device in the amplifier.

The FET bias voltage is derived from a self-bias circuit consisting of resistor R_B shunted by capacitor C_B, which is in series with the FET source electrode. The bias voltage is developed across R_B by the flow of the FET quiescent current through it. This voltage is applied to the gate of the FET by resistor R_G, which has a value in the range 1 MΩ to 10 MΩ. Capacitor C_B is a bypass capacitor whose reactance at the operating frequency is small compared to the resistance of R_B. It effectively provides an a.c. short-circuit to R_B, so that variations in the input signal are closely followed by the output terminal. Capacitors C_1 and C_2 and d.c. blocking capacitors, and permit the input and

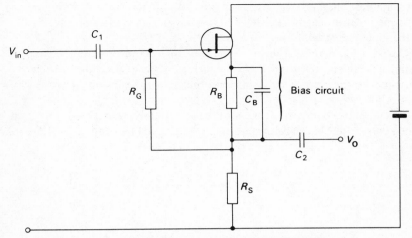

Fig. 14.3   A practical version of a source follower circuit.

output signals V_{in} and V_O, respectively, to be transmitted through them with very little loss.

An increase in the value of V_{in} in Fig. 14.3 causes the current through the FET to increase and, with it, the output voltage increases. As a result, the potential of the output terminal closely 'follows' the input signal variations. The source follower has the following features, which are also common to the emitter follower circuit:

(a) It has a voltage gain of nearly unity and is a non-inverting amplifier.
(b) It has a high input impedance.
(c) It has a low output impedance.

A simplified analysis of the source follower gives

$$\text{Voltage gain, } A_{vf} = g_m R_S/(1 + g_m R_S) \tag{14.5}$$

$$\text{Output impedance, } Z_{2f} = 1/g_m \tag{14.6}$$

$$\text{Current gain, } A_{if} \to \infty$$

$$\text{Input impedance, } Z_{1f} \to \infty$$

Note: the above value of input impedance neglects the effect of the bias circuit. Making allowance for this, the input impedance is

$$Z_{1f} = R_G/(1 - A_{vf}) \tag{14.7}$$

14.5   A series current feedback amplifier

One form of series current feedback amplifier, the *paraphase amplifier* or *single-stage phase splitter,* is shown in Fig. 14.4. This circuit provides two anti-phase outputs V_2 and V_2' which can be used to drive a push-pull output stage. In the latter application, $R_L = R_E$, and since the collector and emitter currents are of the same order of magnitude, the voltage gains at each of the outputs relative to the input are equal.

Output V_2' is derived from an emitter resistor, and this part of the circuit is similar to an emitter follower. Consequently, V_2' is of the same order of magnitude as the input signal, and the output impedance is low by virtue of the emitter follower effect.

This amplifier is almost identical to the one dealt with in section 13.7.5, in which current feedback was applied to a voltage amplifier. In Fig. 14.4, we may

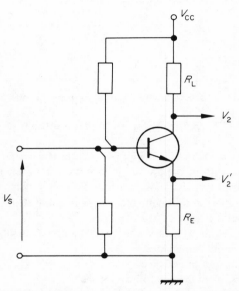

Fig. 14.4   A paraphase amplifier using only one transistor.

assume that $I_c = I_e = I$, say. Now, by emitter follower action, $V_s \simeq V_2' = IR_E$, hence, $I \simeq V_s/R_E$. Also, $V_2 = -IR_L = -V_sR_L/R_E$. Therefore,

$$\text{Voltage gain at the collector} = V_2/V_s = -R_L/R_E \qquad (14.8)$$

and

$$V_2/V_2' = -R_L/R_E \qquad (14.9)$$

14.6   Hybrid feedback circuits

In order to obtain a desired combination of features, it may be necessary to use the combined effects of more than one method of feedback. For example, to achieve a very high gain it may be necessary to incorporate some measure of positive feedback within the amplifier. However, positive feedback can lead to instability (see section 13.9), and it is usual in such cases to apply some overall negative feedback to give stability.

14.7   Operational amplifier circuits

The operational amplifier (see also chapter 11) is a versatile device which can be used in many feedback configurations. An ideal op-amp has an infinitely high value of voltage gain and an infinite input impedance; the values associated with practical amplifiers are not infinite, but are very high (see Table 11.1). The output voltage from an op-amp is given by

$$V_O = A_v V_i$$

where A_v is the voltage gain of the amplifier and V_i is the differential input voltage between the non-inverting and inverting inputs of the amplifier. If A_v is very large (ideally infinite), then

$$V_i = V_O/A_v \to 0$$

For example, if $V_O = 10$ V and $A_v = 10^6$, then $V_i = 10\ \mu$V. When compared to the output of 10 V, the differential input of 10 μV can be taken for all intents and purposes to be zero.

14.7.1   Unity-gain non-inverting buffer amplifier

The circuit is shown in Fig. 14.5, and readers will note that one hundred per cent series negative voltage feedback is applied. From the above theory, $V_i \simeq 0$, hence for Fig. 14.5

$$V_P - V_N = V_i = 0$$

or

$$V_P = V_N$$

hence

$$\text{Voltage gain, } A_{vf} = \frac{V_O}{V_{\text{input}}} = \frac{V_N}{V_P} = +1 \qquad (14.10)$$

The circuit in Fig. 14.5 is a near-perfect voltage follower amplifier (that is, V_O follows V_P) and has a very high input resistance and a very low output resistance.

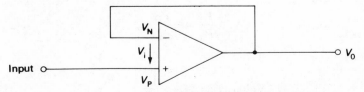

Fig. 14.5   A unity-gain non-inverting buffer amplifier.

14.7.2   A non-inverting amplifier

Series negative voltage feedback is also applied to the amplifier in Fig. 14.6, and once again $V_i \simeq 0$, but in this case V_N is the voltage at the junction of R_1 and R_2, hence

$$V_N = \frac{R_1 V_O}{R_1 + R_2}$$

But since $V_P \simeq V_N$ then

$$\text{Voltage gain, } A_{vf} = \frac{V_O}{V_P} = \frac{V_O}{V_N} = \frac{R_1 + R_2}{R_1} = 1 + \frac{R_2}{R_1} \qquad (14.11)$$

The minimum gain of the amplifier is unity when $R_2 = 0$, and it has a very large value of gain when $R_2 \gg R_1$.

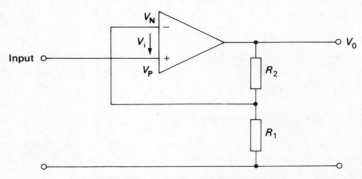

Fig. 14.6   A non-inverting amplifier.

14.7.3   An inverting amplifier

In Fig. 14.7, shunt negative voltage feedback is applied to the amplifier. Again $V_i \simeq 0$, hence $V_N \simeq V_P$; that is V_N is virtually at earth potential and the junction of R_1 and R_f can be regarded as a *virtual earth* point. Since $V_i \simeq 0$, no current flows into the inverting input (the '−' input) of the amplifier, hence $I_1 = I_f$. Now

$$I_1 = (V_1 - V_N)/R_1 \quad \text{and} \quad I_f = (V_N - V_O)/R_f$$

but since $V_N \simeq 0$, then $I_1 = V_1/R_1$ and $I_f = -V_O/R_f$, hence

$$\frac{V_1}{R_1} = -\frac{V_O}{R_f}$$

Therefore

$$\text{Voltage gain, } A_{vf} = \frac{V_O}{V_1} = -\frac{R_f}{R_1} \qquad (14.12)$$

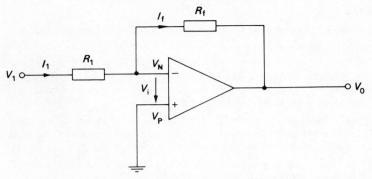

Fig. 14.7   An inverting amplifier.

The negative sign associated with eq. (14.12) implies that the amplifier is phase inverting, and if R_f = 100 kΩ and R_1 = 10 kΩ, then A_{vf} = −10.

14.7.4   Inverting summing amplifier

A simple amplifier circuit which adds several signals together is shown in Fig. 14.8. An expression for the output voltage of this amplifier is

$$V_O = -\left(\frac{R_f}{R_1} V_1 + \frac{R_f}{R_2} V_2 + \frac{R_f}{R_3} V_3\right)$$

For example, if R_f = 100 kΩ, R_1 = 10 kΩ, R_2 = 47 kΩ, R_3 = 100 kΩ, V_1 = +1·5 V, V_2 = −2 V and V_3 = 0·5 V, then

$$V_O = -\left(\left[\frac{100}{10} \times 1·5\right] + \left[\frac{100}{47} \times (-2)\right] + \left[\frac{100}{100} \times 0·5\right]\right)$$

$$= -(15 + (-4·26) + 0·5) = -11·24 \text{ V}$$

This type of amplifier may be used, for example, in an audio mixer unit which mixes signals from three signal sources such as a microphone, a record player and a guitar.

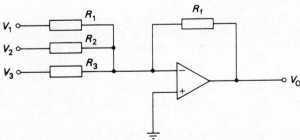

Fig. 14.8   A summing amplifier or voltage adding circuit.

Problems

14.1 (a) Voltage negative feedback is applied to an amplifier. Explain how it affects

(i) the frequency response, and

(ii) variation in stage gain due to fluctuating supply voltage.

(b) Sketch separate typical circuit diagrams to show how current and voltage feedback may be obtained for transistor amplifiers. For each connection state how the feedback fraction may be determined from the component values.

(c) When voltage gain is applied to an amplifier of gain 100 the overall stage gain falls to 50. Calculate the fraction of the output voltage fed back. If this fraction is maintained, calculate the value of the amplifier gain required if the overall stage gain is to be 75.

14.2 (a) List the reasons why negative feedback is frequently employed in amplifiers which form part of instrumentation systems.

(b) An amplifier has a voltage gain A_v without feedback. Derive an expression for the overall gain when a fraction β of the output voltage V_o is fed back in series with the external signal voltage V_i.

(c) What are the special properties of an emitter follower? Give a circuit diagram and quote a typical example of its use in instrumentation.

14.3 Describe the operation of (a) an emitter follower circuit, and (b) a source follower circuit, and enumerate features of importance. Suggest practical applications of both types of circuit.

14.4 Show that the output resistance of a source follower which employs a JUGFET with g_m = 5 mA/V is approximately 200 Ω, and that the input impedance is high.

14.5 Sketch a connection diagram for *either* a FET amplifier *or* a bipolar transistor amplifier with voltage negative feedback. Label (a) input and output connections and (b) the source of the voltage which is fed back. Explain why the phase of this feedback voltage will be in opposition to the input signal.

Indicate how the fraction of the voltage fed back may be estimated from the component values.

A voltage amplifier with a gain of 100 has 1/50th of the output fed back in opposition to the input. Find the new overall gain.

14.6 Draw a circuit diagram of an audio-frequency transistor amplifier comprising a common-emitter stage in tandem with an emitter follower stage. Show clearly the biasing arrangements and briefly explain their operation.

State the order of magnitude of the input and output impedances of the amplifier.

Say what factors will affect the low-frequency response of the circuit you have drawn.

14.7 For a non-inverting amplifier of the type in Fig. 14.6, determine the value of R_1 if the overall gain is to be 10 and R_2 = 18 kΩ.

14.8 A non-inverting amplifier of the type in Fig. 14.6 is to be used to provide a variable voltage gain in the range 1 to 20; this is achieved by replacing R_2 with a potentiometer. Draw a circuit diagram of the arrangement, and suggest a suitable value for potentiometer R_2 given that R_1 = 4·7 kΩ.

14.9 If R_f in Fig. 14.7 is replaced by a capacitor C, show that if V_1 = +2 V, the output voltage changes at the rate of $-2/R_1C$ V/s. If the operational amplifier is supplied by a ± 10 V power source, sketch a graph of the output voltage if R_1 = 100 kΩ and C = 0·1 μF if the input voltage is maintained at +2 V for 1 s.

14.10 In a summing amplifier of the type in Fig. 14.8, if V_1 = +10 V, V_2 = –5 V, V_3 = –8 V, R_1 = 1 MΩ, R_2 = 100 kΩ, R_f = 100 kΩ and V_O = +8 V, determine the value of R_3.

15. Sinusoidal oscillators

15.1 Positive feedback and instability

Consider the operation of the feedback amplifier in Fig. 15.1, which employs a non-inverting amplifier; with this amplifier, the signals V_1 and V_O are in phase with one another. Also, in the circuit shown, the input signal is obtained directly from the output via the β-network.

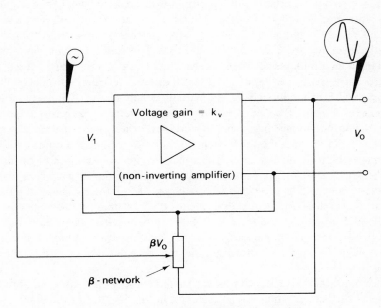

Voltage gain = k_v

V_1

(non-inverting amplifier)

V_O

βV_O

β - network

Fig. 15.1   Illustrating the basis of an oscillator.

223

Let us suppose that the voltage gain A_v of the amplifier is +100, and that the β-network reduces or attenuates this signal by a factor of 0·01 before applying it to the input terminals of the amplifier. Further, assume that the value of V_1 is initially 0·1 V. Since the amplifier voltage gain is 100, then V_O has a value of 100 x 0·1 = 10 V. The β-network reduces this voltage to 10 x 0·01 V. Readers will observe that the value of the voltage fed back to the input of the amplifier is just sufficient to sustain 10 V at the amplifier output terminals. That is, the circuit voltages could theoretically remain indefinitely with V_1 = 0·1 V and V_O = 10 V. This is known as *conditional stability*. Should the above argument be conducted for V_1 = 0·2 V, readers would be forced to the conclusion that the output voltage would remain at a value of 20 V. In fact, when the circuit is in a conditionally stable condition, it is theoretically possible for each and every value of output voltage to supply the correct voltage to the amplifier input which just maintains the output voltage at its original value. For this to occur the *voltage gain around the loop containing the amplifier and the β-network has unity value*. That is,

$$A_v\beta = 1 \qquad\qquad (15.1)$$

In the above case, A_v = 100 and β = 0·01, giving a *loop gain* of unity.

In practice, the instantaneous value of the loop gain is rarely unity, as explained in the following. A practical circuit of the type in Fig. 15.1 is designed so that, when it is first switched on, the loop gain is greater than unity. For example, if the initial value of A_v is 110 and the value of β is 0·01, then the initial loop gain is 1·1. Under this condition, the signal fed back to the amplifier input is greater than that required to maintain the output voltage at a constant value. Consequently, the ouptut voltage begins to rise and with it the signal fed back to the input terminals also rises. This state of affairs cannot be maintained indefinitely since the increasing input voltage eventually causes the transistor at the amplifier input to approach saturation. When this occurs, the voltage gain of the amplifier falls, and with it the rate of rise of output voltage also reduces. Finally, the rate of rise of the output voltage ceases and, momentarily, the output voltage becomes constant. After this instant of time, any small disturbances in the circuit (which occur continuously) cause the output voltage to begin to fall from its high level. The signal fed back to the input of the amplifier also falls, thereby accelerating the reduction of the output voltage. Finally, the output voltage falls to a point where the signal V_1 fed back causes the transistor at the amplifier input to approach cut-off. Once more, the voltage gain of the amplifier is reduced and the rate of fall of the output voltage diminishes until, finally, its value momentarily becomes constant again. Almost immediately, the output voltage begins to rise again; the sequence described above is repeated indefinitely.

The application of sufficient *positive feedback* therefore causes the output voltage to oscillate continuously. The circuit in Fig. 15.1 forms the basis of many forms of *feedback oscillator circuit.* In many of these circuits, the feedback network contains resistors and capacitors and, in others, the feedback network contains inductors and capacitors. The output voltage waveform of some oscillators is sinusoidal, while in others it may be a square or triangular wave.

Although, for oscillations to commence, it is necessary for the circuit to have a loop gain (i.e., the value of the product $A_v\beta$) whose value is greater than unity, it is only necessary for the *average value* of the loop gain to be unity over the complete cycle for the oscillations to be maintained. Once oscillations of the output voltage have commenced, the value of the loop gain is self-regulating to give an average value of unity over the complete cycle.

15.2   R-C oscillators

Oscillators are generally feedback amplifiers which are deliberately designed to be unstable; they can work either as linear (class A) or non-linear (class B or C) networks. In the former case, the amplitude of the sinusoidal oscillations is so small that the excursion of the output voltage lies within the linear part of the characteristics; in the latter case, the amplitude of the output oscillations is large. As with amplifiers, the efficiency of an oscillator working in class A is lower than one working in class C.

High frequency oscillators generally use resonant L-C circuits, since the physical size of these elements is small at these frequencies. However, at low frequency (e.g., in the range 1 Hz to 100 kHz) the physical size of the elements in L-C resonant circuits becomes much larger and manufacturing difficulties present problems; R-C *phase-shift oscillators* are commonly used to generate this band of frequencies.

Broadly speaking, there are two main types of R-C oscillators

(a) Those with ladder feedback networks.
(b) Those with bridge feedback networks.

The type of ladder network used depends to some extent on the device used in the amplifier. Where the input impedance is high, as in a FET circuit or a valve circuit, a 'voltage' transfer stage of the type shown in Fig. 15.2(a) is used in the feedback network. Where the input impedance of the active device is low, as in a bipolar transistor circuit, the 'current' transfer network of Fig. 15.2(b) is used. An essential difference between the two networks is that while the output voltage of Fig. 15.2(a) lags behind the input voltage, the output current of Fig. 15.2(b) leads the input current.

A typical circuit diagram for an R-C oscillator using a bipolar transistor and a 'current' transfer ladder feedback network is shown in Fig. 15.3. The feedback network consists of three identical sections $(R_1 C_1)$, each contributing at the oscillatory frequency a phase-shift of approximately 60 degrees, giving 180 degrees of phase shift through the feedback network. Since the transistor provides a further 180 degrees of phase-shift, the loop phase-shift at the

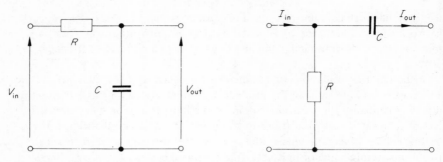

Fig. 15.2   (a) A voltage-transfer ladder network section, and (b) a current-transfer section.

oscillatory frequency is 360 degrees (or 0 degrees) which is a condition for unstable operation. The theoretical oscillatory frequency of the circuit in Fig. 15.3 is

$$f_o = 1/2\pi R_1 C_1 \sqrt{6} \qquad\qquad (15.2)$$

and the theoretical current gain of the transistor amplifier should be at least 29, since the ladder network provides this degree of attenuation at the oscillatory frequency. The equation above ignores the effect of the input impedance and

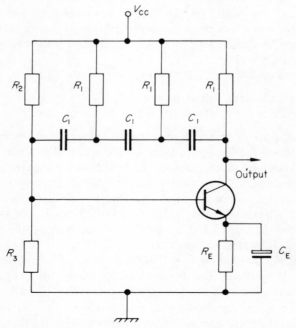

Fig. 15.3   A simple R-C phase-shift oscillator.

output impedance of the transistor amplifier, with the result that the theoretical frequency is generally lower in value than the actual oscillatory frequency. Resistors R_2, R_3, and R_E, and capacitor C_E provide base bias and temperature stabilization. To ensure that an adequate current gain is available to cause oscillation, the transistor used should have an h_{fe} of about twice the theoretical value, i.e., $h_{fe} \geqslant 60$.

The value of R_1 chosen is a compromise between one which is less than h_{oe}, and greater than h_{ie}. The frequency of operation and the output amplitude of this type of circuit are closely related to one another, and an alteration in the circuit loading significantly affects both. Amplitude control of the output signal can be obtained either by replacing R_E by a potentiometer, C_E being connected to the wiper, or alternatively by inserting an emitter follower stage between the oscillator proper and the load. In the former case, the effect of introducing a small unbypassed section of resistor in the emitter circuit increases the input impedance of the transistor amplifier and reduces the base current. In the latter case, the emitter follower presents an approximately constant load of high impedance to the oscillator, the emitter resistor being a potentiometer to allow the output voltage to be controlled.

Another form of R-C oscillator using two transistors and a ladder network is shown in Fig. 15.4. Since both transistors are connected in the common-

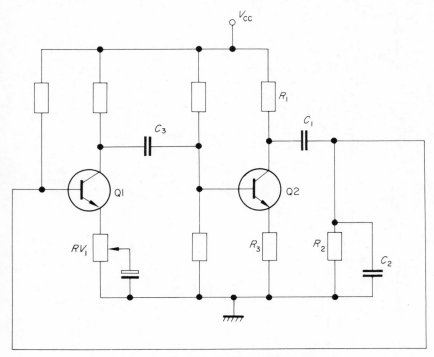

Fig. 15.4　A two-transistor phase-shift oscillator.

emitter mode, the phase-shift between the base of Q1 and the collector of Q2 is theoretically zero. Clearly, instability occurs when the phase-shift introduced by the feedback network $R_1 C_1, R_2 C_2$ is zero. Resistor R_3 in the emitter circuit of Q2 ensures that the second stage has a high output impedance, resulting in Q2 appearing as an ideal constant-current source. The phase lead introduced at the oscillatory frequency by R_1 and C_1 is equal to the phase lag introduced by R_2 and C_2, ensuring the correct phase relationship for oscillatory operation. Potentiometer RV_1 is used to control the amplitude of the oscillations; other resistors are required for bias purposes, and C_3 is an interstage coupling capacitor.

A very popular form of R-C oscillator circuit, known as a *Wien bridge oscillator,* is shown in Fig. 15.5. The name Wien bridge is taken from the fact that the resistance–capacitance circuit at the input of the amplifier is similar to an electrical bridge circuit known as a Wien bridge. This circuit employs an operational amplifier and the output voltage from the amplifier is in phase with the signal applied to the non-inverting input terminal (marked '+') and is antiphase to the signal applied to the inverting input (marked '−'). The signal fed back

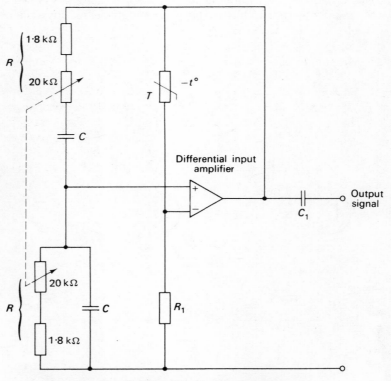

Fig. 15.5   A Wien bridge oscillator.

from the output of the amplifier is applied to both input terminals, the signal
applied to the '+' input applying positive feedback to the circuit and that
applied to the '−' input applying negative feedback. The component values
in the circuit are such that the signal applied to the '+' input has the dominant
effect, and sufficient overall positive feedback is applied to cause oscillations
to occur.

The resistance R in each of the R-C sections consists of two elements as follows.
A twin-ganged variable resistor is used as a means of frequency control, and the
1·8 kΩ fixed resistor is included to ensure that the total value of resistance in
the circuit cannot be reduced to zero when the variable resistance is reduced to
zero. With the values of resistance shown, the frequency of oscillation of the
circuit can be varied over a frequency range of slightly greater than 10:1. The
frequency of oscillation of the circuit is given by the relationship

$$f_O = 1/2\pi RC \quad \text{Hz} \tag{15.3}$$

where the value of R is in ohms and the value of C is in farads. If $C = 0·5\ \mu\text{F}$,
the frequency of oscillation of the circuit ranges from about 15 Hz to about
180 Hz. Reducing the capacitance values to 0·05 μF causes the oscillatory
frequency range to be 150 Hz to 1800 Hz. A simple oscillator can be constructed using a 741-type operational amplifier (see chapter 11), together with
an R53 thermistor (T) and a 470Ω resistor (R_1).

The function of thermistor T and resistor R_1 is to provide the oscillator with
good amplitude stability of output voltage. The way in which these components
provide voltage amplitude stability is described below.

Should the r.m.s. value of the output voltage tend to increase, the current
through the thermistor also increases. The self-heating effect of the current in
the thermistor causes its resistance to reduce, thereby applying a greater proportion of the output voltage to the '−' input of the amplifier. Since this input
signal applies negative feedback to the circuit, it has the effect of reducing the
overall voltage gain of the amplifier. The net result is that the r.m.s. value of
the output voltage is quickly returned to a near-correct value.

Wien bridge oscillators are widely used in laboratories, and provide a stable
sinusoidal signal of very low distortion.

15.3   L-C oscillators

These circuits use a resonant L-C circuit as the frequency-determining element.
They are superior in performance to R-C oscillators at frequencies of about 1
MHz and greater; a number of the more important circuits are described here.

15.3.1   Tuned collector oscillator

A practical circuit is shown in Fig. 15.6 in which the frequency of oscillation,
ω_0, is given by the resonant frequency of the L-C circuit

$$\omega_0 = 1/\sqrt{(LC)} \quad \text{rad/s} \tag{15.4}$$

Base current bias is provided by the resistor chain connected between V_{CC} and the zero volts line. The value selected for the bias current must ensure that the initial value of the loop gain is greater than unity; this ensures that oscillations are self-starting. Feedback between the oscillatory circuit and the input circuit (the base circuit) is provided by the magnetic coupling, the value of the turns ratio (n) of the feedback transformer usually being in the range 5–40.

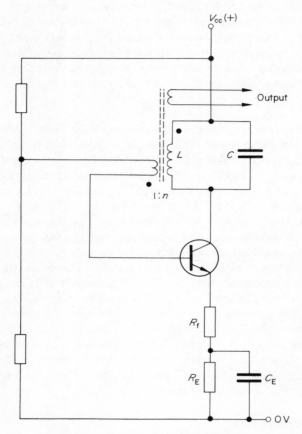

Fig. 15.6   A tuned collector oscillator.

When the feedback fraction is small, the oscillator works in class A; an increase in the feedback fraction causes the oscillator to work in class AB, and a further increase results in it working in class B or in class C. The feedback fraction is changed either by altering the magnetic coupling between the collector and base circuits, or by altering the value of R_f (this resistor introduces series negative current feedback into the circuit).

15.3.2   Colpitts and Hartley oscillators

The basic arrangement of the *L-C* circuit in the *Colpitts oscillator* is shown in Fig. 15.7(a). Capacitors C_1 and C_2 are in series with one another; the resonant frequency is that of the *L-C* circuit which is

$$\omega_0 = \sqrt{\left[\frac{1}{L}\left(\frac{1}{C_1} + \frac{1}{C_2}\right)\right]} \quad \text{rad/s} \qquad (15.5)$$

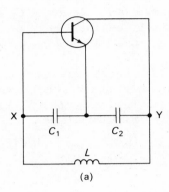

(a)

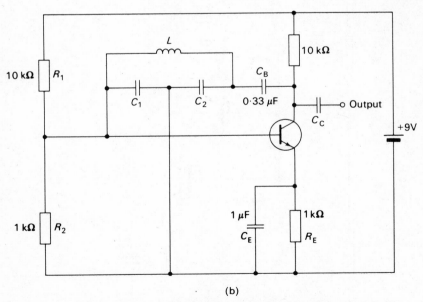

(b)

Fig. 15.7   (a) The basis of the Colpitts oscillator and (b) a practical form of the circuit.

As a general rule, the reactance of C_1 at the resonant frequency is much less than that of C_2 so that the resonant frequency is given approximately by $1/\sqrt{(LC_2)}$ rad/s. The series connected capacitors between points X and Y in Fig. 15.7(a) share the voltage across the resonant circuit, and they act as a reactive potential divider. Since the voltage across C_1 is applied to the input of the oscillator, the capacitance of this capacitor is the primary control on the amplitude of the oscillations; the function of C_2 is to control the frequency of oscillation.

A practical version of the Colpitts oscillator is shown in Fig. 15.7(b). Bias and thermal stability are provided by R_1, R_2, R_E and C_E; C_B is a blocking capacitor whose reactance is small at the oscillatory frequency. This type of circuit can be used to generate sinusoidal oscillations at frequencies between audio frequency and several gigahertz.

The *Hartley oscillator* (see Fig. 15.8) uses a tapped coil together with a single capacitor to form a resonant circuit. If M is the mutual inductance between the two coils, the effective inductance of the coil is $(L_x + L_y + 2M)$, and the resonant frequency of the Hartley oscillator is

$$\omega_0 = 1/\sqrt{[(L_x + L_y + 2M)C]} \quad \text{rad/s}$$

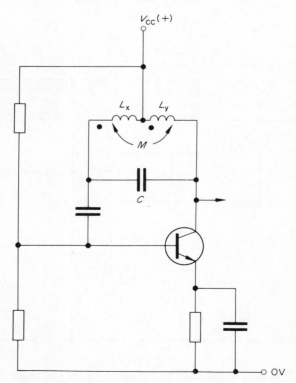

Fig. 15.8   A common-emitter Hartley oscillator.

Inductors L_x and L_y act as reactive potential dividers, L_x having a primary effect on the amplitude of oscillations; L_y primarily affects the frequency of oscillations.

The choice between Colpitts and Hartley circuits is often a question of the relative merits of the use of a two-terminal coil when compared with a tapped coil.

15.4   Oscillator frequency stability

In order that the frequency of oscillation is maintained at a stable value, it is important to ensure that the effects of temperature variation, load variation, etc., are minimized. A change in frequency can result from many factors including (1) a change in the parameters of the tuned circuit, (2) a change in valve or transistor parameters, (3) variation in loading conditions, and (4) variation in supply voltage.

For good frequency stability, the components of the tuning circuit should be mechanically stable; where a very stable frequency is required a crystal-controlled oscillator is used. To isolate the effects of loading in a high stability oscillator, a 'buffer' amplifier is used between the oscillator and the load. It is also necessary in class A oscillators to stabilize the operating point on the characteristics, since a change in the quiescent point gives rise to frequency variation, and may affect the output amplitude and waveshape.

15.5   Crystal controlled oscillators

Certain crystalline substances, notably quartz, exhibit a *piezoelectric effect* which results in a p.d. appearing between the opposite faces of the crystal when it is mechanically deformed, and vice versa. The crystal can be shown to have an

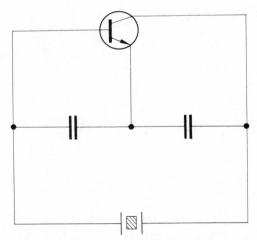

Fig. 15.9   The basis of a crystal controlled oscillator.

'electrical' equivalent circuit which has two resonant frequencies which are very close to one another, and at frequencies between the two resonant frequencies the crystal appears as though it were an inductor having a very high Q-factor. By maintaining the crystal at a constant temperature, it is possible to construct an oscillator with a frequency stability of 1 part in 10^{10}.

The basis of one form of crystal-controlled oscillator is shown in Fig. 15.9; this is a Colpitts circuit with the crystal replacing the inductor.

Problems

15.1   Draw circuit diagrams of *two* different types of resistance-capacitance oscillators and describe the basic action in each case. Compare and contrast the two circuits, particularly from the point of view of convenience of control. Explain why R-C oscillators have generally displaced L-C oscillators for the generation of audio-frequency test signals.

15.2   Draw the circuit diagram of a Colpitts oscillator and explain its operation. By what is the approximate frequency of oscillation determined?

15.3   Draw the circuit diagram and explain the operation of a tuned-circuit oscillator employing a transistor. Explain how the output can be obtained from the oscillator.

15.4   Draw a circuit diagram of a Hartley oscillator using a transistor and briefly explain its operation.
List the factors affecting the frequency stability.

15.5   By means of a circuit diagram, describe in detail how a transistor may be used in conjunction with a tuned circuit to generate oscillations. Explain the operation of the circuit chosen and the function of each component.
Explain the factors which determine the stability of the frequency of the oscillations.

16. Pulse shaping circuits

16.1   Clipping circuits or limiters

The function of clipping circuits is to limit the output signal amplitude to a specific range of values. A basic type of *shunt clipping circuit* is shown in Fig. 16.1; the word 'shunt' implies that the clipping devices (usually diodes) are shunted across the output. When the input voltage applied to Fig. 16.1 exceeds $+E_1$, the diode in series with E_1 is forward biased and conducts; the output voltage is thus clipped or limited at a value equal to E_1. When the input voltage exceeds $-E_2$, the diode in series with E_2 conducts and limits the output voltage to $-E_2$. An alternative arrangement is the series-opposed Zener diode configuration in the inset to Fig. 16.1.

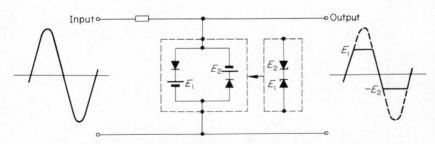

Fig. 16.1   An unsymmetrical shunt clipping circuit.

The circuit shown illustrates a popular method of generating an approximate form of square wave from a sinewave. It has the advantage of simplicity over many other circuits, and its timing accuracy is dependent only on the frequency of the applied sinewave. Its principal disadvantage is that the rising and falling edges of the output waveform are not particularly steep.

235

16.2   Exponential waveforms

16.2.1   Exponentially decreasing waveforms

The general equation of the exponentially decreasing waveform in Fig. 16.2 is

$$y = Ye^{-t/\tau} \tag{16.1}$$

where y is the instantaneous value of the waveform at time t, Y is the initial
value of the waveform, and e is the base of the naperian logarithm system
(= 2·71828). The *time constant*, τ (pronounced 'tor'), is defined as the time
taken for the variable y to change from its initial value (Y) to its final
(zero) if the initial rate of change were maintained, that is

$$\text{Initial rate of change of } y = Y/\tau$$

In electrical circuits we are primarily concerned with a knowledge of the value of
the waveform at certain instants of time, and we shall confine our attention to these.

The *fall-time*, t_f, of the waveform is defined as the time taken for the waveform to change from 90 per cent of the initial value ($0·9Y$) to 10 per cent of its
initial value ($0·1 Y$). We therefore need to estimate the values of t_1 and t_2 in
Fig. 16.2. The *transient period* or *settling time*, t_s, of the waveform is the time
taken for it to have fallen from its initial value (Y) to 1 per cent of its initial

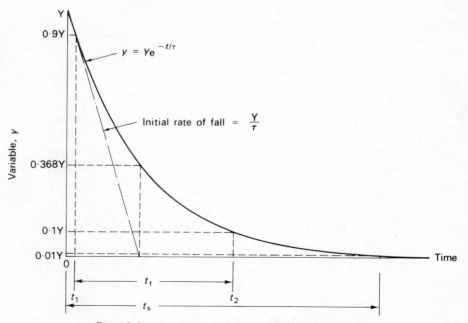

Fig. 16.2   An exponentially decreasing waveform.

value ($0{\cdot}01\,Y$). The values of t_1, t_2 and t_s are determined from the following equations

$$0{\cdot}9Y = Y\mathrm{e}^{-t_1/\tau}$$

$$0{\cdot}1Y = Y\mathrm{e}^{-t_2/\tau}$$

$$0{\cdot}01Y = Y\mathrm{e}^{-t_s/\tau}$$

Solving yields $t_1 = 0{\cdot}1\tau$, $t_2 = 2{\cdot}3\tau$, and $t_s = 4{\cdot}6\tau$, hence

$$\text{fall-time, } t_f = t_2 - t_1 = 2{\cdot}2\tau \tag{16.2}$$

$$\text{settling time, } t_s = 4{\cdot}6\tau \tag{16.3}$$

Thus if a circuit has a time constant of 1 ms, then the fall-time is 2·2 ms and the transient has decayed practically to zero in 4·6 ms. A rule of thumb used in industry is that the settling time is taken to be about five times the time constant of the circuit.

It is also useful to know how long it takes for the variable to have changed by 50 per cent of its initial value. If this time is t_x, then $0{\cdot}5Y = Y\mathrm{e}^{-t_x/\tau}$. Solving gives

$$t_x = 0{\cdot}7\tau \tag{16.4}$$

16.2.2 Exponentially increasing waveform

The general equation for the exponentially increasing waveform in Fig. 16.3 is

$$y = Y(1 - \mathrm{e}^{-t/\tau}) \tag{16.5}$$

the quantities in the equation being defined above. The *rise-time, t_r,* of the waveform is defined as the time taken for it to have risen from 10 per cent to 90 per cent of the final value. The *settling time, t_s,* of the transient is the time taken for the variable to have risen from its initial value (zero) to 99 per cent of its final value ($0{\cdot}99\,Y$). The values of t_1, t_2 and t_s are determined from the following equations

$$0{\cdot}1Y = Y(1 - \mathrm{e}^{-t_1/\tau})$$

$$0{\cdot}9Y = Y(1 - \mathrm{e}^{-t_2/\tau})$$

$$0{\cdot}99Y = Y(1 - \mathrm{e}^{-t_s/\tau})$$

Solving gives $t_1 = 0{\cdot}1\tau$, $t_2 = 2{\cdot}3\tau$, and $t_s = 4{\cdot}6\tau$, hence

$$\text{rise-time, } t_r = t_2 - t_1 = 2{\cdot}2\tau \tag{16.6}$$

$$\text{settling time, } t_s = 4{\cdot}6\tau \tag{16.7}$$

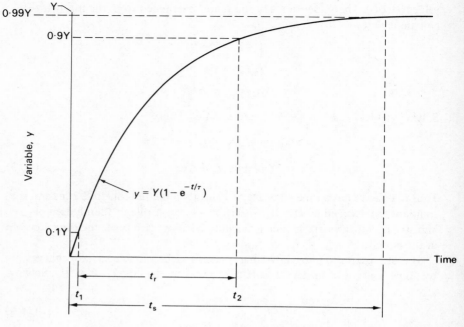

Fig. 16.3   An exponentially rising waveform.

Also the time, t_x, taken for the waveform to have risen to 50 per cent of its final value is

$$t_x = 0{\cdot}7\tau \tag{16.8}$$

16.3   R-C differentiator circuit

The circuit in Fig. 16.4(a) is widely used as an 'approximate' differentiator, providing that the conditions outlined below are fulfilled.

If a rectangular impulse is applied to the input of *a perfect differentiator*, the output voltage should be equal to the rate of change of the input voltage. Thus at times prior to t_a (see upper waveform in Fig. 16.4(b)), and between t_a and t_b, and after t_b the output voltage should be zero. At time t_a the input voltage changes from zero to $+E$ in zero time, so that the differential, (i.e., rate of change) of the input voltage with time is instantaneously $+\infty$. At time t_b the input voltage falls from $+E$ to zero in zero time, so that the differential of the input voltage with respect to time is $-\infty$. The output of a perfect differentiator for the input waveform shown therefore consists of two voltage spikes of opposing polarity at t_a and t_b having infinite height and zero width.

Practical circuits cannot provide the above waveform, and for this reason they are described as approximate differentiator circuits. In the circuit of Fig.

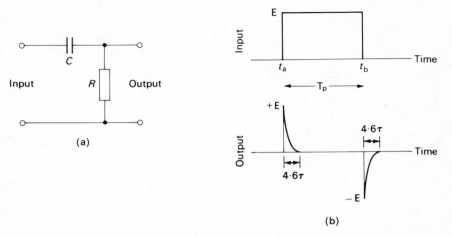

Fig. 16.4   *R-C* differentiator circuit.

16.4(a), the peak output voltage is equal to the peak change in input voltage, and the pulse width is equal to the time taken for the capacitor to charge fully, i.e., a time equal to the 'settling' time defined in earlier sections. Thus at time t_a the peak output voltage is $+E$, and this decays to zero as the capacitor charges in a time of about $4 \cdot 6\tau = 4 \cdot 6RC$. For the circuit to function effectively as a differentiator, the settling time of the transient must be much shorter than the pulse duration, T_p. That is the settling time of the circuit must be much less than T_p, e.g., let

$$5\tau = T_p/100$$

hence

$$\tau = RC = 0 \cdot 002T_p \tag{16.9}$$

If $T_p = 1$ ms and $R = 100$ kΩ, then for the circuit to act as a differentiator

$$C = 0 \cdot 002T_p/R = 0 \cdot 002 \times 1 \times 10^{-3}/100 \times 10^3 \quad F = 20pF$$

16.4   R-C integrator circuit

If a constant is integrated with respect to time, the result is in the form of (time $\times$ a coefficient), that is the integrator output should increase uniformly with time. An *R-C* circuit whose output is approximately equal to the integral of the input signal over a limited interval of time is shown in Fig. 16.5(a). For this circuit to function as an integrator, its settling time ($t_s = 4 \cdot 6\tau$) must be much greater than the period of time, T_p, for which the pulse is applied. The output from the

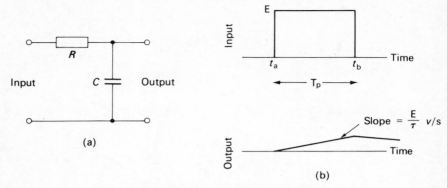

Fig. 16.5   *R-C* integrator circuit.

circuit for a rectangular input pulse is shown in Fig. 16.5(b). For the circuit to function as an integrator let

$$5\tau = 100T_p$$

or

$$\tau = RC = 20T_p \qquad (16.10)$$

If T_p = 1 ms and R = 100 kΩ, then for the circuit in Fig. 16.5 to act as an integrator

$$C = 20T_p/R = 20 \times 1 \times 10^{-3}/100 \times 10^3 \quad F = 0.2\ \mu F$$

Problems

16.1   Explain what is meant by (a) a differentiator circuit, (b) an integrator circuit. If an a.c. waveform of triangular shape is applied to both types of circuit, sketch the waveform you would expect from each circuit. Give reasons for the waveforms.

16.2   The voltage pulse in Fig. 16.6(a) is applied to the circuit in Fig. 16.6(b). Draw the output waveform from the circuit given that V_S = +10 V and that (i) C = 0.1 μF, R = 1 kΩ, (ii) C = 1 μF, R = 20 kΩ.

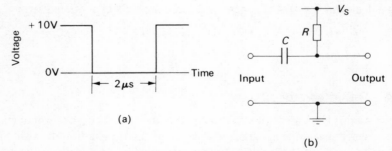

Fig. 16.6   Figure for problem 16.2.

16.3   Draw the output waveforms for the circuit in Fig. 16.6 for the two sets of circuit conditions in (i) and (ii) if V_S is (a) +5 V, (b) −5 V.

17. Multivibrators and non-sinusoidal oscillators

17.1 Multivibrators

Multivibrators are a class of electronic *switching circuits* which depend for their operation on regenerative feedback. They are also a class of *relaxation oscillators*, which generate non-sinusoidal waveforms by gradually charging and then quickly discharging a capacitor through a resistor. The name 'multivibrator' is derived from the fact that a harmonic analysis of the output waveform shows that it is rich in harmonics, or multiple vibrations, of the fundamental frequency. There are three main types of multivibrator:

1. The *monostable multivibrator* or *one-shot circuit,* which has one stable operating state and one quasi-stable state. The application of an input signal triggers the circuit into its quasi-stable condition, in which it remains for a period of time which is dependent upon the value of the circuit constants. After this period of time, the circuit conditions return to their stable state; the process is repeated upon the application of each trigger pulse.

2. The *astable multivibrator* or *free-running multivibrator*, which has two quasi-stable operating states, one following the other in succession.

3. The *flip-flop* or *bistable multivibrator,* which has two stable operating states. The application of a control signal (or signals) causes the output to change from one state to the other. The flip-flop is discussed in chapter 18.

All three types include two stages, and at any one time one of the active devices is saturated and the other is cut off.

17.2 The monostable multivibrator

A popular form of monostable multivibrator is illustrated in Fig. 17.1(a), with typical waveforms in Fig. 17.1(b). In the stable operating mode of the circuit, transistor Q2 is saturated, with v_{BE2} and v_{CE2} both having very small values; Q1 is cut off, having its emitter junction reverse biased and $i_{CE1} \simeq 0$. The

241

circuit is triggered into its quasi-stable state either by turning Q1 on or by turning Q2 off. This is usually accomplished either by applying a positive-going pulse to input A, or by applying a negative-going pulse to input B or at the collector of Q2.

Prior to the application of a trigger pulse, capacitor C is charged to V_{CC} with the polarity shown, since the base of Q2 is approximately at earth potential and the collector of Q1 is at $+V_{CC}$ (since $i_{CE1} = 0$). When a positive-going pulse of sufficient amplitude is applied to input A, it drives Q1 into saturation and effectively connects the left-hand plate of capacitor C to earth.

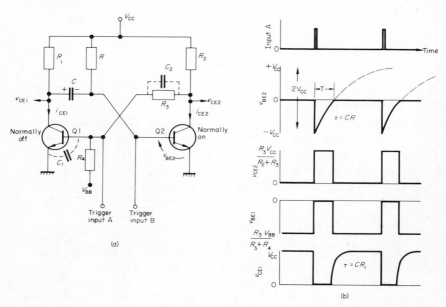

Fig. 17.1   (a) A popular monostable multivibrator circuit,,and (b) typical wave-forms.

As a result, the base of Q2 is driven to $-V_{CC}$ by the charge held on C. This reverse biases the emitter junction of Q2 and its base current and collector current fall to zero. Capacitor C now has to discharge through R; since one end of R is at $+V_{CC}$ and the other end is taken to $-V_{CC}$ when the trigger pulse is applied, the voltage across R at this instant is $2V_{CC}$. The voltage at the base of Q2 thus rises in an exponential fashion from $-V_{CC}$ towards $+V_{CC}$ with a time constant of CR. As v_{BE2} approaches zero, Q2 begins to conduct and its collector potential falls rapidly to zero. This drop in potential is communicated to the base of Q1 by the feedback network R_3R_4, causing the emitter junction of Q1 to be reverse biased. This forces Q1 to be cut off, and the circuit resumes its stable operating state. The period of time that the circuit remains in its quasi-stable state is given by T (Fig. 17.1(b)), which can be determined from the time taken for the voltage across the capacitor to change from $-V_{CC}$ to zero, when

$$V_{CC} = (2V_{CC})(1 - e^{-T/RC})$$

or

$$T = RC \ln 2 \simeq 0 \cdot 693 RC \qquad (17.1)$$

Thus, if $C = 0 \cdot 01 \ \mu F$ and $R = 15 \ k\Omega$, the pulse width is

$$T = 0 \cdot 693 \times 0 \cdot 01 \times 10^{-6} \times 15 \times 10^{3} = 104 \times 10^{-6} \ s$$

$$= 104 \ \mu s$$

The rate of rise of the collector voltage is constrained by the charging time constant $R_1 C$, and the waveform at the collector of Q1 does not have a very good rise time. For this reason, the output from Q1 is generally not used. It can be improved by modifications to the circuit, one example of which is described later in this section.

In practice, the waveforms at the base and collector of Q2 differ very slightly from those shown in Fig. 17.1(b) since, when Q2 turns on, the base potential of Q2 rises rapidly to a positive potential equal to V_{BE2sat}. At the same instant, the collector potential of Q2 falls to V_{CE2sat}, which has a value of about $0 \cdot 2$ V.

A factor which has been overlooked so far is the effect of the input capacitance C_1 of the transistor on the switching performance. When Q2 is suddenly turned off, the rate of rise of the voltage at the base of Q1 is restricted by the charging time constant of the circuit containing C_1. To compensate for this delay, resistor R_3 is sometimes shunted by capacitor C_2, known as a *speed-up capacitor*, which has a value of a few hundred picofarads.

A simple variation which is frequently used to improve the rise-time at the collector of Q1 is shown in Fig. 17.2(a), and is known as the Rozner modification. The circuit includes a diode and resistor R_1' in addition to the normal circuit components. The diode effectively isolates the recharging exponential from the collector waveform of Q1, as follows. At the end of the quasi-stable condition, the emitter junction of Q1 is reverse biased and its collector potential begins to rise; this causes the diode to become reverse biased, so isolating capacitor C from transistor Q1, and the capacitor then recharges through R_1'. If an external load resistor R_L with a high value is connected to the collector of Q1, the output waveform will be a clean square wave with a small rise-time, as shown in Fig. 17.2(b). With a low value of load resistance, the collector potential of Q1 rises rapidly to $V_{CC}R_L/(R_L + R_1)$ until the capacitor has charged to this value. The diode then begins to conduct and the final waveform and voltage level is as shown in Fig. 17.2(c).

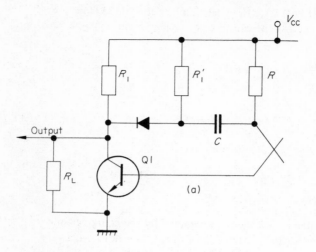

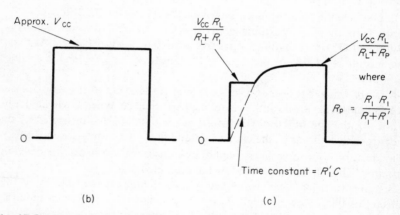

Fig. 17.2   The Rozner modification to give improved output waveshape.

17.3   The astable multivibrator

There are many forms of astable multivibrator, and we restrict ourselves to the most popular form which is shown in Fig. 17.3(a). It consists of two stages which are generally similar to the first stage of the monostable multivibrator in section 17.2.

The operation of the circuit is as follows. When Q2 is saturated, the charge on C_2 causes Q1 to be cut off until v_{BE1} rises to zero, when Q1 saturates. The drop in potential at the collector of Q1 then causes Q2 to be cut off. The circuit remains in the second quasi-stable state until v_{BE2} rises to zero, when Q2 saturates and the circuit is returned to the first quasi-stable state. The process is then repeated indefinitely. The period of time for which Q1 is cut off is given by T_1 in Fig. 17.3(b); T_2 is the period of time for which Q2 is cut off. Their approximate values are

$$T_1 \simeq 0\cdot693 R_4 C_2 \qquad T_2 \simeq 0\cdot693 R_3 C_1$$

The period of time for one complete cycle is $T = T_1 + T_2$, and the frequency is

$$f = 1/T \text{ Hz}$$

For example, if $R_3 = R_4 = 15$ kΩ, and $C_1 = C_2 = 0\cdot01$ μF, then the periodic time for one cycle is 208 μs, and the frequency is 4·81 kHz. The ratio T_1/T_2 is known as the *mark-to-space ratio* or the on-to-off ratio, and it has unity value when $R_3 = R_4$ and $C_1 = C_2$. Accurate control over the mark-to-space ratio is generally difficult to realize with 5 or 10 per cent tolerance components. One method of achieving a given mark-to-space ratio is to connect the top ends of R_3 and R_4 to opposite ends of a potentiometer, with the wiper taken to V_{CC}. Adjustment of the wiper position alters the net values of resistance in the two collector circuits, giving a degree of control over the mark-to-space ratio. However, the simple circuit in Fig. 17.3(a) is unsuitable for mark-to-space ratios greater than about 10:1, and other circuits must be used.

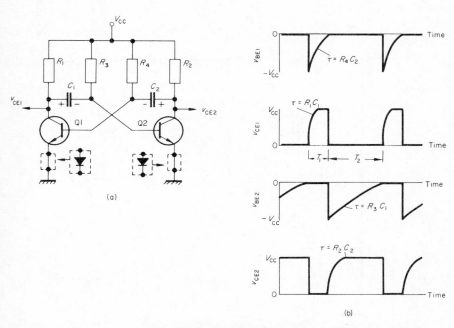

Fig. 17.3 (a) One form of astable multivibrator circuit, and (b) typical waveforms.

It is clear from Fig. 17.3(b) that the output waveforms at both collectors are not good square waves, and are unsuitable for use in circuits where a short rise-time is required. A simple method of improving the rise-time is by using the Rozner modification (Fig. 17.2(a)) in both collector circuits.

Since it is almost impossible to guarantee two identical halves of the circuit in Fig. 17.3(a), the circuit will almost certainly be self-starting, that is to say the output will be oscillatory. However, the circuit is designed to work so that the transistors are driven heavily into saturation. In this state of operation, the current gain of transistors is low, and upon switching it is just possible that the transistors become so heavily saturated that the loop gain is less than unity, and unstable conditions are not achieved. In cases of this kind, it is necessary to take steps to ensure self-starting.

Where the peak negative base-emitter voltage at the instant of switching is large enough to damage the emitter junction of the transistor, a diode can be connected in series with the emitter (shown in the insets in Fig. 17.3(a)) as a means of inverse voltage protection.

17.4   Synchronizing astable multivibrators

The simple astable multivibrator is a *free-running oscillator,* and its output frequency is dependent upon the circuit constants. If accurate control over

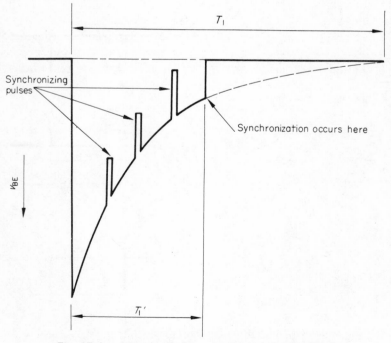

Fig. 17.4   A method of synchronizing a multivibrator.

the frequency is required, it is necessary to provide a means of synchronizing the multivibrator output with an accurate frequency source. A popular method of achieving this end is shown in Fig. 17.4, in which a series of positive-going pulses are applied to the base of one of the transistors. Whenever the externally applied synchronizing pulse forces the base voltage to become positive (in n-p-n transistors), the transistor is switched to its saturated state. As a result, the output duration is T_1', compared with T_1 in the free-running circuit. By this means, the multivibrator may be used as a frequency divider.

For accurate frequency stability, the frequency of the synchronizing signal should not be greater than about ten times the natural frequency of the multivibrator, and the peak of each pulse which is superimposed on the bias voltage should rise above the commencing point of the following pulse by about 20 per cent of the amplitude of the pulse. A smaller trigger pulse (or a larger one for that matter) may cause loss of synchronization.

17.5   A unijunction transistor pulse generator circuit

A simple pulse generator using a unijunction transistor is shown in Fig. 17.5(a). Assuming that the capacitor is initially uncharged, the voltage at point X begins to rise in an exponential manner until it reaches the peak-point voltage of the U.J.T. At this instant of time, the U.J.T. switches to its low resistance conducting mode and the capacitor is discharged through the 22 Ω resistor, causing a positive-going pulse to be generated at Y. The pulse repetition rate is controlled by the value of R, since this controls the time constant RC of the capacitor charging circuit, and the pulse width by R_{B1} since this affects the discharge time constant.

Assuming that the capacitor is initially uncharged, then the voltage at point X prior to breakdown is given by

$$V_X = V_{BB}(1 - e^{-t/RC})$$

where RC is the charging time constant of the resistor-capacitor circuit, and t is the time from the commencement of the waveform. Discharge occurs when V_X is equal to the peak-point voltage, which is taken to be equal to ηV_{BB} (where η is the intrinsic stand-off ratio of the U.J.T., and V_{BB} is the supply voltage). That is when

$$\eta V_{BB} = V_{BB}(1 - e^{-t/RC})$$

Hence, the periodic time is given approximately by

$$t = RC \ln 1/(1 - \eta) = 2 \cdot 3 RC \lg 1/(1 - \eta)$$

A typical value for η is $0 \cdot 55$, giving a periodic time of approximately $0 \cdot 8RC$ s.

The function of resistor R_{B2} is to provide temperature stability, otherwise it has little effect upon the performance of the circuit. However, as a result of this resistor, a negative pulse is generated at base-two and can be used for other control purposes.

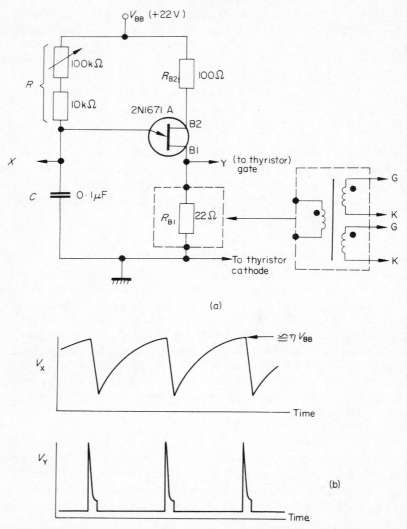

Fig. 17.5   (a) U.J.T. relaxation oscillator, and (b) typical waveforms.

The pulse which is generated at point Y is of short duration, being typically 10 μs to 15 μs, and may be coupled directly to the gate terminal of the thyristor. As an alternative mode of connection, it may be coupled to the thyristor through an R-C network similar to that used between the stages of an R-C coupled amplifier (typical values being $C = 0\cdot1$ μF, $R = 560$ Ω). Where complete isolation is required, a pulse transformer can be used, as shown in the inset in Fig. 17.5(a). The advantage of the pulse transformer is that a number of separate outputs can be used to trigger parallel (or inverse-parallel) connected thyristors.

A complete circuit showing the control and load sections is shown in Fig. 17.6. Resistor R_1 and the Zener diode form a voltage limiting circuit which performs two functions. Firstly, it limits the voltage applied to the control circuit in the positive half-cycle of the supply voltage to the breakdown voltage of the Zener diode. Secondly, during the negative half-cycle it restricts the voltage applied to the control circuit to about -0.8 V, and provides a discharge path for the energy stored in capacitor C. As a result of the latter feature, the

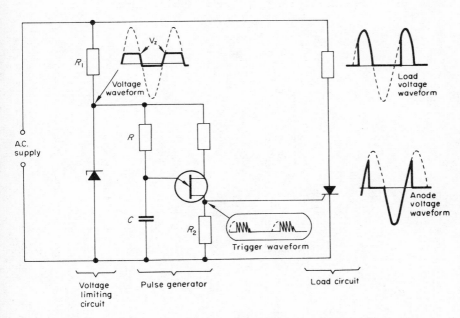

Fig. 17.6   A thyristor circuit controlled by a U.J.T. oscillator.

capacitor is fully discharged at the commencement of each positive half-cycle, ensuring that the first pulse generated by the U.J.T. occurs after a time interval of $(RC \ln 1/(1 - \eta))$ s after the commencement of the positive half-cycle. This also ensures that the thyristor is triggered into conduction at the same point in each positive half-cycle.

The circuit can be modified to be voltage controlled by replacing resistor R by a transistor. The pulse repetition rate is then controlled by the base-emitter voltage of the transistor. In this configuration, the capacitor charging current is a function of the transistor base current. If the base current is constant, then the waveform at the emitter of the U.J.T. is practically a linear ramp.

With a little modification, the circuit in Fig. 17.6 can be used to control a triac. All that is required is to replace the thyristor with a triac, and the supply to resistor R_1 and the Zener diode must be derived from a full-wave rectifier circuit. The latter feature allows pulses to be generated in both half-cycles.

17.6   A pulse generator using a diac

A relaxation oscillator using a diac as the capacitor discharge element is shown in Fig. 17.7; the operation of the circuit is similar to the U.J.T. circuit described in section 17.6. The diac is used as a voltage sensitive switch which partially discharges capacitor C when the voltage at X reaches the breakdown voltage of

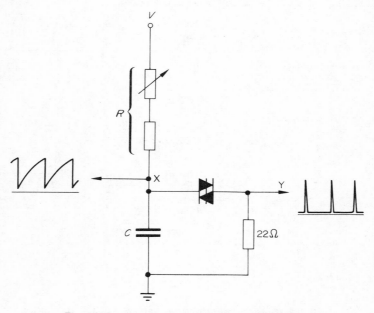

Fig. 17.7   A relaxation oscillator using a diac.

the diac. The capacitor discharge causes a voltage pulse to be developed at Y, so that with a positive polarity supply a positive-going pulse appears at Y, and with a negative polarity supply a negative-going pulse appears at Y. At the same time a sawtooth voltage waveform appears at X having the same polarity as the supply voltage. When the current through the diac falls below its maintaining value, the capacitor discharge ceases and the voltage at X begins to rise again.

Problems

17.1   Explain, with the aid of a circuit diagram and waveforms, the action of a free-running-multivibrator.

State an industrial application.

17.2   Design an astable multivibrator using the principles outlined in this chapter using transistors with $h_{FE} = 100$, $V_{CC} = 6$ V, $I_{CM} = 5$ mA. The mark-to-space ratio is to be unity, and the periodic time is 100 μs.

17.3   Discuss the special problems in astable multivibrators of generating (a) square waves with very long periodic times (i.e. several seconds), and (b) a large mark-to-space ratio (say 100:1).

17.4   Estimate the pulse repetition rate of a U.J.T. relaxation oscillator circuit of the type in Fig. 17.5(a) given that $R = 15$ kΩ, $C = 0.2$ μF and that the intrinsic standoff ratio of the U.J.T. is 0.6.

17.5   A U.J.T. relaxation oscillator of the type in Fig. 17.5(a) is required to produce a pulse train whose repetition rate can be varied over the range 0.4–25 ms. If the capacitor used in the timing circuit has a value of 0.1 μF and the intrinsic standoff ratio of the U.J.T. is 0.57, determine suitable values for the fixed and variable resistors to be used in the timing circuit.

17.6   Estimate the time taken for the first pulse to be generated by a diac relaxation oscillator circuit of the type in Fig. 17.7 after the supply is switched on. The supply voltage is 40 V, $R = 100$ kΩ, $C = 0.1$ μF, and the breakdown voltage of the diac is 40 V.

17.7   If the diac in example 17.6 stops conducting when the voltage across it falls to 28 V, determine the pulse repetition rate of the oscillator.

18. Digital electronics

18.1 The basis of engineering logic

Consider the statement 'X is either a cat or a horse, and X is not a cat. What is X?' This is a simple statement of logical fact, and one way of deducing the answer is to present the facts in the form of a symbolic equation. It is clear that the conventions of symbolic logic or *Boolean algebra*— named after Boole, its inventor—will differ in some respects from conventional algebra. In the following paragraphs, a general insight into the subject is given.

Generally speaking, we require a simple 'true' or 'untrue' answer to any engineering question that we may pose. Suppose that we assign the logical value of unity to an answer which is true, and the logical value zero to one which is untrue. By this simple means, we can readily detect the truth or otherwise of a logical proposition in, say, an electronic logic circuit simply by using a voltmeter which indicates the voltage level at a point in the circuit. If the two voltage levels that are available in the circuit are +10 V and zero, and if we let

$$\text{logic '1'} = +10 \text{ V}$$

$$\text{logic '0'} = 0 \text{ V}$$

then we say we are working in *positive logic,* since the higher of the two potentials represents logic '1'. Most circuits utilizing n-p-n transistors work in positive logic, since it is convenient to think of a signal existing when a positive potential can be detected.

Many early logic systems operated in what is known as *negative logic,* in which the lower of the two potentials is taken as logic '1'. With the above potentials, logic '1' in negative logic would be represented by zero voltage, while logic '0' would be represented by +10 V. Positive logic and negative logic are both employed in present-day engineering systems, and it is often convenient to mix both types of logic levels in order to simplify system design*.

* See *Logic Circuits* by N. M. Morris, published by McGraw-Hill (1976).

In order to reduce logical statements to meaningful symbolic equations we must be able to express such words as AND, NOT, and OR in symbolic form. In the following, circuits are developed which operate in positive logic and satisfy the logical requirements of these statements.

18.2   The AND gate

The most direct approach to the operation of logic circuits is by simple relay circuits, an example of which is shown in Fig. 18.1. Logic circuits are also described as *gates,* since they permit free flow of information when they are *open,* and stop the flow when they are *closed* or *inhibited.*

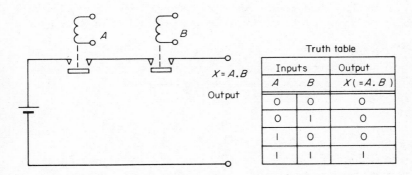

Fig. 18.1   A relay AND gate with its truth table.

Under normal operating conditions, the coils of relays A and B are either energized at their full voltage, or they have no voltage applied to them. In the former case, we say that the signal has unity logical value (full voltage), and in the latter case it has zero logical value (zero voltage). Either coil may be energized at one of the two logic levels, so that there are four possible energization states for the two relays. All possible combinations of the states of inputs A and B are grouped together in the input columns of the *truth table* in Fig. 18.1; the name 'truth table' is derived from the fact that a logic '1' signal represents a state of 'existing' or one which is 'true', while logic '0' represents a state of 'not existing' or one which is 'untrue'.

When either or both of the relay coils are de-energized, one or more sets of contacts remain open and the output voltage is zero. This corresponds to the first three rows of the truth table. Only when both A AND B are energized simultaneously does an output exist, satisfying the fourth row of the truth table. Thus, the gate is closed when either A or B has zero value, and is open only when $A = B = 1$. An inspection of the rows of the truth table for the AND gate shows that the numerical value in the output column has the same value as the mathematical product of the two numbers in the input columns. Accordingly, the logical expression for output X is given by

$$X = A.B$$

where the 'dot' (.) represents the logical AND function. Although the *logical product function* has the same value as the *arithmetic product function* of the variables, great care must be exercised in the use of this relationship, since the two functions do not mean the same thing. Also, the equality sign in the logical equation means logical equality, which is not necessarily the same thing as arithmetic equality.

If several inputs A, B, C, D, etc. are used, then the output of a series relay circuit is the product of the inputs, viz:

$$X = A.B.C.D....$$

A positive logic diode-resistor AND gate is shown in Fig. 18.2(a). The input voltage levels are set by the state of the input switches A and B. When both

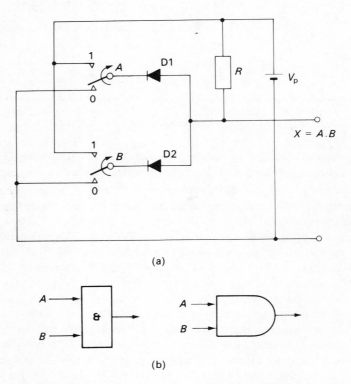

(a)

(b)

Fig. 18.2   (a) A diode-resistor logic (DRL) AND gate, and (b) representative circuit symbols.

input lines are at the zero level, both diodes are forward biased via resistor R, and each carries a current of approximately $V_p/2R$. The output voltage in this condition is the voltage appearing across a forward biased diode, which is generally small. For most practical purposes, the output voltage may be taken to be zero, giving conditions which correspond to the first row of the truth table in Fig. 18.1.

By switching input B to the logic '1' level (with $A = 0$), diode D2 is reverse biased and the current flowing through it falls to zero; diode D1 remains forward biased and continues to pass current. Since the p.d. across D1 remains at a low value, the output signal is still at the logic '0' level. If the states of the input signal levels are reversed so that $A = 1, B = 0$, the roles of the two diodes are reversed, and the output remains at the zero level. This satisfies the second and third rows of the truth table of the AND gate.

When both input lines are connected to V_p (i.e., $A = B = 1$), the return path to the negative pole of the battery is broken, and the current flowing in resistor R falls to zero. As a result, the output potential rises to the logic '1' level, so satisfying the fourth row of the truth table. A number of circuit symbols are used to represent the AND gate, two being shown in Fig. 18.2(b); the left-hand symbol is the B.S. symbol, and that on the right-hand of Fig. 18.2(b) is the American standard symbol.

18.3   The OR gate

A relay version of an OR gate is shown in Fig. 18.3(a), which consists of two parallel-connected relays. When both relays are de-energized ($A = B = 0$), the output is zero; when either relay or both relays are energized the output voltage is $+ V_p$, or logic '1'. A diode-resistor version of the circuit is shown in Fig. 18.3(b) and some circuit symbols in (c). The '1' inside the upper symbol signifies that an output exists when any one of the inputs is energized; the upper symbol is the B.S. symbol, and the '1' inside it may alternatively be replaced by a '$\geqq 1$' symbol. It is left as an exercise for the reader to verify that the diode-resistor circuit satisfies the truth table given in the figure.

The first three rows of the OR gate truth table are satisfied by the arithmetic equation

$$X = A + B$$

and it is for this reason that the 'plus' sign is used to represent the logical OR function. It is only upon investigation of the fourth row of the truth table that any difference between the arithmetic sum function and the logical sum function can be seen. It is observed that, in this case, $1 + 1 = 1$! Again the reader is cautioned to be careful when dealing with the numerical value of a logical equation.

The function generated by the circuits described here is sometimes known as the INCLUSIVE-OR function, since the input combinations which result

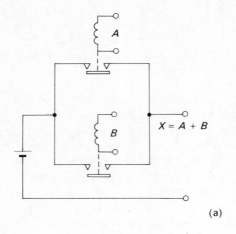

Inputs		Output
A	B	X (A + B)
0	0	0
0	1	1
1	0	1
1	1	1

(a)

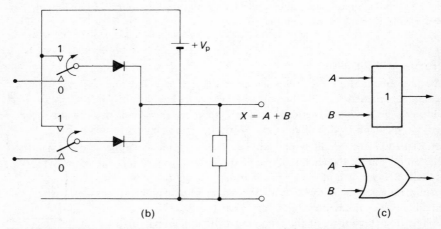

(b) (c)

Fig. 18.3 (a) A relay OR gate with its truth table, (b) a diode-resistor logic OR gate, and (c) representative circuit symbols.

in an output from the circuit include the case where both inputs exist simultaneously. If the gate has N input lines $A, B, C, \ldots, M, N$, the output is expressed in the logical form

$$X = A + B + C + \cdots + M + N$$

It can also be expressed in the form

$$X = A \vee B \vee C \vee \cdots \vee M \vee N$$

where the 'vee' (v) represents the INCLUSIVE-OR function. In some instances, this symbol is preferred to the 'plus' sign as it eliminates any difficulty which may arise when dealing with circuits which involve arithmetic addition.

The maximum number of input signals that can be accommodated by the gate is known as the *fan-in* of the gate, and can have a large value in some circuits. The maximum number of similar gates that may be connected to the output terminal without causing faulty operation is known as the *fan-out* of the gate.

18.4 The NOT gate

A NOT gate gives the *logical complement* of the input signal. It is said to *negate* or *invert* the input signal. Since there are only two possible signal levels, the following relationships hold good.

$$0 = \text{NOT } 1 = \bar{1}$$
$$1 = \text{NOT } 0 = \bar{0}$$

Variables which are complemented are symbolized by placing a bar over the variable.

A relay version of the NOT gate is shown in Fig. 18.4(a), and comprises a relay with normally-open contacts. When the relay is de-energized ($A = 0$), the output signal is logic '1' ($= \bar{A}$); on energizing the relay ($A = 1$), the contacts close and the output falls to logic '0' ($= \bar{A}$).

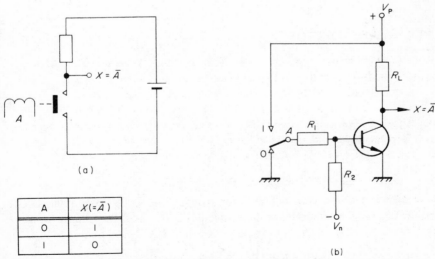

A	$X(=\bar{A})$
O	I
I	O

Fig. 18.4 (a) A relay NOT gate with its truth table, and (b) a resistor-transistor logic (RTL) NOT gate.

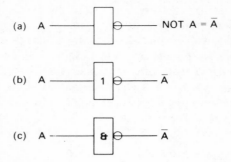

Fig. 18.5   Circuit symbols used for NOT gates.

A transistor version of the circuit is shown in Fig. 18.4(b). When the input line is taken to earth ($A = 0$), the resistor chain $R_1 R_2$ ensures that the emitter junction is reverse biased and the transistor is cut off. In this event, the collector current is zero and the output voltage is at its highest level ($X = 1 = \overline{A}$). The output voltage is dependent upon the current drawn by the load which is driven by the NOT gate.

Circuit symbols used to represent the NOT gate are illustrated in Fig. 18.5. Because Fig. 18.4(b) contains only resistors and a transistor, it is described as a *resistor–transistor logic* (RTL) NOT gate. The RTL family of gates was the earliest type to be introduced in integrated circuit form and has been largely superseded by more sophisticated circuits.

18.5   NAND and NOR gates

A feature of practical forms of electronic gates is that, almost invariably, they provide the NOT function or logical inversion in one form or another.

By combining an AND gate with a NOT gate in the manner shown in Fig. 18.6(a), the output from the combination is the NOT function of the output from the AND gate. The resulting network is known as a NAND gate; typical circuit symbols are shown in diagrams (b) and (c) of Fig. 18.6. Since the output from the gate is NOT (A AND B AND C), it is represented by the expression:

$$\text{Output for the NAND gate} = \overline{A \cdot B \cdot C}$$

A logic function known as a NOR function is generated by combining an OR gate with a NOT gate in the manner shown in Fig. 18.6(d). The output from the gate is the NOT function of the output from the OR gate; hence,

$$\text{Output from the NOR gate} = \overline{A + B + C}$$

Circuit symbols for the NOR gate are shown in diagrams (e) and (f) of Fig. 18.6.

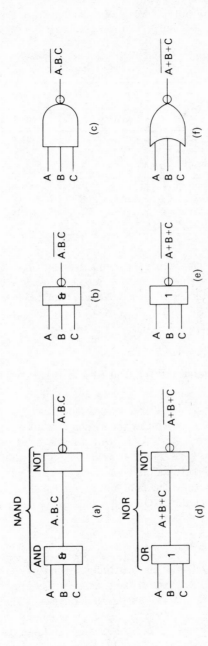

Fig. 18.6 The NAND function is generated by the network in (a); typical circuit symbols are shown in (b) and (c). The NOR function is generated by the network in (d), and typical circuit symbols are shown in (e) and (f).

The truth table of the NAND gate evolves from the fact that the output from the NAND gate is the logical complement of the output from the AND gate. Similarly the NOR gate output is the logical complement of the OR function. Truth tables for 3-input NAND and NOR gates are given in Table 18.1.

Table 18.1

Inputs A B C	Output	
	NAND gate	NOR gate
0 0 0	1	1
0 0 1	1	0
0 1 0	1	0
0 1 1	1	0
1 0 0	1	0
1 0 1	1	0
1 1 0	1	0
1 1 1	0	0

The *NAND gate truth table* may be summarized as follows: when a logic '0' is applied to *any* input line, the output is logic '1'; only when all inputs are logic '1' is the output logic '0'. The *NOR gate truth table* may be summarized as follows: when a logic '1' is applied to *any* input line, the output is logic '0'; only when all inputs are logic '0' is the output logic '1'.

18.6   Function generation using NOR and NAND gates

The most important aspect of NOR and NAND gates to industrial users is that both types can generate any of the normal logic functions, e.g., AND, OR, and NOT functions. Circuits generating these functions are shown in Fig. 18.7.

Thus, a NOR gate or a NAND gate with a single input generates the NOT function of the input signal, shown in (a). Three NOR gates in the configuration in (b) generate the AND function, while the same configuration of NAND gates generates the OR function. The configuration in (c) allows the OR and AND functions to be generated by NOR and NAND gates, respectively.

18.7   The *S-R* flip-flop

A *set-reset (S-R) flip-flop* can be constructed from two NOR gates or four NAND gates, shown in Fig. 18.8(a) and (b), respectively. The flip-flop has two input lines shown as S and $R,$ and two output lines Q and $\bar{Q}$ which provide complementary output signals. When the S-line or *set line* is energized, the logic level of output Q becomes '1', and $\bar{Q}$ becomes '0'. When the R-line or *reset line* is energized, output Q becomes '0' and $\bar{Q}$ becomes '1'. Thus, a signal at the

Circuit	Function generated	
	NOR gates	NAND gates
(a) A ——[ ]o—— f_1	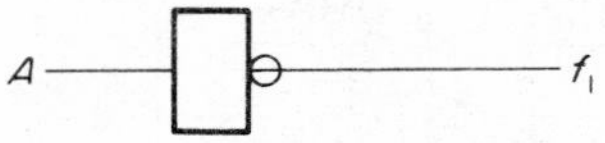 $f_1 = \overline{A}$	$f_1 = \overline{A}$
(b) A —G1—[ ]o $\overline{A}$ ... B —G2—[ ]o $\overline{B}$ ... f_2	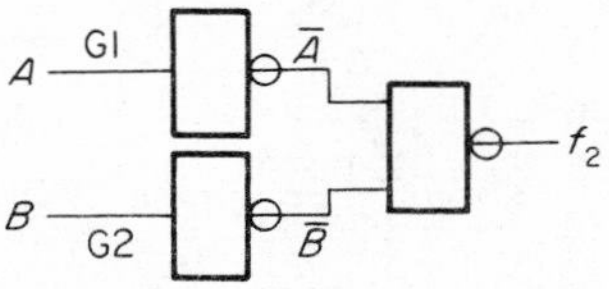 $f_2 = A.B$	$f_2 = A+B$
(c) A —G3—[ ]o—G4—[ ]o— f_3 B	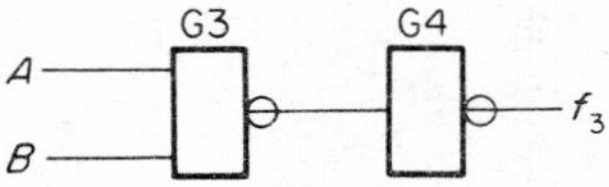 $f_3 = A+B$	$f_3 = A.B$

Fig. 18.7   Some functions generated by NOR and NAND gates.

S-line sets output Q to the '1' state, and a signal at the R-line resets output Q to zero. Under normal operating conditions the logic levels at Q and $\overline{Q}$ are complementary.

Before explaining the principle of operation of the NOR S-R flip-flop, the reader is reminded that the output from a NOR gate is logic '0' when any input is logic '1', and that the output is logic '1' only when both inputs are logic '0'.

When a logic '1' signal is applied to the S-line (with $R = 0$ at this time) it causes output $\overline{Q}$ to be set to logic '0'. Both inputs to G2 are now '0', resulting in Q becoming logic '1'; the latter signal is fed back to the input of $G1$, and this results in output $\overline{Q}$ being maintained at the logic '0' level even if the signal on the S-line is reduced to logic '0'. Thus the signal applied to the S-line can be a pulse of very short duration.

A similar argument shows that when a logic '1' is applied to the R-line (with $S = 0$ at this time), the Q-output is reset to logic '0', (i.e., $\overline{Q} = 1$).

When both input lines are energized with logic '1' signals, both Q and $\overline{Q}$ become logic '0' (in this operating state the outputs are not complementary). Whilst this operating condition is perfectly in order, it is inadvisable to design circuits which use it for the following reason. If the logic signals applied to both input lines is simultaneously changed from '1' to '0', both gates 'race' each other to reach an output of logic '1'. Whichever is the 'fastest' applies its logic '1' to

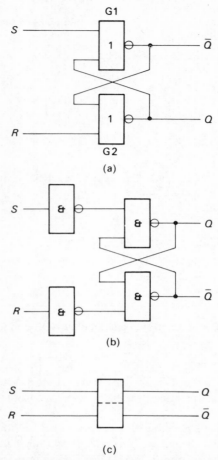

Fig. 18.8   An *S-R* flip-flop using (a) NOR gates, (b) NAND gates. One form of circuit symbol is shown in (c); the broken line may be omitted in some cases.

the input of the other gate and forces the output of the second gate to become '0'. Hence the state of the outputs after a simultaneous input signal change from logic '1' to logic '0' cannot be reliably predicted.

18.8   Logic families

Early versions of logic circuits consisted simply of diode-resistor networks (*diode-resistor logic* or DRL), of the type in Figs. 18.2 and 18.3. Simultaneously, *resistor-transistor logic* (RTL) gates of the type in Fig. 18.4 were developed. These types have been superseded by logic families which were made possible by developments in monolithic integrated circuit technology.

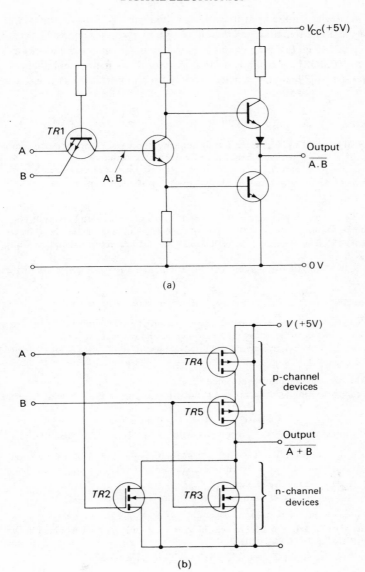

Fig. 18.9   (a) A bipolar transistor TTL NAND gate, and (b) a CMOS NOR gate.

Circuit diagrams of two-input NAND and NOR circuits manufactured in monolithic form are shown in diagrams (a) and (b), respectively, of Fig. 18.9. The NAND circuit, diagram (a), is one of a family known as *transistor–transistor logic* (TTL), and is widely used in commercial, industrial and domestic equipments. An unusual feature of this logic family is the multiple emitter transistor

*TR*1. This device generates at its collector the logical AND function of the input signals. The remainder of the circuit is a high-speed logic NOT gate. The NOR gate, diagram (a), is an example of the *complementary metal–oxide–semiconductor* (CMOS) logic family and employs both p–channel and n–channel MOS transistors. This type of gate is widely used in portable electronic calculators.

Problems

18.1 What is meant by n-type and p-type impurity doping in a semiconductor device? Illustrate your answer with diagrams of the crystal lattice structure.

Explain the principle of operation of an n-p-n transistor and sketch its output characteristics. Show how it may be used as an electronic switch and indicate its limitations in this mode of operation.

18.2 Draw up truth tables for the NAND and NOR logic gates with two input lines.

Show that the logical NOT, AND, and OR functions can be generated using *either* a number of NAND *or* a number of NOR gates. Supplement your explanation with diagrams.

Explain, with the aid of diagrams, the operation of an *S-R* flip-flop constructed from NOR gates.

18.3 Describe the operation of a resistor-transistor NOR element.

18.4 Explain, using suitable diagrams, the operation of diode logic circuits for performing the AND and OR functions, using (a) positive logic, and (b) negative logic.

Discuss briefly the relative merits and disadvantages of diode logic compared with other types of logic circuits.

18.5 Why are logic functions so named?

By means of (a) Boolean algebra and (b) truth tables, prove the following Boolean equations:

$$\overline{A \vee B \vee C} = \overline{A} . \overline{B} . \overline{C} \qquad A \vee \overline{A} . \overline{B} = A \vee \overline{B}$$

Note: 'v' represents logic OR. '.' represents logic AND. '‾' represents logic NOT.

18.6 Describe, with the aid of a suitable diagram, the operation of a bistable circuit using two p-n-p transistors. Discuss the minimum changes necessary to turn the circuit into

(a) A free-running multivibrator.

(b) A monostable circuit (one-shot multivibrator).

18.7 Explain briefly why Boolean algebra is used in the design of modern digital systems.

By means of (a) Boolean algebra and (b) truth tables, prove the following Boolean equations:

$$A \vee \overline{A} . B = A \vee B \qquad \overline{A \vee B \vee C} = \overline{A.B.C}$$

19. Stabilized power supplies

19.1 Basic requirements

The basic block diagram of a regulated power supply is shown in Fig. 19.1.
Broadly speaking regulated power supplies or *stabilized power supplies* can be
reduced to four main areas:

(a) a.c. to d.c. supplies.
(b) d.c. to d.c. supplies.
(c) a.c. to a.c. supplies.
(d) d.c. to a.c. supplies.

Type (a) is used more than any other, and is the subject of this chapter. The
remaining three groups are more specialized.

In a.c. to d.c. supply systems, the unstabilized power supply is a simple
rectifier and smoothing circuit. The output from the unstabilized power supply
is applied to a controlling device which regulates the voltage to give a steady d.c.
output. A proportion of the output signal is fed back, usually from a resistive
type of network, and is compared with a reference signal. The difference
between the two signals is then used to actuate the controlling element in such a
way that it maintains the level of the output quantity at a constant value.

These regulators can be further subdivided into two groups:

(a) Series regulators,
(b) Shunt regulators.

In a *series regulator,* the controlling device is connected in series with the load,
and to regulate the output it must, at all times, absorb some of the supply
voltage. Thus, if the series controlling device is a transistor and the unstabilized
supply voltage is 20 V, then several volts would need to be dropped across the
transistor. This allows the voltage across the transistor to be altered by the
feedback signal to accommodate variations in the supply voltage and load
resistance.

In a *shunt regulator,* the controlling device is in parallel with the load, and to effect output regulation it must pass current at all times. When the current through the controlling device falls to zero, regulating action ceases.

In more sophisticated power supplies, protection circuits are built into the network to limit one or more quantities to a safe level. For example, in the event of an excessive overload or a short-circuit being applied to a semiconductor voltage regulator, to protect the semiconductor regulating device the current must be switched off or reduced to a safe value within 10 μs to 100 μs. Fuses cannot provide this form of protection, and feedback techniques are used. The problem is not so serious in regulators using thermionic devices, and a thermal cut-out can be used. A feature of semiconductor devices is that when they fail

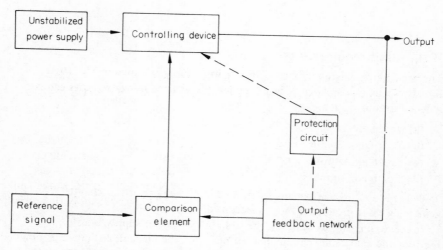

Fig. 19.1   A block diagram of a regulated power supply.

catastrophically, they usually develop an internal short-circuit between the collector and emitter. In series regulators, this means that the unregulated power supply will be directly connected to the output terminals, possibly causing damage to the connected load. One method of protecting the load against this type of fault, known as *crowbar voltage protection,* employs a voltage-sensitive circuit which monitors the output voltage of the regulator; this circuit instantly applies a short-circuit to the output terminals whenever the voltage rises above a predetermined level. A thyristor can be used as a crowbar device. An inherent advantage of a shunt voltage regulator in the above case is that a short-circuit in the regulating device causes the output voltage to fall to zero instantly.

The reference voltage source in regulator circuits is usually a Zener diode.

19.2   Stabilization factor and output resistance

The degree of stabilization against output voltage variation offered by a constant-voltage regulated power supply is given by the *stabilization factor S,* where

$$S = \frac{\delta V_0}{\delta V_1} = \frac{\text{Change in output voltage}}{\text{Change in supply voltage}} \qquad (19.1)$$

the measurements being made with a constant value of load current. Strictly speaking, the stabilization factor should be computed on the basis that *only* V_0 *and* V_1 change. In practice, other quantities do change, e.g., the load resistance, the transistor or valve parameters, etc., but for our purposes they are considered to be constant.

In relatively simple regulators, S may have a value of 0·005 (a change of 5 mV/V), while sophisticated supplies provide values of S which can be smaller than 0·0002 (i.e., $< 0·2$ mV/V). Alternatively, the stabilization against voltage change may be defined as the inverse of S, when it is described as the *stability ratio*; in the above example, the stability ratios are 200:1 and 5000:1, respectively.

The *output resistance* of a power source is defined as

$$R_0 = -\frac{\delta V_0}{\delta I_0} = \frac{\text{Change in output voltage}}{\text{Change in output current}} \qquad (19.2)$$

the measurement being made with a constant value of input voltage. The negative sign in eq. (19.2) implies that an increase in load current results in a reduction in output voltage. The output resistance of a relatively uncomplicated voltage source for low voltage applications (e.g., up to 100 V) may be 20 mΩ, and in an equivalent sophisticated unit it may be 2 mΩ; in a 10 kV e.h.t. supply the output resistance could quite easily be 5 kΩ. The output resistance of a constant current source is, typically, many tens of thousands of ohms.

19.3   A voltage reference source

A popular circuit used as a voltage reference source is shown in Fig. 19.2. It consists of a Zener diode with its cathode connected to the positive pole of the unstabilized power supply via resistor R. The magnitude of the supply

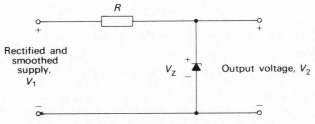

Fig. 19.2   A simple form of voltage reference source.

voltage V_1 is greater than the Zener diode breakdown voltage V_Z; the potential difference between V_1 and $V_Z (= V_1 - V_Z)$ appears across resistor R.

Zener diodes selected for this type of application should exhibit practically no change in breakdown voltage with temperature. The output voltage from this circuit has a value equal to the breakdown voltage of the Zener diode, i.e., $V_2 = V_Z$. Should the value of the supply voltage V_1 alter in value, the p.d. across R alters to compensate for the change, and the output voltage remains constant. If the current in resistor R is I then

$$R = (V_1 - V_Z)/I \qquad (19.3)$$

When the external load resistor, R_L, is disconnected ($R_L = \infty$) the Zener diode must be capable of absorbing the current given by eq. (19.3), hence

$$I \leqslant P_Z/V_Z \qquad (19.4)$$

where P_Z is the power rating of the Zener diode. The circuit ceases to act as a regulator when $I_Z = 0$, i.e., when the load current $= I$; this occurs when the minimum value of load resistance $R_{L(min)}$ is connected, giving

$$\frac{V_Z}{R_{L(min)}} = \frac{V_1 - V_Z}{R}$$

therefore,

$$R_{L(min)} = \left(\frac{V_Z}{V_1 - V_Z}\right) R \qquad (19.5)$$

As a matter of good practice, it is inadvisable to operate the Zener diode near to the zero current condition otherwise the output voltage will vary due to the curvature of the characteristic in the region of the 'knee'.

Example 19.1: Design a voltage reference circuit which uses a 5 V, 400 mW Zener diode. If the supply voltage is 11 V ± 2 V, calculate the value of the resistor R which is to be chosen from a range of preferred resistors with a 10 per cent tolerance. Estimate the lowest value of load resistance that can be connected before the regulator fails to function correctly.

Solution: From eq. (19.4) the current (I) in resistor R is

$$I \leqslant P_Z/V_Z = 400 \times 10^{-3}/5 \quad A = 80 \text{ mA}$$

Resistor R must limit I to this value when the maximum supply voltage, $V_{1(max)}$, is applied

$$R = (V_{1(max)} - V_Z)/I = (13 - 5)/80 \times 10^{-3} = 100 \ \Omega$$

A 100 Ω, 10 per cent tolerance resistor has a minimum value of 90 Ω, which would allow a maximum current of 88·9 mA to flow in the Zener diode when the load is disconnected. As this exceeds the rating of the device, the next higher value of resistance must therefore be chosen, i.e., a 120 Ω, 10 per cent tolerance resistor. Assuming a nominal 120 Ω value, the maximum value of I is 66·7 mA when $V_{1(\text{max})}$ is applied, and the maximum power dissipated by the resistor is 0·53 W.

The value of $R_{L(\text{min})}$ is calculated from eq. (19.5); to allow for 'worst case' conditions, the minimum value of supply voltage is used.

$$R_{L(\text{min})} = R V_Z/(V_{1(\text{min})} - V_Z) = 120 \times 5/(9 - 5) = 150 \ \Omega$$

19.4 The series controlling device

The basis of the series regulator is the emitter follower in Fig. 19.3. The signal V_X applied to the base of the transistor is the output from a voltage reference source similar to that in Fig. 19.2. From the work in chapter 14, readers will

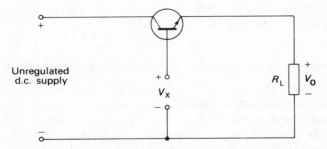

Fig. 19.3 A basic form of series controlling circuit.

appreciate that the value of the output voltage V_O is (by emitter follower action) only slightly less than the value of V_X. Thus, since V_X has a constant and stable value, it follows that the output voltage is also constant and stable.

19.5 A basic series voltage regulator

A simple circuit which provides a stabilized but variable output voltage is shown in Fig. 19.4. The circuit combines the voltage reference source in Fig. 19.2 and the series controlling device in Fig. 19.3. Assuming that a silicon transistor is used, the output voltage (V_{out}) has a value which is about 0·6 V below the voltage at the wiper of RV1. Potentiometer RV1 allows the user to manually adjust the value of the output voltage.

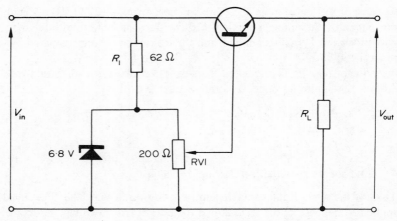

Fig. 19.4   A simple series voltage regulator.

The output resistance of this circuit is reduced and the stabilization factor of this circuit is improved if an amplifier is included in the feedback circuit, in the manner described in section 19.6.

19.6   A series voltage regulator incorporating an amplifier

A series regulator is shown in Fig. 19.5, in which the reader will recognize the rectifier and smoothing circuit, the voltage reference source and the series controlling device. The output feedback network (see also Fig. 19.1) in the circuit consists of the resistive network containing R_1, R_2 and $RV1$; the latter is used to adjust the value of the output voltage. The output voltage V_O and the reference voltage V_Z are applied to the inputs of a differential amplifier (see also chapter 11), whose output voltage is proportional to the potential difference between its input voltages, i.e., $V_Z - \beta V_O$.

The potential at the wiper of the potentiometer RV is a fraction, β, of the output voltage, i.e., it is βV_O. If the gain of the differential amplifier is fairly high, the value of the voltage V_1 between the terminals of the differential amplifier is very small. That is,

$$\beta V_O = V_Z$$

$$V_O = V_Z/\beta$$

For example, if $V_Z = 5$ V and $\beta = 0.4$, then $V_O = 5/0.4 = 12.5$. If the potentiometer slider is moved towards the positive output line so that $\beta = 0.5$, then the new value of output voltage is $V_O = 5/0.5 = 10$ V. Potentiometer $RV1$ may either be a preset potentiometer or, in the case of a general purpose laboratory instrument, it is a potentiometer with its control knob on the front panel of the instrument.

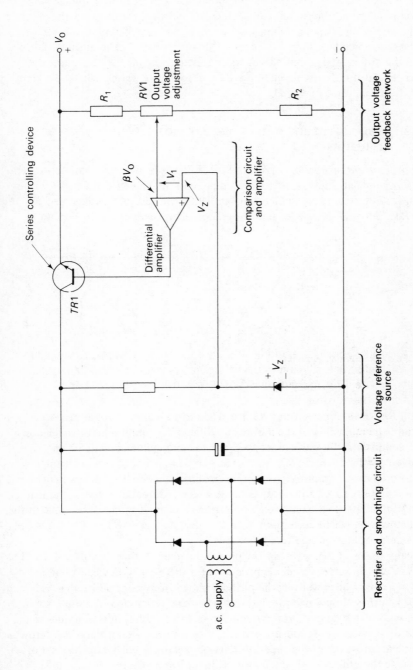

Fig. 19.5   A series regulator incorporating an amplifier in the feedback loop.

The circuit shown regulates its output voltage against supply voltage variations as follows. Should the supply voltage increase in value, the output voltage tends to rise and, with it, the net voltage at the input of the differential amplifier decreases (remember, $V_1 = V_Z - \beta V_O$). This action reduces the output voltage from the differential amplifier which, by emitter follower action, causes the series regulator output voltage to be reduced to a value which is little different from its initial value of V_Z/β.

19.7   Overcurrent and output overvoltage protection of series regulators

The *overcurrent protection* circuit in Fig. 19.6 may be used in conjunction with the series regulator in Fig. 19.5; the components $TR1$ and R_1 in Fig. 19.6 refer to the corresponding components in Fig. 19.5. The additional elements $TR2$ and $RV2$ provide the overcurrent protection. The operation of the circuit is

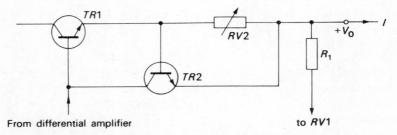

From differential amplifier   to $RV1$

Fig. 19.6   One method of applying overcurrent protection.

as follows. In use, the value of $RV2$ is adjusted so that, at normal values of current, the p.d. across it is insufficient to cause $TR2$ to conduct. Under overload conditions, the p.d. across $RV2$ is large enough to cause $TR2$ to begin to conduct, when $TR2$ diverts some of the current from the output of the differential amplifier away from the base of $TR1$. This causes the collector current of $TR1$ to reduce in value, which reduces the value of the load current to a safe level. *Increasing* the resistance of $RV2$ *reduces* the value of the load current at which current limitation begins, i.e., when RV has a high value, the load current is limited to a low value.

Many forms of logic systems are prone to damage if their supply voltage rises above a certain value. Power supplies used for this type of device should incorporate a means of preventing the output voltage from rising above the safe limit, i.e., they should include output *overvoltage protection*. A simple method of providing this type of protection is shown in Fig. 19.7. In this circuit, in the event of an overvoltage appearing at the output terminals, an electronic 'crowbar' is applied across the output lines; this action instantaneously applies a short-circuit to the output of the regulator. This type of protection is described as

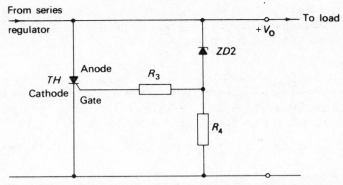

Fig. 19.7   A simple form of 'crowbar' overvoltage protection.

crowbar overvoltage protection. The current flowing in the short-circuit is
either limited by the current limit protection described above, or blows a supply
fuse or operates a cut-out (where fitted). This type of protection is not only
used with IC systems but is widely used in many stabilized power supplies in
colour TV receivers.

The overvoltage protection circuit in Fig. 19.7 operates as follows. The trip-
ping level of the circuit is set by the breakdown voltage of the Zener diode *ZD2*.
When the output voltage from the regulator exceeds the breakdown voltage of
ZD2, current flows through the current limiting resistor R_3 and into the gate of
TH. This has the effect of turning *TH* on, and applies a short-circuit to the out-
put terminals of the regulator.

19.8   Stabilizer with a shunt transistor

A simple shunt regulator consists of a transistor in conjunction with the Zener
diode, as shown in Fig. 19.8. The emitter current of the transistor is the sum
of the base current (i.e., the Zener diode current) and the collector current.
Thus, the shunt circuit handles $(1 + h_{\text{FE}})$ times the current flowing in the
Zener diode.

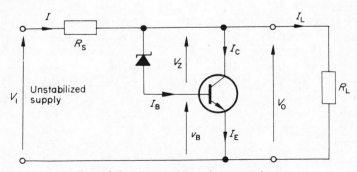

Fig. 19.8   A transistor shunt regulator.

Since the shunt transistor operates in the unsaturated region of its characteristics, the base-emitter voltage drop v_{BE} is of the order of 0·2 to 0·8 V. If the slope resistance of the Zener diode can be neglected, then

$$V_0 \simeq V_Z + v_{BE}$$

Since v_{BE} remains substantially constant over the working range of the transistor, the output voltage is slightly greater than V_Z. The base current is restricted by the current rating of the Zener diode, hence,

$$I_B \leqslant P_Z/V_Z$$

where P_Z is the power rating of the Zener diode.

The maximum load current should be limited to a value which is less than the emitter current of the transistor, otherwise both the diode and the transistor may be damaged if the load becomes disconnected. Hence,

$$I = I_B + I_C = (1 + h_{FE})I_B \leqslant (1 + h_{FE})P_Z/V_Z$$

and the value of R_S is calculated from the equation

$$R_S = (V_1 - V_0)/I$$

and it has a power dissipation of $I^2 R_S$.

19.9   Switched-mode power supplies

Disadvantages of conventional types of series regulator and shunt regulator include (i) the necessity to incorporate a large and costly step-down transformer which operates at mains frequency, and (ii) power is continuously dissipated by the regulating device.

Switched-mode power supplies (SMPS) overcome these disadvantages by operating the transformer at high frequency (typically 20 to 50 kHz, which is beyond the audible range), and by regulating the output voltage by means of a switching device. The switching device (usually a transistor) is either fully turned on (when the p.d. across it is zero, and the power dissipated by it is zero) or is turned off (when the current through it is zero, and the power dissipated by it is zero). However, the reader must not think that the circuit is 100 per cent efficient, since there are other sources of power loss.

The basis of one form of SMPS is shown in Fig. 19.9. The mains supply is rectified and smoothed to provide a high voltage d.c. supply. This is converted into a high frequency a.c. supply by means of a 'chopper' or electronic switch, and the r.m.s. voltage applied to the primary winding of the transformer depends on the mark-to-space ratio (or on-to-off ratio) of the chopping device. Control of the d.c. output voltage from the regulator is therefore exercised by controlling the r.m.s. value of the primary winding voltage—more is said about

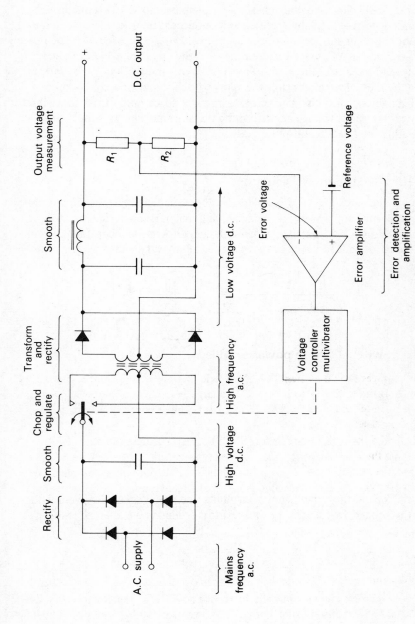

Fig. 19.9   The basis of a switched-mode power supply.

this below. Due to the very high frequency involved, a small ferrite-core transformer can be used which has a very low power loss. The transformer secondary voltage is finally rectified and smoothed. In order to regulate the output voltage, a proportion of the output voltage is compared with the reference voltage, and the difference between the two (the error voltage) is amplified and is used to control the mark-to-space ratio of a multivibrator. The output from the multivibrator controls the action of the semiconductor chopper in the high voltage, d.c. circuit. Hence the mark-to-space ratio of the multivibrator controls the r.m.s. voltage applied to the transformer primary winding, so regulating the final d.c. output voltage.

19.10   Series current regulators

In some applications, it is desirable to be able to maintain a constant current in a circuit, despite supply voltage variations and load resistance changes. A basic circuit is shown in Fig. 19.10, which is designed to deliver a constant current of 10 mA into a load which has a resistance of any value between zero and

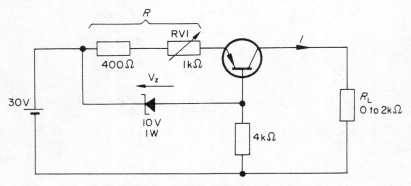

Fig. 19.10   A series current regulator.

about 2 kΩ. In the circuit shown, assuming that v_{BE} is small compared with V_Z, the voltage drop across the two resistors comprising R is equal to V_Z that is,

$$V_Z \simeq IR$$

or

$$I \simeq V_Z/R$$

The load current is set up initially by means of $RV1$, so that with a 10 V Zener diode and a load current of 10 mA, R has a value of 10 V/10 mA = 1 kΩ. The power rating of resistor R must be greater than 10 V x 10 mA = 100 mW. The lower end of the 4 kΩ resistor may, alternatively, be connected to the collector of the transistor instead of the negative supply rail.

Under no-load conditions ($R_L = 0$), the transistor must absorb a voltage $(V_S - IR) = 30 - 10 = 20$ V. The limiting condition for the circuit to maintain the load current constant occurs when the p.d. across the transistor falls to zero. This happens when the p.d. across the transistor is zero, and $IR_{L(max)} = 20$ V, or when

$$R_{L(max)} = 20 \text{ V}/10 \text{ mA} = 2 \text{ k}\Omega$$

In order that the transistor can deal with all possible load conditions, it must have a maximum current rating greater than 10 mA, and a voltage rating greater than 20 V.

Problems

19.1 Draw the static characteristic of a Zener diode, and explain its principle of operation. Show how the diode can be used in a simple shunt regulator.

19.2 Design a Zener diode shunt regulator to supply 0·2 A at 15 V from a 50 V unstabilized supply. Assume that the slope resistance of the diode is zero. State the ratings of the Zener diode and the series resistance.

19.3 A shunt regulator uses the transistor circuit in Fig. 19.8. If $R_S = 50$ Ω, the Zener diode slope resistance is 10 Ω, and the relevant transistor parameters are $h_{FE} = 49$, $h_{IE} = 10$ Ω, calculate (a) the output resistance of the regulator, (b) the change in output voltage when the load current changes by 1·5 A, the supply voltage remaining constant, and (c) the change in output voltage when the supply voltage changes by 5 V, the load resistance being 10 Ω.

19.4 For a regulator of the kind in Fig. 19.4, estimate the input voltage range for which the circuit gives satisfactory stabilization. Assume that the transistor bias current is negligible and that the components have the values given in the figure. The Zener diode current must not be allowed to fall below 1 mA, and its power rating is 750 mW.

19.5 For a circuit of the type in Fig. 19.5, estimate suitable values for R_1 and $RV1$ if $V_Z = 4·7$ V, and if the output voltage is to be regulated between 10 V and 20 V.

20. Electronic measuring instruments

20.1 The cathode-ray oscilloscope

The cathode-ray oscilloscope (C.R.O.) is perhaps the most versatile measuring instrument available for use with electronic circuits. With it, it is possible to measure voltage, current, phase-angle, and a whole host of other quantities, and it gives electronic engineers another eye to 'see' inside the circuit itself. By utilizing a range of probes and plug-in units, measurements from microvolts to megavolts can be made at frequencies from zero (d.c.) to several gigahertz ($1\,\mathrm{GHz} = 10^9$ Hz).

The rudiments of the C.R.O. are shown in Fig. 20.1; the heart of the C.R.O. is the *cathode-ray tube* (C.R.T.), in which a controlled beam of electrons causes an illuminated spot to appear on the *fluorescent screen* of the tube. By controlling the movement of the illuminated spot in both the X-direction and the Y-direction, waveforms and other curves can be traced out on the screen; in some oscilloscopes it is possible to modulate the brilliance of the spot, giving what is known as *Z modulation*. In most modern oscilloscopes, there is a great deal of sophistication, particularly in the amplifiers and circuitry to ensure that the trace or *oscillograph* is a true representation of the input signal or *Y input*.

The input signal is first either amplified or attenuated to give the correct voltage levels to the rest of the circuit; from this section of the circuitry, a *synchronizing signal* or *trigger signal* is derived which initiates the movement of the spot on the face of the tube. Alternatively, the oscillograph may be synchronized with some other external signal by switching S1 to the upper position. The synchronizing signal (*sync. signal*) is applied to the *timebase generator* which causes the spot on the face of the tube to be deflected in the X direction. It is usual in most oscilloscopes to provide switch S2, which allows the operator to choose the sign of the slope at the point at which the trace commences. In some applications, it is necessary to apply signals from an external source directly to the X amplifier; this is achieved by means of switch S3. When the X

278

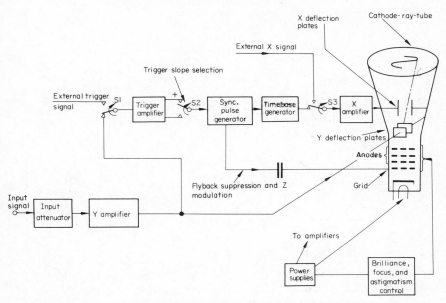

Fig. 20.1   A block diagram of a cathode-ray oscilloscope.

amplifier derives its input from the timebase generator, it traces out a *Y-time graph*, which is a graph of the Y input signal to a base of time. When the input to the X amplifier is derived from an external signal source, it operates as an *X-Y oscilloscope*, since the Y input signal is graphed to a base of the X input. In the X-Y mode, the oscilloscope can be used as an accurate means of measuring phase-shift and frequency.

The power supplies to the grid and anode systems are derived from one or more power sources, and *brilliance, focus,* and *astigmatism* control of the illuminated spot are obtained by potentiometric adjustments. It is also necessary to provide *X shift* and *Y shift* controls to give the operator overall ability to position the trace at any part of the screen.

20.2   The cathode-ray tube (C.R.T.)

The C.R.T. is a funnel-shaped high vacuum valve with an *electron gun* at the end of the long neck of the valve, and a screen treated with a *phosphor* at the flared end. A schematic diagram of a C.R.T. for a typical instrument application is shown in Fig. 20.2. Between the cathode and the display is an array of electrodes which is used to control the electron beam.

The cathode, which is in the form of a flat disc to give high electron emission from one face, is indirectly heated and is completely surrounded by a metallic control grid. The grid has a small hole in one end to allow electrons to escape in

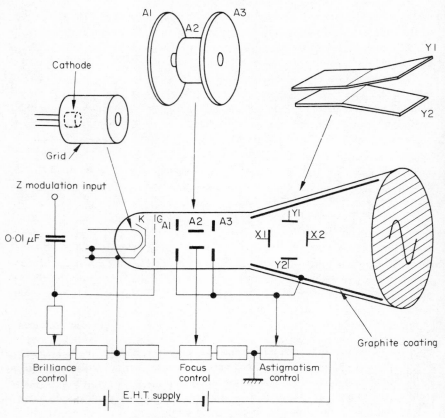

Fig. 20.2   The cathode-ray tube.

the longitudinal direction towards the anodes of the electron gun. As a general rule there are three anodes A1, A2, and A3, each at a positive potential with respect to the cathode. In simple terms, A1 and A3 are discs having a small centre hole, and A2 is cylindrical (possibly with internal diaphragms). The function of the anode system is twofold. Firstly, it accelerates the electron beam, and secondly it takes the convergent beam of electrons which emerge through the hole in the grid and forms it into a divergent beam by the time it has passed through the anodes. As a result of the latter function, this section is known as the *electron-lens system*. Focusing can be achieved by electromagnetic means, and is discussed in section 20.3. The electron beam then enters the deflection system, where it is deflected first in the Y direction and then in the X direction by signals applied between pairs of specially shaped plates. Each pair of deflection plates is flared at the end to prevent the introduction of waveform distortion resulting from electrostatic fringing at the ends of the plates.

In order to ensure that the electron beam continues to travel at a constant longitudinal velocity when it leaves the final anode, the inside of the flared part of the tube is coated with a graphite conducting material known as *Aquadag*, which is maintained at the same potential as the final anode. The Aquadag layer also provides the return path for the current from the screen of the tube.

The general term used to describe the process of converting energy into light is known as *luminescence* (the special case of converting thermal energy into light is known as *incandescence*). When rays or beams of energy fall on certain substances they produce a form of luminescence known as *fluorescence*, which occurs when energy of one wavelength is absorbed by the substance and is emitted as light. In the case of the C.R.T., the cathode rays or beam of high speed electrons produce fluorescence in the film of material laid down on the face of the tube. Luminescence which continues for some time after the excitation energy has fallen to zero is known as *phosphorescence* or *after-glow*. After-glow is due to the release of stored energy in the form of light over a period of time. The *persistence* of the after-glow of a C.R.T. phosphor is generally defined as the time taken for the light output from the phosphor to decline to 10 per cent of the original intensity. Fluorescence and after-glow are always produced together, one generally predominating over the other (depending on the phosphor). The choice of phosphor depends upon the principal application of the C.R.O.

When the primary electron beam arrives at the screen, electrons are released from the phosphor by secondary emission. For a correct potential balance to exist on the screen, the number of primary electrons arriving at the screen must be equal to the net number leaving it. Thus, if *m* electrons arrive in a given time in Fig. 20.3(a), then *m* secondary electrons must be attracted to the Aquadag coat. It is possible that additional electrons may be released from the screen by

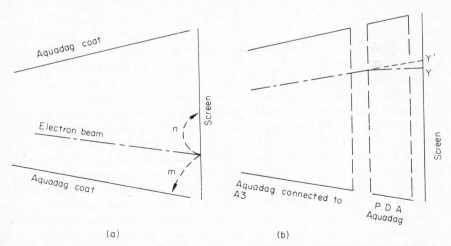

Fig. 20.3   (a) Return path for the screen current; (b) post-deflection-acceleration anode.

secondary emission, leaving the screen with a net positive charge on it. To maintain the potential balance on the screen, the surplus electrons are attracted back to the screen by random routes, path *n* being an example in Fig. 20.3(a). The beam current is controlled by the brilliance control in Fig. 20.2, which controls the grid-cathode potential; if this control is set too high (particularly with a long persistence phosphor), it is possible to *burn* the face of the tube at the point of arrival of the beam. At high beam intensities, the spot on the screen is surrounded by a ring or halo of light, which is due to an excessive number of secondary electrons falling back on the screen to produce secondary illumination.

Despite the fact that the Aquadag coating is provided as a return path for the secondary electrons, there is a net accumulation of negative charge on the screen which leads to a reduction of brightness of the trace. One method adopted to overcome this problem is by backing the screen with a thin layer of aluminium which the electron beam can penetrate. This conducting layer is connected to the final anode, so preventing the formation of a negative charge on the screen. Such a tube is said to be *aluminized.*

One method which is sometimes adopted to increase *either* the brilliance *or* the deflection sensitivity is to use a *post-deflection-acceleration (p.d.a.) anode.* This is simply an Aquadag coat around the screen end of the tube which is isolated from the main Aquadag coat, and is maintained at a potential of 2 kV to 4 kV above the final anode. The net result, illustrated in Fig. 20.3(b), is that the electron beam is deflected. In the absence of the p.d.a. anode, the beam would reach the screen at point Y', but when p.d.a. is applied the additional longitudinal acceleration causes the beam to arrive at point Y. Clearly, if p.d.a. is to be used to increase the brilliance of the trace (due to the increased final velocity), then the deflection sensitivity is reduced since a smaller deflection results. On the other hand, for a given brilliance, p.d.a. allows a greater deflection sensitivity to be achieved since the final anode is run at a much lower voltage, allowing the beam to pass more slowly through the deflection system. In the latter case, the individual electrons stay under the influence of the deflecting voltage for a longer period of time, and suffer a greater deflection.

There are some interesting variations on the C.R.T. which are worthy of mention here. In some applications, it is necessary to study a series of simultaneous events, in which case multiple traces must be drawn out on the screen, and there are various ways of doing this. Firstly, the main beam can be divided into two by a *splitter plate,* each half of the beam then being processed by an independent electron-lens and Y deflection system (the X deflection system being common to the two beams). Secondly, two completely separate electron guns and Y deflection systems can be used. Thirdly, a control circuit can be used to cause a single beam to trace out a number of curves by switching each input signal to the Y amplifier in succession. By the latter means, it is not uncommon to have up to four or more independent traces on the face of the tube. While the C.R.O. is a versatile instrument, its measuring accuracy is usually not much better than 3 per cent, which is futher reduced if the rectangular grid (called a *graticule*), which is placed in front of the tube for measuring purposes, is some distance from the screen. This introduces parallax errors. Where a high degree of accuracy is required, a tube with the graticule scribed on the inside face of the screen should be used.

The trace drawn out on the screen is subject to several forms of distortion peculiar to C.R.T.s, which include *trapezoidal distortion, pincushion distortion,* and *barrel distortion.* Trapezoidal distortion or trapezium distortion can be recognized as a change in deflection sensitivity as the spot sweeps across the screen, resulting in a signal of constant r.m.s. amplitude tracing out a trapezoidal area on the face of the screen. This defect is generally overcome by feeding opposite deflection plates (e.g., Y1 and Y2) from the outputs of a paraphase amplifier such as a long-tailed pair. Pincushion distortion and barrel distortion cause an otherwise rectangular display to be pincushion-shaped and barrel-shaped, respectively. One method of overcoming these defects is to place a shield between the X plates and the Y plates which is at the average potential of the two sets of plates.

20.3 Deflection systems and focusing systems

In the tube in Fig. 20.2, the beam is focused and deflected by electrostatic forces, and is of the type commonly used in electronic instruments. The velocity of the electrons leaving the electron gun is proportional to the final anode potential, and the greater the value of this voltage the smaller is the time that they dwell in the deflection system. Consequently, the deflection sensitivity is inversely proportional to the final anode voltage, since the deflection is proportional to the length of time the electrons spend in the deflection system.

The principle of *electromagnetic focusing* can be understood by reference to Fig. 20.4(a). If a longitudinal magnetic field is set up along the axis of the tube by an electromagnet or a permanent magnet which is external to the tube, then electrons which travel in a direction parallel to the field (i.e., into or out of the page) do not experience any force to deflect them in one direction or the other, and will continue to travel along the tube in a straight line. However, in the general case, electrons leave the electron gun at an infinite variety of angles, with the result that they enter the longitudinal magnetic field with a transverse velocity v, illustrated in Fig. 20.4(a). Since this motion is perpendicular to the magnetic field, the electron experiences a force which is mutually perpendicular to the transverse motion of the electron and the direction of action of the magnetic field. In the case illustrated, the magnetic flux enters the page, and the electron experiences an upward force at the instant considered. A study of its motion at subsequent intervals of time reveals that the electron travels in a circular orbit so long as it remains in the magnetic field. The magnets commonly used for this purpose provide a stronger field near to the envelope than they do at the centre. As a result, electrons with a wide angle of divergence enter a stronger magnetic field than those with a small divergence, causing the former to be turned toward the axis more rapidly than the latter. This enables all electrons to be focused accurately, even with a wide range of angles of divergence.

The principle of *electromagnetic deflection* is much the same as that for electromagnetic focusing, except that the magnetic field is applied in a transverse direction *across* the neck of the tube, as shown in Fig. 20.4(b). After the electron leaves the focusing system, it enters the transverse magnetic field and is deflected, the deflection being dependent on the initial velocity of the electron and the current flowing in the deflecting coils.

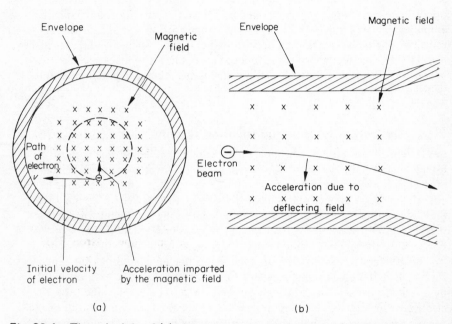

Fig. 20.4   The principle of (a) electromagnetic focusing, and (b) electromagnetic deflection.

Electromagnetic focusing is fundamentally more satisfactory than electrostatic focusing, since the electrons approach the screen from a variety of angles. In electrostatic focusing, the electrons approach the screen in the form of a beam, and the mutual repulsion between the electrons can cause defocusing. Electromagnetic deflection allows a much greater angle of deflection to be obtained without defocusing than is the general case with electrostatic deflection. However, electromagnetic deflection systems cannot handle high frequency signals (higher than about 20 kHz) due to the inductance of the coils. In some applications, notably domestic television tubes, a hybrid system with electrostatic focus and electromagnetic deflection is used.

20.4 Power supplies and C.R.O. controls

Owing to the wide variety of equipment used in oscilloscope circuits, a number of separate power supplies is required. The C.R.T. heater is supplied from an isolated winding on the main transformer, so that it can be directly coupled to the cathode of the tube, thus avoiding applying an excessive voltage to the insulation which separates them.

The final anode voltage may be anything from +1 kV to +20 kV or more with respect to the cathode. In a typical tube with a p.d.a. voltage of +3 kV, the A3 anode voltage may be about +250 V, with an A2 anode voltage of −500 V, and a cathode potential of −1 kV. The main controls of the circuit are as shown in Fig. 20.2, the brilliance control effecting control of beam current and the brilliance of the spot. The focus control alters the potential of the A2 anode and modifies the electric field within the electron lens. The astigmatism control enables the operator to adjust the shape of the spot on the screen so that it remains circular over its full scan. An unfortunate feature of many simple oscilloscopes is that the brilliance and focus controls interact upon one another, and increasing the brilliance of the trace causes defocusing.

In addition, a supply must be maintained to the amplifiers. In sophisticated units, the power supply is obtained from a stabilized voltage source, the design principles of which are dealt with in chapter 19. In less complex oscilloscopes, the power supply to the amplifiers is smoothed but not regulated, and to account for mains voltage variation the gain of the amplifiers used can be made inversely proportional to the supply voltage over a limited range of supply voltages. It is common to provide a calibration signal output on the front panel of the oscilloscope, in order to permit easy calibration of the gain and time controls. This signal is usually of the order of 1 V peak-to-peak at mains frequency.

20.5 Oscilloscope amplifiers

Almost without exception in oscilloscopes used as measuring instruments, the Y amplifiers consist of long-tailed pair stages. In a simple circuit, one stage of amplification would be used, and in more advanced equipment a number of cascaded stages are employed.

In an X-Y oscilloscope the X amplifier and the Y amplifier should be identical in all respects. To increase the usefulness of the C.R.O., Y shift and X shift controls are added to allow the trace to be located at any point on the screen. This is generally achieved by adjusting the bias voltage applied to the amplifier, causing a shift in output voltage.

Conventional oscilloscopes use *real time* scanning, that is to say that only waveforms that exist within the bandwidth of the amplifier system can be accurately observed. Developments in *sampling oscilloscopes* have, however, allowed repetitive events in the gigahertz region to be viewed. Amplifiers used in sampling oscilloscopes 'sample' the input waveform periodically, and display

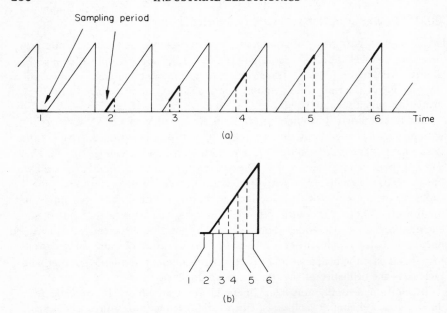

Fig. 20.5   Reconstruction of a waveform by a sampling oscilloscope.

the magnitude of the sample on the screen. Thus, if the waveform takes the form in Fig. 20.5(a), and is sampled at the instants 1 to 6 shown, the waveform can be reconstructed in the form in Fig. 20.5(b). By this means, a waveform which has a frequency above the normal range of real time systems can be displayed.

20.6   Horizontal deflection circuits

The function of the horizontal deflection circuit is to provide a voltage which causes the electron beam to be deflected in the X direction. In this section, we shall consider several circuits which generate *sawtooth waveforms,* so providing suitable constant-velocity waveforms in order that periodic waveforms may be displayed on the screen.

    The prime function of the timebase circuit is to generate a signal which causes the spot to scan across the face of the tube so that its displacement from the point of its commencement is proportional to the time which has elapsed from the start of the sweep. The *timebase* is the time taken for the spot to make one sweep in the X direction, and the circuit which develops the signal is known as the *timebase generator* or *sweep generator.*

    In a tube with electrostatic deflection, the ideal timebase waveform is shown in Fig. 20.6(a). The signal applied to the X_1 plate rises linearly from zero to a maximum value, after which it falls to zero voltage in zero time. A signal of the

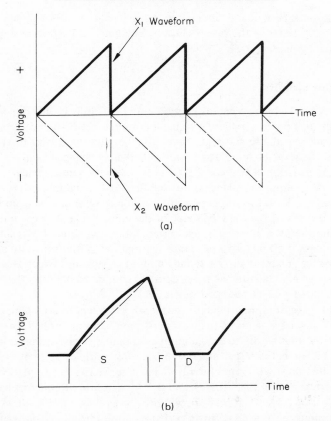

Fig. 20.6   (a) Idealized timebase waveform, and (b) a practical waveform.

opposite polarity is applied to the X_2 plate. An imperfect practical version of
the waveform is shown in Fig. 20.6(b), in which the voltage rise is non-linear
during the *sweep time S*, there is a finite *flyback time F* during which the spot
returns to the commencement of the sweep, and there is a *delay time D* before
the commencement of the next sweep. In addition, the voltage does not always
fall to zero due to the p.d. developed across some component in the circuit.
Normally, the flyback time is made as short as possible, but where the sweep
time is short (as is the case when high frequency phenomena are being investiga-
ted), the flyback time takes up an increasing proportion of the timebase and
may represent as much as 20 per cent of the total time. The flyback causes a
line to be drawn on the face of the tube, in much the same way as the trace is
drawn during the sweep. To eliminate this line, since it has only nuisance value,
a *flyback suppression* pulse is generated and is applied to the grid of the C.R.T.
during the flyback period. This has the effect of reducing the beam current

during the flyback period, and eliminating the flyback trace. Broadly speaking, timebase circuits generate the sweep signal by charging a capacitor, and the flyback signal by discharging it.

20.7   Input circuits

The accuracy with which a signal is presented on the C.R.T. is only as good as the circuits which process it allow it to be; input circuits are no exception to this rule. The input impedance and capacitance on all input ranges must be standardized on all settings of the input attenuator, otherwise a change of input impedance alters the load that the C.R.O. presents to the circuit being monitored. If the input impedance is not standardized, a change in the attenuator setting leads to an apparent difference in several factors including the magnitude, the phase, and the waveshape of the input signal. As a general rule, the input impedance of an oscilloscope is standardized at about 1 MΩ shunted by a capacitance of 20 pF to 50 pF. Since the input amplifier generally has an input impedance greater than 1 MΩ, and an input capacitance which is less than the standard value, a resistor and a capacitor are connected between the amplifier input terminals to give the standard values.

A normal range of input attenuator settings is 0·1 V/cm to 50 V/cm, corresponding to the voltage required to give a deflection of 1 cm on the face of the C.R.T. Suppose that we are to design input attenuators to give calibrations of 0·1 V/cm, 0·2 V/cm, 0·5 V/cm, and then in decade multiples up to 50 V/cm, what procedure must we adopt? Firstly we must derive the basic equations of the simple attenuator in Fig. 20.7(a), and then design four attenuators based on these equations. The final network will then be as shown in Fig. 20.7(b). A prime requirement of each network is that its input impedance must be 1 MΩ when it is terminated in a load of 1 MΩ. In the following all values are in megohms. Since the input impedance of Fig. 20.7(a) is $R_1 + [R_2 \times 1/(R_2 + 1)]$ MΩ, and this must have a value of 1 MΩ, then

$$1 = R_1 + \frac{1 \times R_2}{1 + R_2} \text{ M}\Omega \qquad (20.1)$$

Now, if the ratio V_2/V_1 of the circuit is N, then

$$N = \frac{V_2}{V_1} = \frac{(1 \times R_2)/(1 + R_2)}{R_1 + (1 \times R_2)/(1 + R_2)} \qquad (20.2)$$

But, from eq. (20.1), the denominator of eq. (20.2) has unity value, hence

$$N = R_2/(1 + R_2)$$

or

$$R_2 = \frac{N}{1 - N} \qquad (20.3)$$

R_1 can then be evaluated from eq. (20.1)

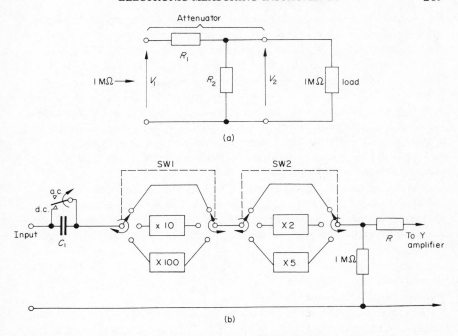

Fig. 20.7   (a) The basic attenuator circuit, and (b) the layout of a typical oscilloscope input circuit.

Since the oscilloscope calibration is 0·1 V/cm when the input is directly coupled to the Y amplifier, then an attenuator with $N = 0·5$ calls for an input voltage of 0·2 V to give a deflection of 1 cm on the screen. Substituting $N = 0·5$ into eq. (20.3) gives

$$R_2 = 1\ \text{M}\Omega$$

and R_1 is evaluated by substituting this value into eq. (20.1).

$$R_1 = 0·5\ \text{M}\Omega$$

For our purposes, we will describe this as a 'times two' attenuator, since it doubles the input voltage required to produce a given deflection on the screen. The combinations of resistor values for the four switched attenuators in Fig. 20.7(a) are listed in Table 20.1. If accuracy and repeatability are required,

Table 20.1

Attenuator	N	R_1 (MΩ)	R_2 (MΩ)
x 2	0·5	0·5	1·0
x 5	0·2	0·8	0·25
x 10	0·1	0·9	0·111
x 100	0·01	0·99	0·0101

high stability resistors with a tolerance of 1 per cent or better must be used in the attenuators.

The circuit in Fig. 20.7(b) highlights two other aspects of oscillography. Firstly, it may be desirable to monitor either the total instantaneous input signal (i.e., the d.c. component + the a.c. component) or only its alternating component. In the former case, the input signal is connected directly to the attenuator networks, and in the latter case it is coupled through capacitor C_1 which blocks the d.c. component of the input signal. C_1 typically has a value of 0·1 μF. Secondly, it is possible to apply an excessive voltage to the input circuit; to prevent an excessive current flowing into the Y amplifier, a resistor R is included in series with the input line.

In a practical attenuator, the input capacitance of the amplifier causes a reduction in input impedance at high frequency. In Fig. 20.8, this is represented by capacitor C_2. This must be compensated for in some way in order to reproduce high frequency phenomena faithfully. One method commonly used

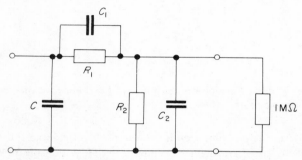

Fig. 20.8   A frequency compensated attenuator.

is to shunt the series resistor R_1 by capacitor C_1, which is adjusted in value until a square wave at the input is correctly traced out on the screen of the C.R.T. If C_1 is too small, the corners of the leading edge of the wave are rounded, and if too large the leading corners have overshoots or 'spikes'. In fact, much as R_1 and R_2 form a d.c. potential divider chain, C_1 and C_2 form an a.c. potential-divider chain. Capacitor C which is connected across the input of the attenuator is adjusted to give a total input capacitance which is equal to the standard value of input capacitance for that oscilloscope. When these adjustments have been made, the attenuator is described as a *frequency compensated attenuator*.

20.8   Oscilloscope probes

A *probe* is simply a test lead which contains either a passive network or an active network at its end or at some point along the lead.

A *simple voltage-divider probe* looks like the basic attenuator in Fig. 20.7(a), and may be used for voltages up to about 15 kV. In this type of probe, the input resistance is generally much greater than 1 MΩ, and a fairly complex frequency compensating network is employed to achieve a good high frequency response. A disadvantage of this arrangement is that the signal attenuation may be severe (up to about 1000:1 in some probes) which may be unacceptable in some instances due to the small size of the trace on the C.R.T.

If alternating voltages of the order of 50 kV are to be measured, a *capacitive potential-divider probe* is employed. In its simplest form, it consists of two series-connected capacitors as shown in Fig. 20.9. The input voltage divides between the two capacitors in inverse proportion to their capacitances.

In other circuits, the 1 MΩ input impedance of the C.R.O. may not be large when compared with the output impedance of the circuit. In this case, a high input impedance probe is required. A *resistive potential-divider probe* is commonly used in this application, the resistor being mounted in the tip of the probe. This type of probe presents an input impedance of the order of 10 MΩ, and has a voltage gain of the order of 0.1.

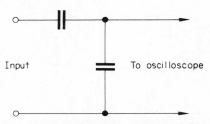

Fig. 20.9   A simple capacitive voltage-divider probe.

The simplest method of measuring current is to connect a low value of resistance in series with the circuit, and monitor the voltage across the resistance. Alternatively, a *current probe* can be used, which consists of a clip-on transformer with a secondary winding which is connected to the oscilloscope input.

20.9   Electronic voltmeters

Electronic voltmeters fall into two main groups. The first group contains *electronic voltmeters* (E.V.M.) proper, which are analogue (i.e., continuous reading) instruments which usually use a moving coil voltmeter as the read-out device. E.V.M.s are, more often than not, built around a linear amplifier with a high input impedance and high gain. The second group contains a range of instruments which give a digital readout, and are collectively known as *digital voltmeters* (D.V.M.)

20.10   Analogue Electronic Voltmeters

Electronic voltmeters can be used to measure unidirectional (d.c.) quantities as well as alternating quantities. The vast majority of E.V.M.s use a moving-coil meter in which the torque acting on the movement is proportional to the average current flowing through it; consequently, E.V.M.s are basically instruments which read unidirectional quantities, but they can be calibrated to read r.m.s. alternating quantities if the input signal is a pure sinusoid. The readings may be considerably in error if the input signal is non-sinusoidal.

One form of FET circuit used in d.c. instruments is shown in Fig. 20.10. It is in the form of a bridge circuit, with the two FETs forming one half of the bridge, and the source resistors R forming the other half. The meter (which usually has a full-scale deflection of between 200 μA and 1 mA) is coupled between the two sources which are the 'corners' of the bridge circuit. The network R_1C_1 serves to attenuate any a.c. signals which may be super-imposed upon the steady input voltage. The value of R_1 lies between 100 kΩ and 5 MΩ, while C_1 has a value between about 0·025 μF and 0·1 μF. With zero

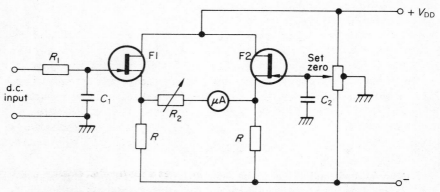

Fig. 20.10   One form of d.c. electronic voltmeter.

input signal, the bridge is balanced by the set zero control which alters the bias applied to FET F2; capacitor C_2 decouples the gate of F2 to earth.

When the gate of F1 is raised to a positive potential, the potential of the source is raised by a similar amount and current flows through the meter from the source of F1 to the source of F2. In order to provide a means of cali-brating the instrument, a variable resistor R_2 is connected in series with the meter; this resistance is adjusted at the time of the final calibration. The sensitivity of this type of instrument (i.e., the current flowing in the meter for a given input voltage) is very approximately $g_m/2$, where g_m is the mutual con-ductance of the FET. Thus, if g_m = 1 mA/V then the sensitivity of the instrument is approximately 0·5 mA/V.

Another circuit which is in common use in d.c. instruments is the long-tailed pair; in transistor circuits, the meter is connected between the two collectors.

Alternating quantities can be measured by rectifying the signal at some stage. Broadly speaking, a.c. instruments are either of the rectifier-amplifier type or of the amplifier-rectifier type. In the former, a d.c. amplifier is used and the instrument can be used to measure either alternating or direct quantities. In the latter type, a straightforward a.c. amplifier is used, and rectification takes place at the output. In this type of instrument, which only measures alternating quantities, overall negative feedback is applied to overcome the effects of temperature variation, ageing, etc. The output rectifier is usually included in the feedback loop to reduce the effects of the non-linear diode characteristics on the reading of the output meter. These instruments give full-scale deflections for inputs between 1 mV and several hundred volts in the frequency range 10 Hz to 10 MHz.

20.11 Digital voltmeters (D.V.M.)

In this section of the book, the more popular types are described. D.V.M.s are direct potential reading instruments, and require additional circuitry to enable them to read other quantities.

The terminology used in specifying the voltmeters can sometimes be confusing. For instance, the maximum reading on a four digit voltmeter is theoretically 9999, but the design of the circuit may limit the useful range to a maximum reading of, say, only 1999; in this case, the most significant digit can only assume either of the values zero or unity. An instrument with the latter type of display is known as a $3\frac{1}{2}$ digit D.V.M. Ideally, the limit of the accuracy of the instrument corresponds to the smallest digit displayed. However, factors such as the design of the circuit, electrical noise, input impedance, etc., mean that the value of the least significant digit is sometimes suspect.

A block diagram of one type of D.V.M. known as a *continuous balance voltmeter* is shown in Fig. 20.11. The counter is initially set to zero at the beginning of the measuring process. At a later point in the measuring process, the counter holds a succession of numbers, and these are converted into an analogue (i.e., continuous as distinct from digital) signal V_2 by the digital-to-analogue (D/A)

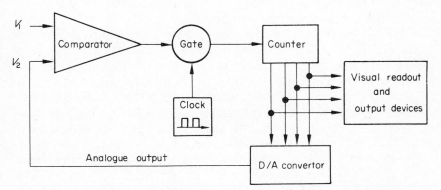

Fig. 20.11 A block diagram of one form of digital voltmeter.

convertor. The output from the D/A convertor is compared with the input signal V_1 in an electronic comparator. When $V_1 > V_2$, the output voltage from the comparator is at its highest level, causing the electronic 'gate' to be opened to allow the 'clock' pulses to be fed into the counter. So long as the gate remains open, the number stored in the counter continues to increase as it counts the clock pulses. This number is converted into an analogue voltage by the D/A convertor, giving a steadily increasing value of V_2. When $V_2 = V_1$, the output voltage from the comparator suddenly falls to zero, so closing the electronic gate and freezing the number held in the counter. The value of the input voltage is then displayed on the visual read-out device and other output devices which are connected to the D.V.M. The counter is usually a reversible counter so that it can change its value 'up' or 'down' as the input voltage changes.

Successive-approximation types of D.V.M. use a variant of the above principle. Let us first consider the operation of a D.V.M. of the type in Fig. 20.11. Suppose that we are using a two-digit D.V.M. with a maximum reading of 15 V, and the input voltage is 13 V. Since the counter commences at zero, 13 steps of 1 V are necessary to reach final balance. The essential difference between the continuous balance D.V.M. and the successive-approximation D.V.M. lies in the sequence of test voltages used to balance the voltmeter. Suppose that we were to try the sequence 8, 4, 2, 1. The first clock pulse in the successive-approximation type sets the counter to 8. This is compared with V_1, and since $V_1 > V_2$ the comparator allows the count to continue in the 'up' direction. The next clock pulse adds another 4 to the count, which now becomes 12; this is compared with V_1, and the count continues in the 'up' direction. The next clock pulse adds 2 to the count stored in the counter, making it 14. The comparator must then instruct the counter to count 'down' by the previous count, reducing the number in the counter to 12 again. The comparator now recognizes that $V_2 < V_1$, and the counter then counts 'up' by the next sample number which is unity, making the stored number equal to 13. At this point, after five steps, the D.V.M. balances. Clearly, the successive-approximation D.V.M. is potentially far more rapid in operation than the more simple continuous balance D.V.M., but only at an increase in complexity and capital cost.

In both types of D.V.M. described above, there is a danger of error due to induced voltages in the leads to the instrument. For this reason, a filter is usually included in the input circuit of the D.V.M.; in some applications this may have the undesirable effect of reducing the response of the instrument.

In another type of D.V.M., known as a *dual-ramp D.V.M.,* a capacitor is charged by the input voltage. The capacitor is then disconnected from the input, and connected to a constant-current discharge circuit. To determine the input voltage, clock pulses are gated into a counter during the discharge period. By a suitable choice of capacitance value, clock frequency, and sampling rate, the input voltage can be displayed directly.

Yet another type uses a *voltage-to-frequency convertor,* in which the input voltage controls the frequency of an oscillator. In this oscillator, the number of pulses per second is linearly proportional to the input voltage. By a suitable choice of the counting period and pulse frequency, the visual display is made equal to the input voltage.

Digital voltmeters often form the basis of *data processing systems* or *data logging systems*. In these systems, a number of analogue input signals are scanned sequentially by an electronic system; each signal is then converted into an equivalent digital value by the D.V.M. The digital value is then transmitted to a printer, together with information about the input line from which the signal is derived, and the information is printed out. In this way, a large number of input signals can be automatically scanned or processed, and their values printed or logged.

Problems

20.1 Draw a block diagram of a cathode-ray oscilloscope and briefly explain the purpose of each portion. Detailed circuit diagrams are not required.

An oscilloscope is to be used to examine waveforms occurring in a high quality audio amplifier. Briefly discuss the requirements for the bandwidth of the deflection amplifier and the velocity of the timebase.

20.2 With the aid of a diagram, and starting with electron-emission from the cathode, describe the complete path taken by the current in a cathode-ray tube circuit.

Make a list of the important properties of the fluorescent material which is used to coat the screen of the tube.

Why, in practice, is a saw-tooth the most common of all time-base waveforms?

20.3 Make careful sketches to show the appearance of the following waveforms when displayed on a cathode-ray oscilloscope:

(a) a sinewave of frequency 1 kHz and 2 V peak, to which has been added 50 per cent second harmonic. Use scales of 1 inch = 1 V and 1 inch = 0·5 ms;

(b) a sinewave of frequency 1 kHz and 2 V peak to which has been added 50 per cent third harmonic. Use scales as in (a);

In both cases assume that the oscilloscope provides a linear timebase.

20.4 Draw diagrams to illustrate the effects on the trace of a sinewave signal of (a) a non-linear timebase, and (b) lack of flyback blanking.

20.5 Describe how a single-beam cathode-ray oscilloscope could be calibrated and used to measure:

(a) a d.c. voltage.

(b) the r.m.s. value of a sinusoidal a.c. voltage.

(c) the frequency of a sinusoidal a.c. voltage.

(d) the phase difference between two a.c. voltages.

20.6 If a supply frequency, $f = 1/2\pi\sqrt{(R_1 R_2 C_1 C_2)}$ is applied across XZ in Fig. 20.12 then the voltage across YZ will be in phase with that supply. Describe a test, using an oscilloscope, which would confirm this fact and suggest how the circuit could be adapted to measure an unknown frequency.

20.7 Draw a diagram to show how a diode and a simple d.e. amplifier may be used as a valve voltmeter, and briefly describe its operation.

What limits the frequency range of the instrument you have described?

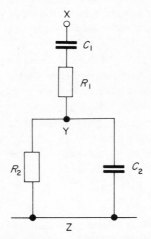

Fig. 20.12   Figure for problem 20.6.

20.8 Why is the input impedance of an electronic voltmeter high?

How can an electronic voltmeter be used to measure r.f. current?

A series circuit ABC consists of a 100 Ω resistor between points A and B, and a coil of effective resistance *r* and inductance of 0·001 H between points B and C. An electronic voltmeter reads 5 V when connected across AB and 43·9 V when across BC. If the supply frequency is 100 kHz, determine the values of (a) the circuit current, and (b) the effective resistance *r* of the inductor.

20.9 State Thevenin's Theorem.

A signal generator has its output terminals connected to a variable resistor in parallel with a valve voltmeter. The indication of the voltmeter as the resistance is varied is shown in the table below. Determine the e.m.f. of the generator and the internal resistance.

V (μV)	33	50	67
R (Ω)	25	50	100

What is the maximum power available from the generator?

20.10 Draw the circuit diagram of a transistor and briefly describe its operation.

What precautions must be taken when using such a voltmeter in conjunction with a signal generator to determine the resonant frequency of a tuned amplifier?

A peak reading voltmeter has been calibrated with a sine-wave signal and is scaled in r.m.s. volts. What will the meter indication be when a square-wave signal of +1 V peak amplitude is applied?

20.11 Enumerate the general principles of *three* types of digital voltmeters, and describe *one* in detail.

20.12 Explain how a cathode-ray oscilloscope may be used to measure the amplitude of an alternating voltage, and explain how it may be calibrated on direct current.

Discuss the advantages and disadvantages of this method of voltage measurement as compared with the use of a valve voltmeter.

20.13 Describe the relative advantages of magnetic and electric deflection in cathode-ray tubes used (a) in television receivers, (b) in oscilloscopes.

Explain how a circular trace may be produced on a cathode-ray tube with electrostatic deflection. How may this be used to compare two frequencies, one many times the other?

20.14 A digital voltmeter (D.V.M.) often forms the basis of a data processing system. Draw a block diagram of a simple D.V.M. and explain briefly the circuit operation.

Solutions to numerical problems

Chapter 1

1.9   4·7 V.
1.10 0·68 V, 0·52 V; 5 mA.

Chapter 2

2.2   100 Hz.
2.4   (c).
2.5   5 kΩ; (a) 221 V; (b) 196 V.

Chapter 3

3.3 $E_S = 10$ V, $r = 100$ Ω; $I_S = 0·1$ A, $R_S = 100$ Ω.
3.8   99; −0·988.
3.9 $h_{ie} = 1800$ Ω; $h_{re} = 8 \times 10^{-4}$; $h_{fe} = 82$; $h_{oe} = 128$ μS.

Chapter 4

4.5 $g_m = 3·6$ mA/V; $r_d = 10$ kΩ

Chapter 5

5.2   50 MΩ.
5.4   8·9 Ω.

Chapter 7

7.2   0·00854 mA/V; 60 V; 5·55 mA.
7.5 $g_m = 4$ mA/V; $r_a = 5$ kΩ.
7.6   3·33 kΩ; 10; 3 mA/V.

7.7 $\mu = 19.5, g_m = 2.75$ mA/V.

7.8   333 kΩ; 333 kΩ; 666 kΩ; 666 kΩ; 2930.

7.9 $\mu = 1200, r_a = 200$ kΩ.

7.10 $g_m = b + 2cv_G$; 9.

Chapter 8

8.9 $R_1 = 6$ $\Omega, R_2 = 295$ Ω.

Chapter 9

9.3   (a) 6.54 mA; (b) 6.54 V; (c) 42.8 mW; (d) $h_{fe} = 101, h_{oe} = 87$ μS.

9.4   (a) 250; (b) 300; (c) 400; 270.

9.5 $R_C = 3$ k$\Omega; R_B = 300$ kΩ.

9.6 -135; 6075.

9.7 -22.5.

9.9 $S = k(1 + h_{FE})$.

9.10 $R_C = 6.25$ k$\Omega; R_3 = 80.6$ k$\Omega; R_4 = 11.4$ k$\Omega; C_2 > 50$ μF (Note: the values of R_3 and R_4 are based on the assumption that the current drawn by them is ten times greater than I_B).

9.13 (a) 985 Ω; (b) 39.5 Ω.

9.14 4.34 V; 57 mW.

9.15 (i) 6.05 mA, 147 V; (ii) 42.5 V; (iii) -15; (iv) 72.25 mW.

9.16 $R_1 = 45$ k$\Omega; R_2 = 6$ kΩ; 5.73 mA.

9.17 (a) 30 dB; (b) 20 dB; (c) 10 dB; (d) 0 dB; (e) -10 dB; (f) -40 dB.

9.18 10.2 dB.

9.19 32.36 mV.

9.20 -9.8 dB; 16.2 mV.

9.21 (a) 40 dB; (b) 20 dB; (c) 10 dB; (d) -10 dB.

9.22 270 Hz, 3.2 kHz; 370 Hz, 3 kHz; 3.34 V.

9.24 0.25 A, 1 A; 50 W, 50 W; 4:1.

9.26 2250 Ω.

9.29 (i) -47; (ii) -32.

9.30 (a) (i) 100 kΩ; (ii) 4.15 mS; (b) -6.15; (c) 1.88 kΩ (Note: the value of the load resistor must be calculated from the d.c. conditions).

9.31 (c) (i) 5 dB, (ii) 3.16.

Chapter 10

10.4 44.1, 0.978; (a) -17.1 V; (b) 39.3; (c) -47.1.

10.5 $V_{CC} = 14$ V; $I_C = 1.8$ A; $R_B = 490$ Ω; 23 V, 4 V (for a $\pm$ 20 mA base current swing).

10.6 (a) 5; (b) 0.465 W; (c) 1.16 W; (d) 1.16 W.

10.7 (b) 500 μF or greater, 6.25 W.

Chapter 13

13.2 0.02; (i) 20 per cent; (ii) 11.2 per cent.

13.3 A reduction of 8.34 per cent or 0.76 dB.

13.4 100; (a) 20 per cent; (b) 2.5 per cent.

13.5 2 kΩ; 0.05 Ω; 0.5 per cent.

13.6 0·0167; (i) 33·3 per cent; (ii) 25 per cent.
13.7 (a) 1510 Ω; (b) 510 Ω; $\beta = 0 \cdot 184$.
13.8 29·8 dB (or a numerical gain of 30·9).

Chapter 14

14.1 0·01; 300.
14.5 33·3.
14.7 2 kΩ.
14.8 90 kΩ.
14.10 200 kΩ.

Chapter 17

17.4 2·75 ms.
17.5 Fixed = 4·7 kΩ, variable = 291·5 kΩ.
17.6 16·1 ms.
17.7 4·06 ms.

Chapter 19

19.2 $R = 175$ Ω, 7 W; diode −15 V, 3 W.
19.3 (a) 0·397 Ω; (b) 0·595 V; (c) 0·038 V.
19.4 9 to 13·6 V.
19.5 $R_1 = 10 \cdot 6$ kΩ; RV1 = 4·7 kΩ.

Chapter 20

20.8 (a) 0·05 A; (b) 614 Ω.
20.9 0·102 mV, 52·5 Ω; 49·5 pW.
20.10 0·707 V.

Index

Printed in Great Britain by Spottiswoode Ballantyne Ltd., Colchester and London

AMP - POWER DISSIPATION AND HEAT SINK CAL.

$$P_D = \frac{T_j(max) - T_A}{R_{\theta jc} + R_{\theta ch} + R_{\theta HA}}$$

T_j = Maximum junction temp.

T_A = Ambient temp.

$R_{\theta jc}$ = Thermal resistance from transistor junction to case package.

$R_{\theta ch}$ = Thermal resistance from case to heat sink.

$R_{\theta HA}$ = Thermal resistance from heat sink to ambient air.

also:-

T_j = 200°c for silicone transistors.

$R_{\theta jc}$ ≅ 2.0 c/w for steel bottom TO-3 PACKAGE with die attachment to beryllia substrate. to header

$R_{\theta ch}$ = 0.045°c/w for 1mil thickness of Wakefield type 120 THERMAL JOINT-COMPOUND.

$R_{\theta HA}$ = WAKEFIELD 403 HEATSINK WITH FREE AIR.

2.0°c/w

$$P_D = \frac{200°C - T_A}{2.0°c + 0.17° + 2.0} = \frac{200 - 25°c}{4.17 c/w} = 42W.$$